SPACE STATIONS AND PLATFORMS

by
Gordon R. Woodcock

with Foreword by
Dr. Edward G. Gibson

ORBIT BOOK COMPANY

MALABAR, FLORIDA
1986

Original Edition 1986

Printed and Published by
ORBIT BOOK COMPANY, INC.
2005 Township Road
Malabar, Florida 32950

Printed and Published in the United States of America

Library of Congress Cataloging in Publication Data

Woodcock, Gordon R.
    Space stations and platforms.

    Includes index.
    1. Space stations—Design and construction.
II. Title.
TL797.W66   1986   629.44'2   84-25442
ISBN 0-89464-001-1
10   9   8   7   6   5   4   3   2

To my wife Linda who is almost always patient and to
all the space enthusiasts who are impatient for great
things to happen

Series editors
Joseph A. Angelo, Jr., Ph.D.
Edwin F. Strother, Ph.D.

Contents

Foreword

It's time. Explorers, move farther out. The settlers are on their way.

Like New England in the early 1500s, the edge of space near Earth has been probed and explored. At the boundary of our inhabited world, it stands in the way of a relentless expansion. The inevitable permanent residency in "New Earth" is at hand.

Permanent presence in permanent facilities is as meaningful to us as it was to New England settlers. The size of the facilities required to begin manned use of space in earnest, and the required cost effectiveness of their transportation, dictate their permanent placement. And, just as the permanent occupation of New England settlements led to dynamic growth, so will the permanent occupation of New Earth.

Skylab was our nation's first but temporary station in space. We verified that the formula for man's real progress in space is the same as on Earth. We must be there, on the job, day after day, in facilities whose quality matches the challenge. We must be able to observe, learn, ask new questions, develop new techniques, and build new hardware. We must work in permanent space facilities that can grow in capability, nature, and size.

This is an exciting book, an excellent book about Space Station, our first such permanent residence in New Earth.

Some who plan to settle New Earth are scientists and engineers. They seek knowledge. They are attracted by the opportunity to look down and make synoptic observations of the Earth, to look out and make distortion-free, full-spectrum observations of the Sun and stars, and to study the effects of zero gravity on materials and the human body.

Others who will settle New Earth are businessmen. They come for profit. They are attracted by the potential of large markets for rare medicines and new engineering materials, some worth millions of dollars a pound. Initially, their progress will be slow and steady. However, as commercial processes are developed and markets established, the pace will accelerate. Discovery of "California gold" in one or more commercial processes, with its impetus to space development, is a constant possibility.

Space Station, through its ability to service space hardware, will give itself and New Earth a level of autonomy. It will assemble, deploy, repair, maintain, test and check out itself as well as other space facilities. Extravehicular activity (EVA) servicing of space equipment, which has become an operational reality, will be further developed and utilized.

Space Station will consist of a manned station and unmanned free-flying platforms. The platforms will be in both the station's orbit and polar orbit. They provide an environment that is relatively free of disturbances and contamination and can satisfy unique pointing requirements. They will have commonality with the station at the subsystem or component levels, enhancing their ease of servicing and logistics resupply. In all of station operations, automation and robotics are being developed to provide a mix of man and machine that will both be efficient in space and stimulate technology on the ground.

Like the New England colonies, Space Station will provide not only a toehold in the new world but also a launch site for further missions of exploration. In addition, it will develop the durable system and crew capabilities that are required for multiyear missions that include return to the Moon, flight to Mars, and flights to other planets, other moons, and other worlds farther out.

Over the past 300 million years, it has been our nature always to expand into new territory. In time, we have never failed to go beyond the next hill, over the next river, across the ocean, into the air, and now, into space. A permanent station in space is but one inevitable step in this outward growth of human occupation. And with each step, those who demand that all advantages of the "wilderness" beyond be defined, before we establish residence, enjoy only temporary credibility. Once the move is made, its benefits are taken for granted and the controversy moves on to the next step.

The permanent occupation of space is already under way. We can but influence its rate, quality, and leadership—its identification as New Earth or New Russia. For two decades Space Station has not been an issue of technical feasibility but one of national will. Now participation in the program has been broadened to obtain the added benefit of international cooperation with Canada, Europe, and Japan.

In this book, Gordon Woodcock has made a clear and comprehensive presentation of Space Station's background, general design features, operations, and supporting analysis. He has presented a systematic approach to the basics which underlie the station's implementation. In addition, through his direct involvement in station design for several years, he has provided exceptional insight into its technical issues. Over the coming years, this work should become a classic space station reference. It has high value for those who desire to understand, appreciate, or contribute to our first permanent settlement in New Earth.

EDWARD G. GIBSON

Preface

In this book I have attempted to offer a broad systems view of the engineering of space stations and platforms on a project scale. Although space stations and platforms will be large and complex structures, this book presents the technical aspects of the many disciplines in enough depth for sound systems analysis and architectural design. Interrelationships among the disciplines and their influences on design decisions are highlighted. Since the technical disciplines involved are applicable to most other space systems, it is anticipated that this book will become a vehicle for teaching contemporary fundamentals of space systems design.

People especially skilled in systems thinking often become systems architects and systems engineers. Relying on specialists for up-to-date knowledge and technical detail, systems architects conceptually put entire systems together. A big program like the development of a space station may employ thousands of engineers, but the important systems architecture decisions (What should it look like? How should it work?) will be determined, at most, by a handful of people. Many more will be involved, of course, but not in a central way.

The space field needs people highly skilled in engineering specialties such as heat transfer and digital design, but with enough exposure to systems thinking and to the main principles of many different engineering disciplines to understand how their specialty fits into an entire project. This contextual knowledge is essential to maintaining high productivity of and job satisfaction for the individual engineer. The engineers involved in even the detailed design portions of a larger project must understand how their work fits in, or much effort will be put into unnecessary work and rework.

We in the aerospace industry often find that new graduate engineers, although very well educated in many respects, need significant on-the-job training. One reason is that our large projects are thousands of times bigger in total labor expended than anything new graduates have been exposed to. Project Apollo consumed on the order of a billion man-hours. A typical senior class design project involves about ten thousand man-hours, and many graduates lack exposure even to one of those. Another perhaps more cogent reason is that most graduates have had too little exposure to space systems design. Furthermore, most design project classes are taught without a textbook because none are suitable. This book is intended as a start toward filling that gap.

Few English language texts exist on any broad aspect of space systems design and analysis. By contrast, such works are numerous in Soviet technical literature. This would indicate that the Soviets consider space achievement and superiority to be an important instrument of national policy. This is reflected in their educational technical literature.

Space is a growing field of engineering endeavor. The NASA program is building an infrastructure of space transportation and space stations and platforms designed to serve aggressive and exciting mission needs far into the next century. Defense uses of space are growing, and commercial applications are beginning to display an economic and technical significance similar to that of other existing government programs. For example, commercial satellite communications is already a mature industry and the privatization of remote sensing is well under way. Although the first true commercial success in spaceborne materials processing has yet to be registered, the number of companies funding research in this area is nearly doubling every year. While current projections of the commercial future of materials processing in space vary wildly, given a few successes it could financially outrank government spending in space by the end of the century.

Space technology began about thirty years ago as a highly experimental and exploratory field. There is no end of exploration to be done—space has been aptly called the endless frontier—but, despite its youth, the space field has reached a level of engineering maturity where there are established fundamentals. These fundamentals, especially in the ways they are applied by practicing space technologists, are unique to the field. Founded on well-known scientific and engineering principles, they will change only gradually as the field continues to mature. With this in mind, it is hoped that *Space Stations and Platforms* will provide positive assistance to a wide range of students, graduate engineers, and space technologists.

Chapter 1
Space Station: The Next Logical Step

Space Evolution and History

"[The scientific revolution] was not quick, and except in its later stages it was not violent; moreover it happened a long time ago and was virtually complete well before the end of the seventeenth century. And yet it resulted in probably the most radical change in outlook that mankind has ever known. To his dismay, homo sapiens found that he was not the lord of the universe; instead, he was confined to a small planet in the Sun's family." Patrick Moore, in *Watchers of the Skies*.

One result of the scientific revolution was the idea of space travel. Johannes Kepler wrote an early story of a trip to the Moon, but his means of getting there involved demons and was hardly scientific in modern terms. Perhaps the first *science* fiction story of space travel was Verne's *De la Terre á la Lune* in 1865; roughly contemporary was E. E. Hale's short story *The Brick Moon*. The latter introduced the concept of a manned space station orbiting the Earth.

Genuinely scientific thought about space stations began with the work of the Russian physicist Tsiolkovskii about the turn of the century. His work, however, was written in Russian and received little notice until recent times.

In the 1920s speculation about space flight was popularized in Europe by the writings of Hermann Oberth and many others. The enthusiasm quickly spread across the Atlantic. Rocket and space flight societies were formed; some began experiments with rocket propulsion. Dr. Robert Hutchins Goddard, working in the United States with at most a handful of assistants, accomplished the first liquid-propellant rocket flight in 1926 and by the late 1930s had pioneered nearly all of the basic features of modern rocket propulsion systems.

As the rudiments of early space flight engineering took shape through the labors of these enthusiasts, the accompanying scientific speculation dealt mostly with flights to other worlds. Imaginings about life on Mars were in vogue. The ferment in technical circles was mirrored in the entertainment media by the adventures of Buck Rogers and Flash Gordon. There was little mention of Earth-orbiting space stations.

In 1939 the industrialized world was plunged into World War II. The quixotic rocket experimenters suddenly were no longer crackpots. The German group, for example, became the nucleus of the Peenemünde engineering team that developed the V-2 rocket. After the war, the technical feasibility of space flight was no longer in question. There remained only the questions of when, and which nation would be first.

Technical discussion of space flight was, by the late 1940s, making its way into serious engineering and scientific literature, although the concept retained an aura of flakiness. The space station idea bloomed afresh in 1952 with Wernher von Braun's proposals for a very ambitious space station program—ambitious even by today's standards. Von Braun's design, shown in Figure 1.1, offered a rotating wheel-shaped station large enough to house dozens of people. It was to be supported by a fleet of giant reusable rocket ships.

Von Braun's space station was designed to provide artificial gravity to its residents by way of rotation of the wheel-shaped structure. In 1952, nothing was known of the ability of humans to operate or even survive in zero g. Consequently the conservative approach clearly dictated artificial gravity. One of the more popular speculations of the time was that people could not sleep in zero g because the "falling" sensation would wake them as soon as they began to doze off. Although there was no conceivable way to avoid at least a few hours of zero g in transit to and from a space station, at least Von Braun's design avoided long periods of it.

Although the engineering architecture of Von Braun's scheme was presented in impressive detail, the mission needs were somewhat hazy. A serious proposal was made that the United States embark on such a program. It would have been, however, quite expensive and some people began to ask "why?"

During World War II, giant strides in the electronics arts had made it possible to imagine an automated spacecraft, a prospect not foreseen by the visionaries of the twenties and thirties. The need for humans in space, assumed in the Von Braun proposal, was not entirely obvious. The issue of "man versus robot" was born.

Figure 1.1   Wernher von Braun's space station concept of 1952. *Painting by Chesley Bonestell, reprinted by permission of Bonestell Space Art.*

As these matters were debated in public, national plans for space programs were being developed, somewhat shrouded in secrecy. The United States program aimed at a limited objective, the orbiting of a few scientific satellites. The Soviet Union, however, forged a comprehensive program beginning with automated *and* manned space flight, contemplating a relentless evolution, including space stations and platforms and eventually reaching other worlds.

The United States viewed space technology as serving specialized scientific ends. The Soviets saw it as a logical evolution of their socialist ideal, extending their ideology and their civilization not only throughout the world but throughout the universe.

The Soviets opened the space era with their Sputnik I on 4 October 1957. They dominated the first several years of space exploration and accomplished the first manned space flight, a single orbit of the Earth by Yuri Gagarin on 12 April 1961. (John Young and Bob Crippen piloted the first Space Shuttle into orbit 20 years later to the day.)

The U.S. reaction to early Soviet leadership in space was a technically awesome challenge: to land a man on the Moon and return him safely to Earth, all within less than 10 years. The National Aeronautics and Space Administration (NASA) and the aerospace industry mobilized toward this goal and performed magnificently. The first Moon landing was achieved 8 years after the Kennedy decree, and a total of six landings were made. Twelve U.S. astronauts left

footprints on the Moon. American technological supremacy was upheld in the eyes of the world. And the space flight dream of the 1920s, reaching another world, had become reality!

During the Apollo years, far-reaching planning studies by NASA explored many alternative futures of space technology, exploration, and utilization. NASA conducted internal studies of space stations as early as 1959. Contracted studies were initiated in 1963, with the Manned Orbiting Research Laboratory (MORL) studies. The MORL was to support about six astronauts in reasonable comfort and was viewed as a scientific laboratory in Earth orbit. One of the MORL concepts is shown in Figure 1.2.

The MORL was a zero-g space station. By this time, initial manned flights into orbit had been made and concerns about zero g were diminishing.

Later NASA studies of future missions considered reusable launch vehicles, lunar bases, manned flights to Venus and Mars, and automated spacecraft for exploration of all the planets. Some form of space station occurred in most of these scenarios. As the Saturn V lunar rocket was developed, large space station designs aimed at using the Saturn heavy lift capability emerged. One of these is illustrated in Figure 1.3; it was sized to house 60 people! This station had a zero-g core and artificial-g habitats on the rotating arms depicted in the figure.

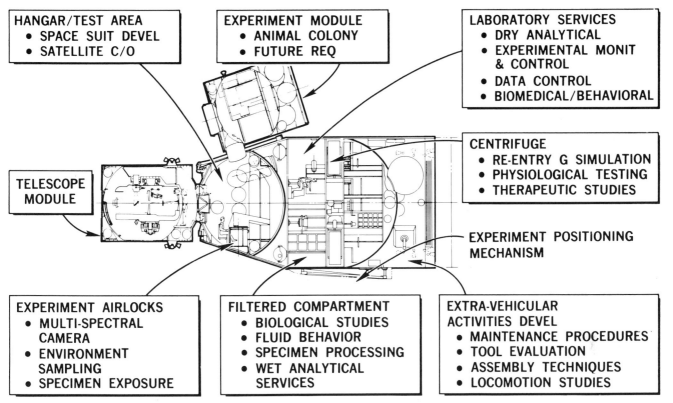

Figure 1.2 Manned Orbiting Research Laboratory (MORL) space station concept. *Courtesy of McDonnell-Douglas.*

In 1968, as the Apollo lunar landing program neared its goal, NASA outlined an integrated plan for space development, including a space station, a permanent manned base on the Moon, and manned expeditions to Mars. The plan included a standardized vehicle set, including a reusable Earth launch vehicle, and space-based vehicles using conventional as well as nuclear rocket propulsion.

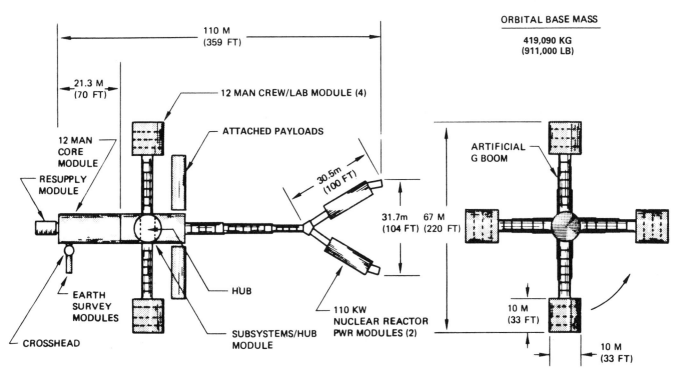

Figure 1.3 Sixty-man space base from Rockwell study circa 1971. *Courtesy of Rockwell International.*

Figure 1.4 Skylab. *Courtesy of NASA.*

Fiscal pressures caused all of this plan to be abandoned except for the launch vehicle and the space station. Phase B preliminary design studies of a space shuttle and a space station were begun in 1970. (Phase B, in the NASA procurement system, is the final study phase before project approval and issuing of hardware development contracts.) The inexorable fiscal vise created by the "war on poverty" and the Vietnam War then forced NASA to choose between these two projects. NASA opted for the Shuttle, sensing that routine manned access to space is an essential precursor to a permanent manned presence.

As these events were occurring, NASA utilized some remaining assets from the Apollo program to launch and periodically occupy a temporary space station, the Skylab. Skylab, shown in Figure 1.4, was occupied by three crews of three men each, for 28, 54, and 84 days respectively, in 1973 and 1974. Figure 1.5 shows a typical interior view of Skylab. (A Skylab space vehicle is on display at the Smithsonian Air and Space Museum in Washington, D.C.)

NASA had hoped to revisit Skylab with the Space Shuttle, but Skylab, having no orbit makeup propulsion, entered the atmosphere and was destroyed in 1980, before the first Shuttle flew.

The Skylab missions were very successful in many respects and proved that people in space, given adequate equipment and other resources, can do anything that people on Earth can do, as well as many things not possible in a one g environment. The Skylab crews conducted Earth, stellar, and solar observations, life sciences and human factors research, exploratory materials processing science, and technology experiments.

Meantime, the Soviet Union, having lost the race to the Moon (and then having claimed that they were never in it), proceeded with their own space station program. After a few years of difficulties and one fatal flight accident, the Soviet program has become mature. Their Salyut 6, shown in Figure 1.6, operated successfully for several years, and has now been superseded by Salyut 7. The Soviets have gained an order of magnitude more long-term manned space flight experience than the United States and enjoy a growing lead. It was 1985 before Shuttle flight crews accumulated the total number of crewperson days on orbit booked just by the 210-day mission of Salyut 7 in 1982. Long-duration missions, of course, provide scientific data not obtainable on numerous short missions of the same total duration.

NASA renewed studies of space stations during the Shuttle development effort. A very modest space station design called the Manned Orbiting System Concept (MOSC) was developed under contract to the Marshall Space Flight Center. During this period, studies of unmanned space platforms were also conducted. Platforms designed to carry various types of scientific instruments, with periodic servicing by

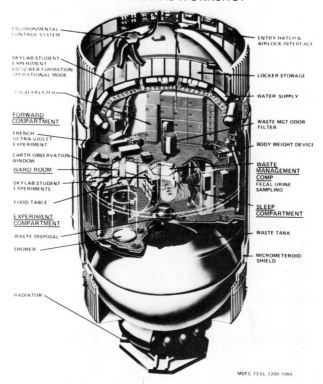

SKYLAB ORBITAL WORKSHOP

Figure 1.5 Interior cutaway of the Skylab space station. *Courtesy of NASA.*

the Space Shuttle, as well as communications platforms in geosynchronous orbit, were defined in several studies. Representative examples are shown in Figures 1.7 and 1.8. Some of these were designed to grow into space stations through the addition of pressurized habitat modules; a typical concept of a space station derived from a design for a large platform is shown in Figure 1.9.

The term *space platform* originally implied a large, permanent (i.e., serviceable) spacecraft intended to host a number of payloads, probably belonging to more than one owner. Payloads could be more or less as permanent as the platform, as in the case of a communications platform, or could be occasionally exchanged or modified as in the case of science and applications platform concepts. The term *platform* has become popular, almost faddish, and has been applied to a wide variety of vehicles, some not at all fitting the original description. "Platform" originally implied unmanned, where "station" usually (but not in Soviet usage) implied manned. In the title of this book I refer to large, relatively permanent, either manned or unmanned, spacecraft to be operated in Earth orbit. I am inclined still to use "platform" to infer unmanned, but "platform" can, and has been, applied to all sorts of spacecraft. The present NASA space station program includes a manned core as well as one or more unmanned platforms.

KEY CONTINUED. 21. TELEVISION CAMERA FOR AFT DOCKING OPERATIONS. 22. SANITARY FACILITIES. 23. TOILET. 24. FOOD LOCKERS. 25. SIGHTING DEVICE (12 x MAGNIFICATION, FOR ALIGNING THE BST-1M TELESCOPE). 26. CONTAINER FOR SCIENTIFIC INSTRUMENTS (BST-1M TELESCOPE). 27. FRESH WATER STORAGE. 28. GARBAGE CONTAINERS. 29. ELECTRONIC CONTROL PANELS FOR INSTRUMENT MODULE. 30. RUNNING TRACK FOR COSMONAUT EXERCISES. 31. VELOERGOMETER EXERCISER. 32. PHOTOGRAPHIC APPARATUS. 33. ELECTRONICS BAY. 34. SOLAR PANEL ROTATING MECHANISM. 35. COMMANDER'S CONTROL PANEL. 36. TELEVISION CAMERA. 37. EVA SPACESUITS (STOWAGE). 38. TRANSPORT SPACESHIP SOYUZ. 39. ACTIVE DOCKING SYSTEM OF SOYUZ SHIP. 40. PASSIVE DOCKING SYSTEM OF THE SALYUT STATION. 41. SUN SENSOR. 42. PORTHOLE. 43. COMPRESSED AIR CYLINDERS. 44. OXYGEN CYLINDERS FOR STATION'S ATMOSPHERE. 45. FRESH WATER TANK. 46. VACUUM CYLINDER. 47. ATTACHMENT POINT FOR LAUNCH SHROUD. 48. MKF-6M PHOTOGRAPHIC APPARATUS. 49. HIGH PRESSURE AIRLINES. 50. HIGH PRESSURE AIR STORAGE CYLINDER. 51. COMMUNICATIONS ANTENNA. 52. PROPELLANT TANK. 53. MAIN PROPULSION SYSTEM ENGINE. 54. VISUAL DOCKING TARGET. 55. SOYUZ ORBITAL MODULE. 56. SOYUZ DESCENT MODULE.

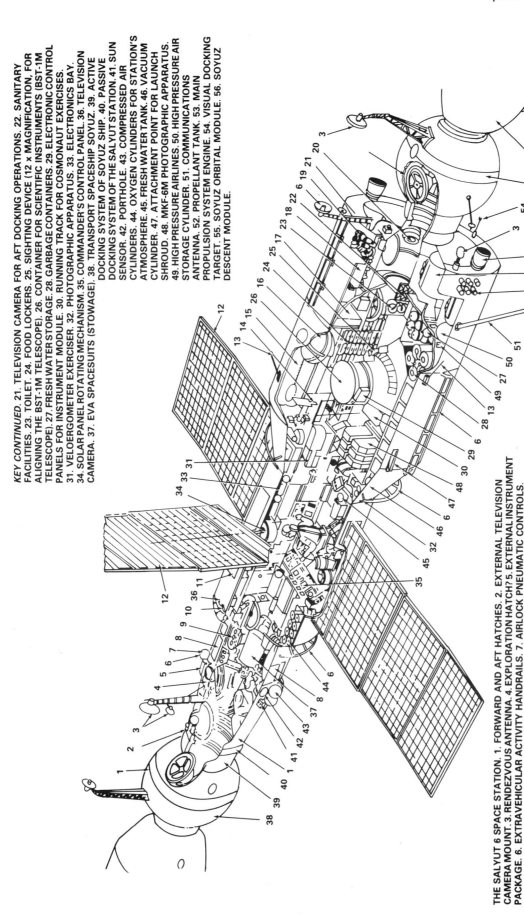

THE SALYUT 6 SPACE STATION. 1. FORWARD AND AFT HATCHES. 2. EXTERNAL TELEVISION CAMERA MOUNT. 3. RENDEZVOUS ANTENNA. 4. EXPLORATION HATCH 5. EXTERNAL INSTRUMENT PACKAGE. 6. EXTRAVEHICULAR ACTIVITY HANDRAILS. 7. AIRLOCK PNEUMATIC CONTROLS. 8. EXTERNAL THERMAL CONTROL PANEL. 9. AIRLOCK CONTROLS. 10. SUN SENSOR. 11. PROTECTIVE SCREEN. 12. ROTATING SOLAR ARRAYS. 13. TELEMETRY ANTENNAE. 14. ZERO-GRAVITY COSMONAUT WEIGHTING SCALE. 15. SLEEPING BERTH. 16. AIRLOCK FOR DEBRIS EJECTION. 17. DUST FILTER. 18. PNEUMATIC AND HYDRAULIC SYSTEMS FOR ATTITUDE CONTROL AND MAIN PROPULSION ENGINES. 19. ATTITUDE CONTROL ENGINES. 20. AIR VENTILATOR.

Figure 1.6 The Soviet Salyut-6 space station. *Courtesy of the British Interplanetary Society.*

DRAWINGS ARE ADAPTED FROM ORIGINAL SOVIET MATERIAL. WE SHOULD PARTICULARLY LIKE TO ACKNOWLEDGE THE NOVOSTI PRESS AGENCY. 'AVIATSIYA I KOSMONAVTIKA' AND THE CZECHOSLOVAKIAN PUBLICATION 'I. & K.'

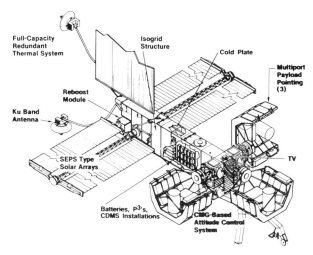

Figure 1.7 Space platform concept designed by McDonnell-Douglas. *Courtesy of McDonnell-Douglas.*

Figure 1.8 The TRW space platform concept as a long-term host vehicle for scientific payloads. *Courtesy of TRW.*

As Shuttle development proceeded, innovative thinking was applied to new uses for the anticipated routine access to the space environment. Among other things, concepts for use of large space structures were explored. Ideas ranged from large antennas and optical systems to the very ambitious solar power satellites proposed by Dr. Peter Glaser of Arthur D. Little. The latter included structures tens of square kilometers in area. At the same time, renovation of old ideas for basing orbit-to-orbit transportation systems in space occurred through studies of future space transportation. This ferment of new thinking, stimulated by the anticipated Space Shuttle, congealed into the concept of space operations.

In 1979, the NASA Johnson Space Center undertook studies of a new space station concept built around these ideas, the Space Operations Center (SOC). SOC studies were contracted by JSC in 1980 and continued for about two years. The resulting SOC design concept is illustrated in Figure 1.10.

At the same time, the Marshall Space Flight Center (MSFC) was refining its designs for a manned platform that would evolve from earlier unmanned platforms. A typical MSFC concept is illustrated in Figure 1.11.

One could hardly imagine two approaches more opposed in philosophy. The MSFC system was evolutionary, dedicated to space science and applications, used off-the-shelf hardware where possible, and was intended to be low in technical risk. The JSC design was an all-up design to be directly built, dedicated solely to space operations, and was technologically aggressive.

Both approaches, of course, had many attractive features. Science and operational applications are both credible. The benefits of these concepts as well as the disputes between them caused NASA headquarters to take control of the emerging program. Their first step was to place with the

Figure 1.9 MSFC concept for evolution of a space platform into a manned station through addition of manned modules. *Courtesy of MSFC.*

aerospace industry a set of eight mission analysis studies in order to clearly identify mission needs before proceeding with a detailed design. Concurrently, a Concept Development Group was established in NASA headquarters. This

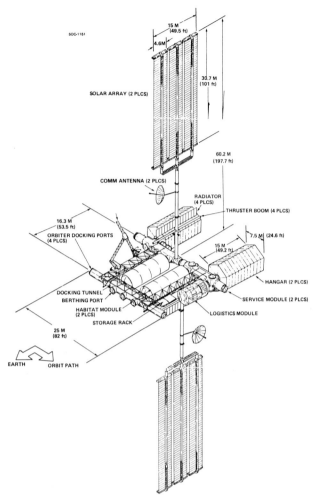

Figure 1.10 The "Space Operations Center" space station concept. *Courtesy of Boeing.*

proach, employs 2 degrees of freedom of the solar array system to cause the arrays to continually track the sun while the station itself is oriented toward the Earth by gravity gradient forces.

Concept designs with solar arrays on booms or masts tend to have very low natural frequencies of structural oscillation, on the order of 0.05 hertz. Early concern as to the controllability of such flimsy structures led to concepts for much stiffer structures such as the "delta" and "tee" concepts developed by the Johnson Space Center. These designs incorporate large space structures to achieve stiffness. The "spinner" concept, offered by the Hughes Corporation, employs a spinning solar array suspended by a quadriform assembly of Shuttle external tanks to achieve high structural and dynamical stiffness. Figure 1.13 categorizes these space station concepts based on how their solar arrays track the sun and how they are flown.

These concepts, presented here by way of introduction to the subject, are discussed and analyzed further in Chapter 8. They represent the range of configurations presently recognized as viable space station designs. Future studies may identify additional generic design approaches, although it presently seems that the concepts depicted cover the range of conceivable approaches.

A subtle evolution is evident in the progression of concepts from the early Von Braun wheel to the concepts arising from the studies of the early 1980s. This evolution has been largely driven by concern for missions. The early concepts were merely habitats in space. One is reminded of Tom

group, in concert with aspiring space station contractors, explored space station configuration issues during 1983 and 1984.

During 1983 and 1984, NASA studies selected the primary features of the space station program NASA was to recommend to the Reagan administration. These were:

- Crew of six to eight
- 75 kW of busbar electrical power
- Two laboratories, one each for life sciences and materials processing
- Two associated unmanned platforms, one in 28.5 degree orbit and one in polar or sun-synchronous orbit

The NASA task force and concept development activity also developed the generic design concepts displayed in Figure 1.12. The "modular" approach is conventional; solar arrays and radiators are carried on extremities in order to track the sun and to place these essential items out of the way of operational activities. The "power tower" approach is stabilized by gravity gradients, and like the modular ap-

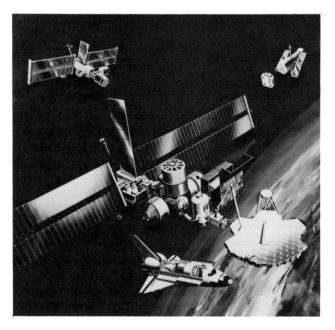

Figure 1.11 MSFC space station concept circa 1982. *Courtesy of NASA-MSFC.*

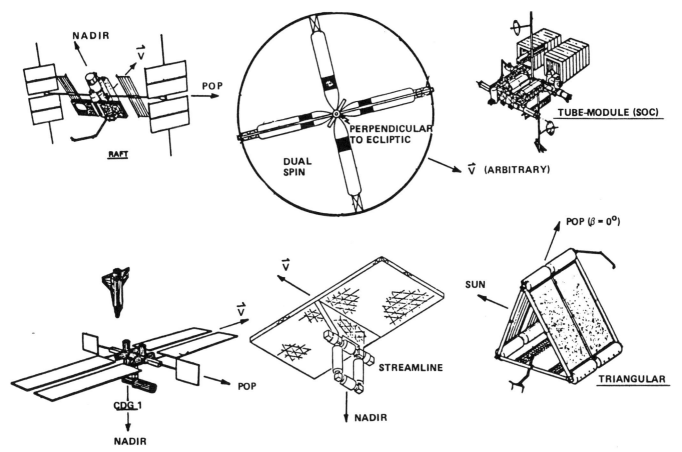

Figure 1.12 NASA concept studies in 1983 which considered a broad range of space station concepts. *Courtesy of NASA.*

		SUN-TRACKING			
		NO TRACKING OR LIMITED β-TRACK	0 DOF (SLEW SPACECRAFT)	1 DOF (SPACECRAFT PEP, ETC.)	2 DOF
F L I G H T M O D E	GRAVITY GRADIENT	BIG T			
	INERTIAL	INERTIAL WITH BORESIGHTED INSTRUMENTS	DELTA ● HUGHES SPINNER ● SKYLAB	PLATFORM CONCEPTS	
	OPTIONAL	INERTIAL/EARTH ORIENTED) WITH BORESIGHTED INSTRUMENTS			SOME PLANAR VERSIONS POWER TOWER
	BODY EARTH-ORIENTED, ARRAY INERTIAL (SUN TRACK)				SOC, CDG PLANAR

Figure 1.13 Space stations categorized by flight mode and sun-tracking mechanism. *Courtesy of Boeing.*

Wolfe's reference to ''Spam in a can'' (describing early engineering concepts for the Mercury spacecraft). This is true of the Von Braun wheel and to a lesser degree to the circa 1972 Phase B study concepts. Concepts that evolved during the mid-seventies began to show configuration impacts for mission integration, and the most recent thinking about space station configurations is becoming dominated by mission accommodation matters. Specific needs for mission accommodations are described later in this chapter.

Space stations and platforms have been seriously studied for over 20 years. Both the United States and the Soviet Union have flown experimental space stations and platforms. With the new NASA space station initiative, the time of permanent operational systems is nearing. This book provides a survey and summary of design considerations and technical information needed to accomplish systems design and analysis for space stations and platforms.

The Meaning of Permanent Presence

Early in our space program, many objects launched were called probes. The term *probe* of course implies temporariness. Early space probes explored aspects of the space environment for a few hours, days, or weeks.

As spacecraft became more utilitarian, longevity became important. The value of a utilitarian spacecraft is the total data returned; a spacecraft that lasts ten times as long can be worth ten times as much. Great effort has been invested in making spacecraft long-lived. The results are eminently realized in communications spacecraft that often last 10 years, as well as in the outer planet Pioneers and Voyagers that have survived a decade or more on epic odysseys covering billions of miles.

The best so far achieved in long life of spacecraft, however, falls far short of what we expect in useful lifetimes of terrestrial facilities. The Paris Observatory was established in 1670, the U.S. Naval observatory in 1830, the Lick Observatory in 1888. Palomar began service almost 40 years ago and is still in the forefront of astrophysical research. Things built for scientific, social, and other ends on Earth last from decades to hundreds of years. Spacecraft last an average of five or so. The theme of *permanent presence* aims to bring space systems into the realm of permanence.

Permanence will fundamentally change the way we conduct space missions. Today a significant part of space programs costs is replacing temporary systems. Granted that the replacements often represent design and capability improvements; still the cost of replacement is much higher than that of upgrade. The instrumentation used at the Lick Observatory today bears no resemblance to that used in its early days. But the *facility* is still there and still productive.

Avoiding the costs of replacing basic facilities can bring about a new approach to space utilization, one of accumulating space assets rather than replacing them. We are already moving in this direction with the Space Telescope, designed to be serviced by Space Shuttle (and later by space station). It will serve as a national research facility for decades.

The permanence approach is probably the only way, for example, to achieve the scientific goals of a space astrophysics program. We would like to establish observatory-class systems (like Space Telescope) that cover the entire range of wavelengths from RF to gamma rays as well as cosmic ray particles. To do this, we probably need as many as eight observatory-class systems. A representative list is as follows:

- A radio telescope of large aperture to cover the RF and microwave spectra.
- An optical/IR reflector telescope to cover millimeter wave and long-wave IR. Such an instrument, of roughly 20 meters aperture, is under study by the Ames Research Center. It would operate in both coherent (i.e., using communications detection techniques) and radiometer modes.
- A cryogenically cooled infrared telescope to extend the research initiated by the IRAS spacecraft. This instrument would require resupply of cryogenic coolant every few months.
- The Space Telescope (visible and ultraviolet light) now under development.
- A large thinned-aperture multimirror telescope for high-resolution searches for extrasolar planets and other specialized purposes.
- An advanced x-ray astronomy facility (AXAF), presently in a study phase.

- A gamma-ray observatory (GRO), also in a study phase.
- A large deployable particle detector array (LDA) for detection and analysis of high-energy cosmic rays.

Assembly of optical systems in space is an essential part of the growing ferment in physics and cosmology. To see this in perspective, recall the turn of the century. A ferment had then begun with the discovery of radioactivity in 1895, at a time when many scientists believed that all the fundamental discoveries had already been made. The revolution that resulted in what is known as "modern physics" accelerated in the early twentieth century with Einstein's relativity and the beginnings of quantum theory. In the 1920s, astronomers discovered that many "nebulae" were star systems, galaxies like our own, and by 1930 it was known that the galaxies are as numerous as the billions of stars in our own galaxy, and that the universe was expanding as if from a "big bang." This revolution in knowledge slowed in the 1930s. Perhaps the final event was the discovery of uranium fission in 1938.

A new ferment is now in progress. We do not enjoy the comfortable vantage point of the historian, but one might argue that it began with the quark theory of structure of elementary particles, with the discovery of quasi-stellar objects (quasars), and with the discovery of the "microwave background," the remanent radiation of the cosmic "big bang." All were events of the early 1960s. It is in full swing now with the Grand Unified (GUT) theories and the inflationary universe models of the beginnings of things.

And what of optics assembled in space? IRAS found dusty matter around certain nearby stars, evidence of processes akin to planetary system formation. There are many star nurseries out there, in giant molecular clouds (GMCs). We urgently need high-resolution optics in the infrared and millimeter wave bands to get a clearer look at the births of stars, to understand whether planets are a natural outcome. Large thinned-aperture visible light or infrared systems might give us a direct glimpse of planets accompanying the nearer stars. Observatory-class instruments covering all wavelengths are needed in space, to look as far toward the edge of things knowable and as far back in time as possible. Surely we can gain some additional insight into the ultimate beginnings.

A space station is almost certainly necessary for assembly and commissioning of such systems. Further, a full array of observatories is not likely to be affordable except in a permanence mode of operations. Observatories will probably average $500 million each. Suppose we had an annual budget of $500 millions to invest.

If one assumes a replacement mode of operations and a 5-year half-life, typical for *complex* scientific spacecraft, the rate of accumulation of capital facilities may be related to the annual budget by $dC/dt = B - RC$, where dC/dt is the

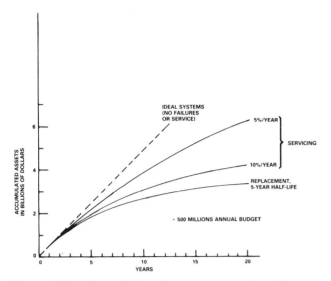

Figure 1.14 Accumulation of space assets under replacement and servicing assumptions.

rate of accumulation, B is the annual budget, and R is the replacement rate, $R = 0.693/5$, based on the 5-year half life. The value 0.693 is ln(2), and serves to convert half-life to exponential decay terms.

Accumulation of assets under this replacement assumption is graphed in Figure. 1.14.

The permanent presence assumption leads to a budgetary dispensation divided between accumulation of assets and their servicing and repair. The rate of accumulation of assets is simply $dC/dt = B - fC$, where annual servicing/repair/upgrade cost as a fraction of initial cost is represented by the term f. This equation has exactly the same form as the previous one. The physical significance of this is of course that replacement of complete assets after failures resulting in mission loss is just an extreme case of servicing—one in which the entire spacecraft is replaced.

The annual servicing term f is presently believed to be between 5 percent and 10 percent of the initial investment cost for these systems. The accumulation of assets under the servicing assumption is also graphed in Figure 1.14. This simple model demonstrates expectation of much more return for a given investment with permanence.

This *permanence* concept has evolved over the past several years. The Space Shuttle, with its routine human access to space, was the key to introducing the concept. Shuttle provides human presence in orbit on a routine basis.

A natural outgrowth of the Shuttle was the space platform concept. Such a platform was conceived of as a spacecraft in which the utilities (power, propulsion, attitude control, and data) would be provided on a permanent and serviceable platform bus, and the experimental and instrument systems would be client payloads on the bus, installed in a servicing mode and replaced, maintained, or upgraded as necessary

to serve mission ends. Because the platform was to be maintainable and modifiable on orbit, it had the attribute of permanence. (As noted previously, the term "platform" now has a much broader connotation than it originally did.)

Routine access to low Earth orbit with a return capability naturally leads to the idea of spacecraft with the attributes of a space platform rather than the expendable, inaccessible, mission-dedicated spacecraft designed for launch by expendable launch vehicles. This represents a technological culture change. It offers great potential for achievement of space mission goals and objectives more effectively at lower cost. But because it is a culture change, a new and nontraditional way of carrying out space missions, the benefits may be slow to become recognized and realized.

The Shuttle itself serves a limited role as a space platform. The synthetic aperture radar flown on STS-2 is a typical platform mission; the Shuttle provided the platform for operation of this instrument for several days on orbit. The European Spacelab has platform and space station functions. The Spacelab flies in the Shuttle payload bay as an attached payload and can be used in a platform-like configuration as illustrated in Figure 1.15 or in a laboratory (station-like) configuration as illustrated in Figures 1.16 and 1.17. The Spacelab equipment lends itself to arrangement in many alternative configurations to serve various mission ends, as diagrammed in Figure 1.18.

One may contrast the platform idea with the observatory idea. Both are essentials of the permanence concept. The difference is that the platform was conceived as a multi-mission, modifiable vehicle while the observatory is a mature mission system, involving a single major instrument that will be used over periods of decades. The platform is best suited to periodic exchange of science payloads while the observatory is a permanent science instrument with exchangeable sensory equipment, e.g., at the focal plane.

Manned Presence

Permanence in space does not necessarily require a permanent manned presence. The platform systems offer a measure of permanence with intermittent manned presence. The issue of the permanently staffed space station still must be addressed. This means that the utility of man in space is at issue.

We first must put the man-in-space issue into perspective. There is, of course, no such thing as an unmanned space system. Most space systems, however, involve humans only on Earth in a remote control role. Manned spacecraft add a human presence in space.

The manned space program has always been highly politicized. In the days of Mercury, Gemini, and Apollo, the manned program was motivated largely by competition with the Soviet Union for an image of technological supremacy.

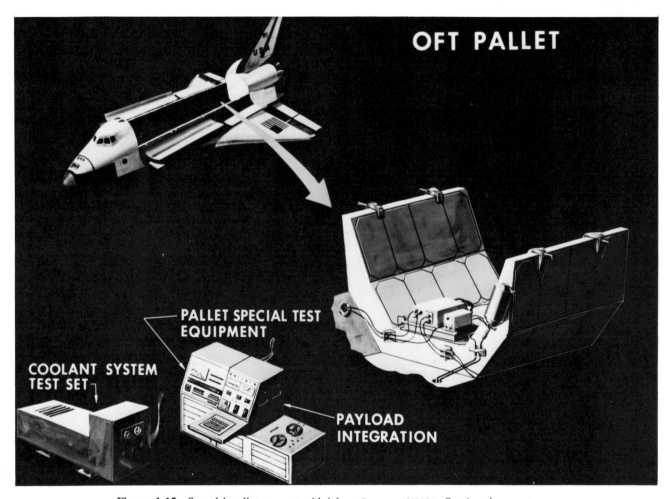

Figure 1.15 Spacelab pallet segment with igloo. *Courtesy of NASA. Continued on next page.*

Further, manned space activities have been NASA's most visible and heavily funded programs. They entail the glamour of the astronaut corps and the drama of heroism and risk. They receive intense media coverage, concentrating on mission events rather than true accomplishments. They are often perceived, especially by scientists, as taking funds from other deserving projects.

Because true accomplishments, and especially the understanding thereof, usually come much later than the mission events themselves, the accomplishments of manned missions are grossly underrecognized. Almost everyone old enough to have watched remembers TV coverage of the Apollo astronauts on the Moon, but how many know that the lunar samples, films, and data returned by the Apollo missions totally changed scientific understanding of the formation and evolution of our solar and planetary system? How many are aware of the many oceanographic phenomena discovered through visual observations by astronauts in low Earth orbit on flights from Mercury to Shuttle? How many realize that the remarkable advances in electrophoretic processing of biologicals now being made by McDonnell-

Douglas trace their origins to pioneering experiments carried out on the Skylab space station over 10 years ago?

The simple truth is that presence of humans in space has always been beneficial and always will be. The issue is whether the benefits are worth the cost. Benefits are often unquantifiable. How valuable, for example, are the revolutionary Apollo advances in scientific understanding of solar system evolution?

Here is one of the real benefits of space station. Space station dramatically lowers the cost of human presence in space, e.g., to about 1 percent of the cost per man-day for Apollo. At the same time, it aggregates many missions that benefit from human presence in space, none of which, alone, would benefit enough to justify the cost. Space station, by bringing many missions together, makes the benefits of human presence affordable.

Space station can enable the second phase of space industrialization. The first began over 20 years ago with the launch of the first commercial communications satellite by NASA; it was turned over to COMSAT Corporation after

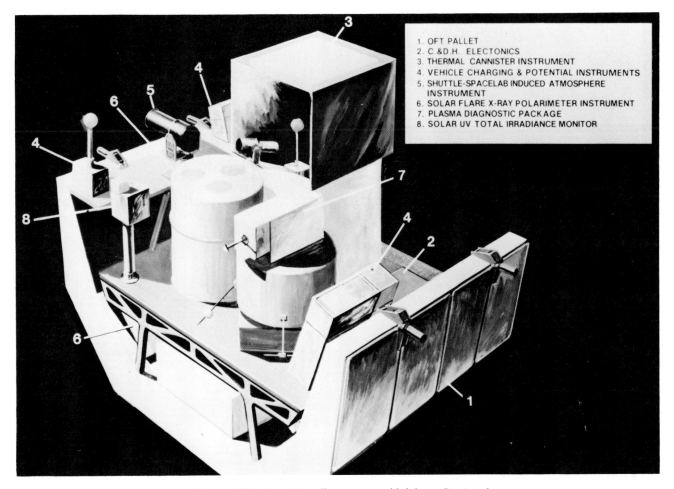

1. OFT PALLET
2. C.&D.H. ELECTONICS
3. THERMAL CANNISTER INSTRUMENT
4. VEHICLE CHARGING & POTENTIAL INSTRUMENTS
5. SHUTTLE-SPACELAB INDUCED ATMOSPHERE INSTRUMENT
6. SOLAR FLARE X-RAY POLARIMETER INSTRUMENT
7. PLASMA DIAGNOSTIC PACKAGE
8. SOLAR UV TOTAL IRRADIANCE MONITOR

Figure 1.15 Spacelab pallet segment with igloo—*Continued.*

demonstration tests. The second is now beginning with initial efforts toward commercial microgravity manufacturing processes. Major advances in this field need permanent human presence, for broad-based and innovative research and development programs, and for servicing of automated factories. (Even Earth-based automated factories need continual human presence, to service the robots.)

Finally, human presence in space will not always be confined to low Earth orbit. We have already set our sights on geosynchronous orbit (GEO), where there is much valuable work to be done once we have reduced the cost of human presence enough. We have been on the Moon, albeit briefly. Someday we will return, to begin the third phase of space industrialization, exploiting the plentiful material resources there. The planet Mars beckons; eventually the stars. The space station is the logical stepping-stone to these long-range goals. It offers a base camp in low Earth orbit. With synergistic advances in space transportation technology, space station promises low costs for manned sortie missions to GEO. Repair and servicing of the valuable and accumulating assets there would then be economical. Station-based lunar

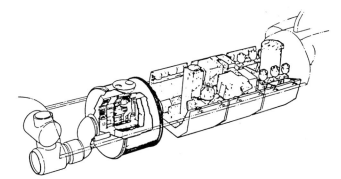

Figure 1.16 Spacelab short module with pallets. *Courtesy of NASA.*

mission modes could enable support of a small but permanent human settlement on the Moon for less annual resupply cost than the cost of a single Apollo lunar flight. A manned Mars mission could be launched from space station, a concept first described over 20 years ago by NASA studies. The stars? Someday. For that, we'll probably need an entire shipyard in orbit.

As H. G. Wells said, "There is no turning back. It's the universe or nothing."

Figure 1.17 Spacelab long module with pallets in Shuttle Orbiter payload bay. *Courtesy of NASA.*

Missions for Space Stations and Platforms

The uses of space cover a wide range of scientific, practical, commercial, and industrial applications. Mission analyses, i.e., the determination and evaluation of needs and utility for new capabilities, are speculative and uncertain inasmuch as established requirements for new capabilities are recognized only in cases of dire need. Most potential users of a new capability ''have no requirements,'' because their plans were formulated without the assumption that new capabilities would exist.

The problem of mission analysis is somewhat eased by categorizing missions according to user communities and economic factors. This is important because it permits evaluation of mission utility in light of user needs and user funding capabilities. This practice is consistent with that employed by NASA in their 1983-84 mission requirements working group activities leading to space station mission models.

Mission models, of necessity, represent a sort of forecast of the future. As such, they suffer by virtue of being far too specific. Forecasts of the specific applications, requirements, and utility of individual missions in such a model are almost certainly inaccurate. Whether any specific mission in the model will even be undertaken is highly uncertain. In the aggregate, however, the accommodations requirements estimated from well-thought-out mission models have proven very useful. Although the details of any *individual* mission are of very low probability, the overall accommodations requirements of the aggregated missions are indeed representative of actual needs.

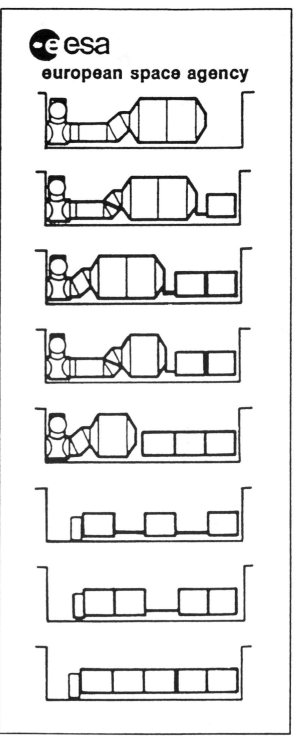

Figure 1.18 Spacelab configuration options. *Courtesy of NASA/ESA.*

This observation, based on the experiences of development and use of the Space Shuttle mission models, is especially valuable in the following light: If one specific mission forecast is generating a tent-pole accommodations requirement, the analyst should be skeptical. The expression ''tent pole'' come from thinking of a bar chart or schedule chart: the longest bar was originally called the "longest pole in the tent." In other words, since any one mission requirement forecast is unreliable, any one requirement that sticks out from the rest should be regarded with suspicion. Similar requirements coming from several missions, however, should be regarded as reliable.

The mission model data presented herein were adapted from a version of the NASA space station mission model known as the "Langley Data Base." It includes only U.S. missions. The space station program, by policy, is international. Many nations have aggressive space programs including missions of the types described here. Later versions of the "Langley Data Base" included international as well as U.S. missions. For the objectives of this book, no purpose is served by trying to capture the "latest" mission model. Mission models are always in flux. The missions described here are representative and that is all that is intended.

The mission types described below are aligned with user community institutions and economic categories related to public or private sector financing of the missions. The following categories are presently recognized for space stations and platforms.

Space Sciences and Applications

U.S. space sciences are funded primarily by NASA, with some support from the National Academy of Sciences, the Department of Defense, academia, and industry. The recognized categories of space science generally follow the NASA practice of discipline categories: (1) space environment, (2) astrophysics (includes solar physics), (3) Earth environment, (4) life sciences, and (5) materials sciences. Planetary science is an additional category but space stations and platforms are little influenced by the current planetary science model except where the latter may be served by using a space station as a launch or recovery platform. Such uses are included in the operations category described below. (Space station will play a central role in future manned lunar and planetary exploration.)

Space applications missions include those disciplines of space science that are far enough advanced to have practical applications of immediate benefit to society. Examples include weather prediction, remote sensing for oceanography, land use analysis, crop forecasting, etc., and certain classes of communications such as search and rescue. Applications missions overlap science missions and possibly even commercial missions in Earth observations. The distinction between applications and science is especially unclear, as particular instruments and equipment can, and often do, serve both science and applications ends.

From an economic viewpoint, applications missions are those that offer economic or service benefits to society, but missions for which the benefits cannot readily be captured as profits to a commercial enterprise. Weather forecasting is a prime example. Those Earth observations missions that involve scientific development of new observational, data processing, or instrument techniques, may properly fit into a space science category. Such missions may also, of course, move into the commercial category if capture of profits becomes practical.

Space sciences remote sensing missions for the space station era are projected to include observatory-class missions as well as lesser instrument and exploratory missions. Observatory missions include the Space Telescope, advanced x-ray astronomy, and gamma-ray astronomy facilities. Radio and infrared telescopes are also possible. Lesser instruments and exploratory missions include the Shuttle infrared telescope (SIRTF) and other Shuttle payloads as well as developmental missions for advanced Earth observations instruments for climatology, oceanography, and land surface observation.

Observatory-class payloads are those that require special capabilities such as extreme pointing precision, greater than expected possible from a space station or platform. The Space Telescope, for example, needs pointing stability of 0.007 arc second. A space station is expected to provide stability on the order of an arc minute; subplatforms attached to a space station can probably improve this figure to something rather better than an arc second. Unmanned space platforms will presumably have better pointing accuracy than stations because crew-induced disturbances will not be present, but the best accuracy will always be provided by a dedicated spacecraft.

Remote sensing missions include stellar and planet pointing as well as solar and Earth pointing. Stellar and solar pointing are very similar in that stellar pointing is fixed in inertial space; solar and planetary pointing involve very gradual motions relative to inertial space. Earth pointing requires Earth orientation, i.e., pointing "downward" as the spacecraft orbits the Earth about every hour and a half.

Most Earth-pointing missions need a full-Earth coverage orbit, either polar or sun-synchronous (see Chapter 3). The present NASA space station plans include a space platform in a sun-synchronous orbit for Earth observations. The platform will be serviced by the Shuttle and orbital maneuvering vehicles (OMVs). A small manned space station may eventually be placed in a polar orbit.

Representative concepts for stellar and Earth-pointing instrument payloads are depicted in Figures 1.19 and 1.20. An example of an applications and science Earth observation package is the "System Z" concept developed by the NASA Goddard Space Flight Center and the Jet Propulsion Laboratory (JPL). This system includes a variety of instruments. Described in Figure 1.21, the System Z package is representative of missions and instruments for the polar (or sun-synchronous) orbit platform planned as a part of the NASA space station system.

SUMMARY DESCRIPTION FOR SIRTF PAYLOAD

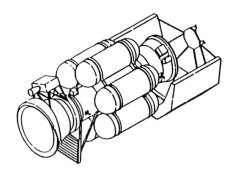

CHARACTERISTICS

MASS UP/DOWN (kg):	8103/6853
LENGTH IN CARGO BAY (m):	11.3
POWER AVG./PEAK (kW):	1.1/2.3
HEAT REJ., ACT./PASS. (kW):	0.8/0.3
SCIENCE DATA (Mbps):	1
TELEMETRY (kbps):	~7.2*
POINTING CATEGORY:	CELESTIAL (IR)
OPERATING CONDITION:	CONTINUOUS

*PLUS REAL-TIME IMAGE

SPECIAL CONSIDERATIONS

VENTS HELIUM

SENSITIVE TO USUAL OPTICAL/IR CONTAMINANTS

AVOIDANCE ANGLES: 90 DEGREES WITH RESPECT TO THE SUN

60 DEGREES WITH RESPECT TO EARTH, MOON, AND PLATFORM SURFACES

SUPPORT FRAME (NOT SHOWN) ASSUMED USED FOR DELIVERY/RETURN IN CARGO BAY

INSTRUMENTS/FACILITIES

SHUTTLE INFRARED TELESCOPE FACILITY (SIRTF)

Figure 1.19 Shuttle infrared telescope facility (SIRTF). *Courtesy of Teledyne-Brown/NASA.*

Uses of crews in this mission category include the servicing and calibration of instruments, observation and targeting of transient events, especially on the Sun, and handling of film in cases where film is preferable to electronic media for recording of science data. Further, the space station offers the benefits of the permanent presence and permanent facilities described earlier in this chapter.

The present NASA science and applications mission set for the initial space station (from the NASA mission model)

SUMMARY DESCRIPTION FOR UPPER ATMOSPHERE RESEARCH SATELLITE (UARS) PAYLOAD

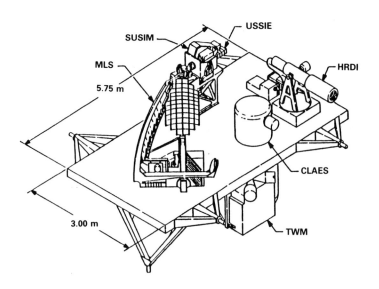

CHARACTERISTICS

MASS UP/DOWN (kg):	2367/2347
LENGTH IN CARGO BAY (m):	5.8
POWER AVG./PEAK (kW):	1.34/TBD
HEAT REJ., ACT./PASS. (kW):	0.83/TBD
SCIENCE DATA (Mbps):	0.02
TELEMETRY (kbps):	2.0
POINTING CATEGORY:	MULTIPLE DIRECTIONS
OPERATING CONDITION:	CONTINUOUS

INSTRUMENTS

CLAES
HALOE
HRDI
ISAMS
MLS
SUSIM
TWM

SPECIAL CONSIDERATIONS

CRYOGEN SYSTEM ON CLAES VENTS HYDROGEN

Figure 1.20 Upper Atmosphere Research Satellite (UARS) payload. *Courtesy of Teledyne-Brown/NASA.*

INSTRUMENT USE MATRIX

INSTRUMENT CLASSES	ATMOSPHERIC CHEMISTRY	ATMOSPHERIC CIRCULATION	GLOBAL CLIMATE	OCEAN DYNAMICS – CIRCULATION	OCEAN DYNAMICS – SEA ICE	HYDROLOGY	BIOGEOCHEMICAL CYCLES	BIOMASS DYNAMICS	LAND COVER/ LAND USE DYNAMICS	CONTINENTAL GEOLOGY
VIS/IR MODERATE & WIDE FOV IMAGERS		X	X	X		X	X	X	X	X
VIS/IR HIGH RESOLUTION IMAGERS						X	X	X	X	X
LASER RANGERS/ALTIMETER				X				X	X	X
LIDAR FACILITY	X	X	X	X		X	X			X
PASSIVE CHEMICAL SPECIES SENSORS	X		X				X			
MICROWAVE RADIOMETERS		X	X	X	X	X	X			
IR & MICROWAVE SOUNDERS	X	X	X			X				
SCATTEROMETERS		X	X	X	X	X				
REAL APERTURE RADARS		X	X	X		X				
SYNTHETIC APERTURE RADARS				X	X		X		X	X	X
SOLAR SENSORS	X		X							
DATA COLLECTION LOCATION PLATFORM		X	X	X	X	X	X	X	X	X

830816-9

Figure 1.21 Summary of System Z instrument uses. *Courtesy of NASA.*

includes a number of payloads, including those installed on the Space Station as well as payloads designated for a platform, and observatory missions represented by dedicated space craft. The mission set is summarized in Table 1.1.

Commercial

Commercial missions are those conducted by business entities for profit. Commercial missions may either earn profits, as do communications satellites, or be directed to the development of capabilities that will earn profits, as is true of some current ventures in the field of zero-gravity processing technology. Commercial missions are funded by the private sector of the economy.

Potential commercial uses of a space station clearly include research, developmental, and pilot production activities in the field of materials processing. Mature commercial processing activities might also occur at a NASA space station, but present thinking is that these would use dedicated manned or automated facilities, serviced from the NASA space station.

The near-term commercial potential of materials processing has been somewhat exaggerated, in that a perception exists of great reserves of venture capital waiting in the wings to be invested in materials processing developmental projects. There is indeed some such capital. But investors more often seek practical projects offering near-term payoff rather than research and development opportunities leading to uncertain long-term returns. The present lack of a space station forces exploratory research projects into a very long-term situation. Conducting enough experiments to convert promising ideas into solid commercial propositions could well require many years. The McDonnell-Douglas electrophoresis project is relatively far advanced because the scientific principles were proved on the Skylab flights over a

decade ago and further research was funded by the U.S. government in the late 1970s.

Other microgravity processing ventures, however promising in principle, have less foundation in flight experience. Investor willingness to undertake the lengthy path from proof of scientific principle to development of a commercially viable product remains to be demonstrated. The one true commercial success in space indusrialization, communications, is instructive.

In the early 1960s, NASA researched the concept of the geosynchronous-orbit communications satellite and launched an experimental model, Syncom-1. At the same time, the U.S. government created the COMSAT Corporation. After experimental demonstration tests, the NASA satellite was turned over to COMSAT for initial profitable operations. In this instance, the government created not only the technology but also the business entity that would achieve commercial exploitation of the technology. The materials processing situation is different inasmuch as no one expects the government to establish a processing corporation. Yet, the benefits of a space station in offering a comprehensive research environment, as well as opportunity for quick research turnaround, are keys to aggressive exploitation of the potentials of this new frontier of industrial research and development.

There may be limited opportunities for the space station to serve commercial communications. Suggestions include storage and launch of replacement spares for high-value and time-critical communications satellites, servicing of communications assets in GEO orbit (considered an operations mission), and space-based research or testing of advanced communications equipment. None of these ideas has been validated as a genuine commercial venture.

The commercial mission set for the initial space station, from the NASA space station mission model, is summarized in Table 1.2. These missions include research and development and pilot production. At least some commercial capital has been invested in all of the opportunities represented, but in some cases the investments have been no more than token.

Benefits of crew involvement are principally the accomplishment of developmental research, where immaturity of knowledge precludes automation, and intervention in automated processes, typically a daily necessity for Earth-based automated systems.

Operations

Operations missions are conducted as intermediate means to a later end in one of the other categories. They include spacecraft servicing and repair missions as well as those devoted to space transportation operations. Examples include basing transportation vehicles in space, and assembly and construction operations serving missions that need this capability, e.g., for assembly of large, complex vehicles in

Space Stations and Platforms

18   Space Stations and Platforms

Table 1.1 Summary of NASA space station mission model for science and applications (April 1984 version). *Courtesy of NASA/Boeing.*

NASA INDEX NO.	NAME	CATEGORY	LOCATION	FIRST ACTIVE YEAR	SIZE (M)	MASS (KG)	POWER (KW)	POINTING	DATA
SAAX0001	COSMIC RAY SPECTRA (SCRN)	ASTRO-PHYSICS	ON SPACE STATION EXTERNAL	1991-1992	3x4x5	3,100	0.8	140° FOV ANTI-EARTH	100 KBPS 24 HRS
SAAX0004	SHUTTLE INFRARED TELESCOPE FAC. (SIRTF)	ASTRO-PHYSICS	ON SPACE STATION, EXTERNAL	1992	4 DIA x 8.5L	4,000	0.7 AV 2 PK	0.15 ARC SEC STELLAR	10 KBPS UP 1 MBPS DOWN
SAAX0005	TRANSITION RAD & ION CALORIMETER	ASTRO-PHYSICS	ON SPACE STATION, EXTERNAL	1992	3.3x4.8x 4.8	5,750	0.5	120° FOV ANTI-EARTH	100 KBPS
SAAX0006	STARLAB	ASTRO-PHYSICS	ON SPACE STATION, EXTERNAL	1991	2 DIA x 7L	3,200	2.2 AV 3.9 PK	2 ARC SEC STELLAR	16 MBPS
SAAX0007	HIGH-THROUGHPUT MISSION (X-RAY)	ASTRO-PHYSICS	ON SPACE STATION EXTERNAL	1993	2x2x2	10,000	2 AV 3 PK	~1 ARC SEC STELLAR	300 KBPS
SAAX0008	HIGH ENERGY ISOTOPE EXP 4	ASTRO-PHYSICS	ON SPACE STATION, EXTERNAL	1994	3x5x4	3,000	0.3	10° STELLAR	100 KBPS
SAAX0009	PINHOLE/OCCULTER FACILITY	SOLAR PHYSICS	ON SPACE STATION EXTERNAL	1993	50m BOOM	3,600	0.5	SOLAR; FEW ARC SEC	1,400 KBPS + TV
SAAX0010	SOLAR CORONA DIAGNOSTICS	SOLAR PHYSICS	ON SPACE STATION, EXTERNAL	1995	8x5x5	1,250	?	SOLAR; FEW ARC SEC	650 KBPS
SAAX0011	ADVANCED SOLAR OBSERVATORY	SOLAR PHYSICS	ON SPACE STATION EXTERNAL	1995	8x5x5	12,500	4.1	SOLAR; 1 ARC SEC	42 MBPS
SAAX0012	SPACE TELESCOPE (SERVICING)	ASTRO-PHYSICS	FREE-FLYER OBSERVATORY	1986	4.3D x13L	11,350	HAS ITS OWN	0.01 ARC SEC STELLAR	HAS ITS OWN
SAAX0013	GAMMA RAY OBSERV (GRO) (SERVICING)	ASTRO-PHYSICS	FREE-FLYER OBSERVATORY	1988	4.5D x7.6L	14,000	HAS ITS OWN	STELLAR 1 ARC SEC	HAS ITS OWN

NASA INDEX NO.	NAME	CATEGORY	LOCATION	FIRST ACTIVE YEAR	SIZE (M)	MASS (KG)	POWER (KW)	POINTING	DATA	
SAAX0014	X-RAY TIMING EXPLORER (XTE) (SERVICING)	ASTRO-PHYSICS	FREE-FLYER SPACECRAFT	1991	4x4x8	850	HAS ITS OWN	STELLAR 1 ARC SEC	HAS ITS OWN	
SAAX0015	OPEN	SOLAR/ EARTH PHYSICS	FREE-FLYER SPACECRAFT	1990	—	1,000	HAS ITS OWN	N/A	HAS ITS OWN	▷
SAAX0016	SOLAR MAX	SOLAR PHYSICS	FREE-FLYER SPACECRAFT	1980	3x3x5	3,000	HAS ITS OWN	SOLAR FEW ARC SEC	HAS ITS OWN	▷
SAAX0017	ADVANCED X-RAY (AXAF) (SERVICING)	ASTRO-PHYSICS	FREE-FLYER OBSERVATORY	1991	4.3D x13L	10,267	HAS IT OWN	STELLAR FEW ARC SEC	HAS ITS OWN	
SAAX0018	VERY LONG BASE-LINE (VLBI)	ASTRO-PHYSICS	ON SPACE STATION (EXT) OR FREE-FLYER	1995	15m DIA ANT	1,350	0.9	STELLAR FEW ARC SEC	12 MBPS	
SAAX0019	FAR UV SPECT-ROSCOPY EXPLORER (FUSE) (SERVICING)	ASTRO-PHYSICS	FREE-FLYER SPACECRAFT	1993	5x4x4	1,350	HAS ITS OWN	STELLAR 1 ARC SEC	HAS ITS OWN	
SAAX0020	LARGE DEPLOYABLE REFLECTOR (LDR) CONSTR & SERV	ASTRO-PHYSICS	FREE-FLYER SPACECRAFT	1997	20m OPTICS	55,000	HAS ITS OWN	STELLAR 1 ARC SEC	HAS IT OWN	
SAAX0022	SOLAR SEISMOLOGY (SERVICE)	SOLAR PHYSICS	FREE-FLYER	1993	8x5x5	5,540	HAS ITS OWN	SOLAR 1 ARC SEC	HAS ITS OWN	
SAAX0101-0109	VARIOUS PLANETARY S/C	PLANETARY	VARIOUS TARGETS	1990-2000	VARIOUS	VARIOUS	HAS ITS OWN	N/A	HAS ITS OWN	②▷
SAAX0110	MARS SURFACE SAMPLE RETURN	PLANETARY	MARS AND RETURN	1996	N/A	9,045 PAYLOAD ONLY	HAS ITS OWN	N/A	HAS ITS OWN	

▷ NOT REALISTIC AS SPACE STATION MISSION
②▷ PLANETARY LAUNCHES FROM SPACE STATION NOT REALISTIC UNLESS PAYLOAD OUTGROWS SHUTTLE/CENTAUR CAPABILITY

Table 1.1 continued on next page

Table 1.1 Summary of NASA space station mission model for science and applications (April 1984 version)—*Continued*.

NASA INDEX NO.	NAME	CATEGORY	LOCATION	FIRST ACTIVE YEAR	SIZE (M)	MASS (KG)	POWER (KW)	POINTING	DATA
SAAX0201	LIDAR FACILITY	EARTH OBSER	ON SPACE STATION EXT & INT	1991	2.5x2.5 x2.5	1,900	4.5	EARTH, 1°	250 KBPS
SAAX0202	EARTH OBS SYS (PLATFORM)	EARTH OBSER	SUN SYNCH ORBIT	1992	4 DIA x19L	10,000	12	EARTH	300 MPBS
	CARRIES INSTRUMENTS SAAX0208-0220:								
SAAX0208	IMAGING SPECTROMETER								
SAAX0209	HIGH-RESOLUTION IMAGING SPECTROMETER								
SAAX0210	HIGH-RESOLUTION MICROWAVE RADIOMETER								
SAAX0211	LASER ATMOSPHERIC SOUNDER								
SAAX0212	SYNTHETIC APERTURE RADAR								
SAAX0213	RADAR ALTIMETER								
SAAX0214	SCATTEROMETER								
SAAX0215	TROPOSPHERIC COMPOSITION MONITOR								
SAAX0216	DIRECT TROPOSPHERIC WIND SENSING								
SAAX0217	UPPER ATMOSPHERE COMPOSITION								
SAAX0218	UPPER ATMOSPHERE WIND SOUNDING								
SAAX0219	ENVIRONMENTAL MONITORS								
SAAX0220	AUTOMATED DATA COLLECTION/LOCATION SYSTEM								

NASA INDEX NO.	NAME	CATEGORY	LOCATION	FIRST ACTIVE YEAR	SIZE (M)	MASS (KG)	POWER (KW)	POINTING	DATA	
SAAX0203	OCEAN TOPOGRAPHY (TOPEX)	OCEAN-OGRAPHY	63°x1,330 KM	1989	SMALL SPACE-CRAFT	327	HAS ITS OWN	EARTH	HAS ITS OWN	▷3
SAAX0204	GEOPOTENTIAL RESEARCH	EARTH PHYSICS	90°x160 KM	1990	SMALL SPACE-CRAFT	8,000	HAS ITS OWN	NONE	HAS ITS OWN	▷3
SAAX0205	GEOSYNCHRONOUS PLATFORM (ASSEMBLY; OTV SERVICE)	EARTH SCIENCE	GEO-ORBIT	1999	30x30x10m	7,000-15,000	5 (ITS OWN)	EARTH; FEW ARC SEC	100 MPBS	▷4
SAAX0206	UPPER ATMOSPHERE RESEARCH SATELLITE	ATMOS-SCIENCE	57°x 600 KM	1989	NOT GIVEN	NOT GIVEN	NOT GIVEN	EARTH	32 KBPS	▷3
SAAX0207	SPACE PLASMA PHYSICS	SPACE PHYSICS	SPACELAB PALLET ON SPACE STATION	1992	SL PALLET; LONG DIPOLE ANTENNA	3,200	3; 12 PK	EARTH & ANTI-EARTH	12 MPBS	
SAAX0221	LARGE MICROWAVE ANTENNA	EARTH SCIENCE	ON SPACE STATION	1999	30m ANTENNA	2,000-5,000	1	EARTH	100 KBPS	
SAAX0222	INFRARED SOUNDING	ATMOS-SCIENCE	ON SPACE STATION	1999	2m DIA x5 LONG	500-1,000	1	EARTH; FEW ARC SEC	5 KBPS	
SAAX0223	LARGE IMAGER	EARTH SCIENCE	ON SPACE STATION	1999	3m DIA x10L	2,500-5,000	3	EARTH; FEW ARC SEC	90 MPBS	

▷3 NOT A SPACE STATION MISSION

▷4 NOT TO BE CONFUSED WITH COMMERCIAL COMMUNICATIONS PLATFORM

Table 1.1 continued on next page

Table 1.1 Summary of NASA space station mission model for science and applications (April 1984 version)—*Continued.*

NASA INDEX*	NAME	CATEGORY	LOCATION	FIRST ACTIVE YEAR	SIZE (M)	MASS (KG)	POWER (KW)	POINTING	DATA	
SAAX0301	HEALTH MAINT CLINICAL RES	LIFE SCI HUMAN	IN SPACE STATION	IOC (1992)	NOT GIVEN	NOT GIVEN	NOT GIVEN	N/A	50MBPS	5▷
SAAX0302	ANIMAL/PLANT VIVARIUM & LAB	LIFE SCI NON-HUMAN	IN SPACE STATION	1995	13X1X2	4320	12	N/A	50KBPS	6▷
SAAX0303	HUMAN RESEARCH LABORATORY	LIFE SCI HUMAN	IN SPACE STATION	IOC (1992)	NOT GIVEN	NOT GIVEN	NOT GIVEN	N/A	50KBPS	5▷
SAAX0304	CELSS EXP'T'L SYSTEMS	FOOD GROWTH	IN SPACE STATION	1992	3X3X3	2625	10	N/A	50KBPS	
SAAX0305	DEDICATED CELSS MODULE	FOOD GROWTH	IN SPACE STATION	1999	4.4D X 5.5L	10500	30	NA	100KBPS	7▷
SAAX0306	CELSS PALLET	FOOD GROWTH	INSPACE STATION	1993	1X2.5X 0.5	1300	1	N/A	100KBPS	
SAAX0307	LIFE SCIENCES LAB	LIFE SCI ALL	IN SPACE STATION	IOC (1992)	4.4D X 7L	12000	10	N/A	50KBPS+	7▷
SAAX0401	MICROGRAVITY & MATLS PROC FAC	MATLS PROC SCIENCE	IN SPACE STATION	IOC (1992)	4.4D X 7L	12000	20 OR MORE	N/A	50KBPS +TV	7▷
SAAX0402	MICRO-G VARIABLE-G FREE FLYER	MATLS PROC SCIENCE	CO-ORBIT FREE FLYER	1998	6X2X2	5000	HAS ITS OWN	N/A	50KBPS + TV	
SAAX0403	MICROGRAVITY & MAT'LS PROC FAC	MATLS PROC SCIENCE	IN SPACE STATION	1993	13X1X3(?)	12000	60	N/A	50KBPS + TV	8▷
SAAX0501	EXPERIMENTAL GEO PLATFORM	COMMUNI- CATIONS	GEO ORBIT	1994	LARGE ANTENNA	5450	HAS ITS OWN	EARTH	HAS ITS OWN	

5▷ RESOURCES INCLUDED IN LIFE SCIENCES LABORATORY, SAAX0307

6▷ ROLE FILLED BY SAXX0307 BEFORE 1995

7▷ DEDICATED LAB MODULE

8▷ REPRESENTS GROWTH OF SAAX0401

space. Servicing operations, of course, are the key to *permanence* in space.

Space-basing of transportation vehicles such as orbit maneuvering vehicles and orbit-to-orbit stages (often called orbit transfer vehicles or OTVs) imposes significant configuration and operational requirements on a space station. Space transportation vehicles and operational infrastructures are described in the following chapter.

A space-based transportation vehicle requires storage and handling provisions, turnaround and maintenance provisions and facilities, propellant storage and stage refueling provisions, and a work area and support equipment for mating and integrating payloads with the transportation vehicle. A concept for a storage and maintenance area is shown in Figure 1.22. An integrated OTV handling facility concept is shown in Figure 1.23. This figure includes provisions for temporary storage of payloads as well as vehicles and a mating and launch platform for integration of payloads with OTVs.

The mission set for the initial space station includes operation of a space-based OMV (intended mainly for servicing operations) but not an OTV. The latter is intended as a delivery system for heavy payloads to high-energy orbits. Examples include communications platforms as well as manned sortie missions destined for GEO. These are forecast by the present mission models as needs falling in the 1995 and later time period.

Servicing operations as well as turnaround operations for space-based propulsive stages are predicted to be crew-intensive. Each and every maintenance and repair operation conducted up to the present time has involved direct crew participation. Most if not all of these operations have been conducted on equipment not designed to be serviced in space. Even if this problem is not present, however, crew involvement is seen as a necessary part of the operations missions planned for the space station. Servicing missions are included in Table 1.2.

Technology Development

Technology development missions are ordinarily viewed as government-funded. As a space station program evolves, opportunities for private funding of technology development missions will probably arise. Present mission analysis practice would place privately funded activity in the commercial category.

The development of large space structures assembly technology is a good example of a government-funded activity. Figures 1.24 and 1.25 illustrate examples of large space structures technology development missions defined by recent studies. The first of these figures illustrates a large-aperture microwave or radio telescope antenna; the second, a multimirror infrared or optical telescope system supported by a space-assembled structure. Figure 1.26 shows astronauts assembling an experimental structure from the Shuttle payload bay.

Table 1.2 Space station mission model—commercial mission set. *Courtesy of NASA.*

NASA INDEX*	NAME	CATEGORY	LOCATION	FIRST ACTIVE YEAR	SIZE (M)	MASS (KG)	POWER (KW)	POINTING	DATA	
COMM1014	REMOTE SENSING TEST, DEV, & VERIF	EARTH OBS	ON SPACE STATION	1993	3X4X2	1500	25(?)	EARTH 360 = ARC SEC	NOT GIVEN	[10]
COMM1019	MULTILINEAR STEREO ARRAY	EARTH OBS	POLAR PLATFORM	1991	1X1X1	92	1.4	EARTH FEW = ARC SEC	2.4 MBPS	
COMM1023	STEREO SAR, MLRA, CRCS	EARTH OBS	COMMON POLAR PLAT	1999	3X4X2	1500	30	EARTH FEW = ARC SEC	300 MBPS	
COMM1105	COMMUNICATIONS TEST LAB	COMMUNI-CATIONS	ON SPACE STATION	NOT GIVEN	NOT GIVEN	NOT GIVEN	NOT GIVEN	NOT GIVEN	NOT GIVEN	
COMM1110	CLASS IV COM-SAT DELIVERY	COMMUNI-CATIONS	GEO ORBIT	1998	FULL P/L BAY	5000	HAS ITS OWN	EARTH	HAS ITS OWN	[11]
COMM1115	CLASS IV COM-SAT DELIVERY	COMMUNI-CATIONS	GEO ORBIT	1996	4.5D X 12L	2500	HAS ITS OWN	EARTH	HAS ITS OWN	[11]
COMM1116	CLASS II COM-SAT DELIVERY	COMMUNI-CATIONS	GEO ORBIT	1995	4.5D X 6L	1800	HAS ITS OWN	EARTH	HAS ITS OWN	[11]

[8]> APPARENTLY A DEDICATED FACILITY BUT IS NOT CALLED OUT AS SUCH

[9]> DUPLICATES SAAX0403

[10]> COMMERICAL USE OF TDMX2260

[11]> TRANSPORTATION MISSION FOR SPACE STATION

NASA INDEX*	NAME	CATEGORY	LOCATION	FIRST ACTIVE YEAR	SIZE (M)	MASS (KG)	POWER (KW)	POINTING	DATA	
COMM1117	CLASS I COM-SAT DELIVERY	COMMUNI-CATIONS	GEO ORBIT	1995	4.5D X 3L	900	HAS ITS OWN	EARTH	HAS ITS OWN	[11]
COMM1124	CLASS IV COM-SAT SERVICING	SERVICING	GEO ORBIT	1998	4.5D X 3L	1000	HAS ITS OWN	N/A	HAS ITS OWN	[12]
COMM1125	CLASS III COM-SAT SERVICING	SERVICING	GEO ORBIT	1999	4.5D X 3L	1000	HAS ITS OWN	N/A	HAS ITS OWN	[12]
COMM1126	CLASS II COM-SAT SERVICING	SERVICING	GEO ORBIT	2000	4.5D X 3L	1000	HAS ITS OWN	N/A	HAS ITS OWN	[12]
COMM1201	MPS PROCESSING LAB I	MPS	ON SPACE STATION	1991	13X1X3(?)	16000	16	N/A	NOT GIVEN	[8][13]
COMM1202	EOS PRODUCTION UNITS	MPS	ON SPACE STATION	1991	3.5X3.5X4	4500	15	N/A	5KBPS	
COMM1203	ECG PRODUCTION UNITS	MPS	ON SPACE STATION	1991	1X1X3	5000	20	N/A	5KBPS	
COMM1204	MPS PROCESSING LAB II	MPS	ON SPACE STATION	1994	18X1X3	16000	40	N/A	5KBPS	[8]
COMM1205	ECG PRODUCTION UNITS NO. 2	MPS	ON SPACE STATION	1999	1X1X3	5000	20	N/A	5KBPS	

[12]> ASSUMES ROBOTIC OR TELEOPERATED SERVICER, MANNED SERVICES PAYLOAD WOULD BE ABOUT 3000KG PAYLOAD

[13]> APPEARS TO DUPLICATE OR OVERLAP SAAX0403, STATED TO INCLUDE TDMX2020

NASA INDEX*	NAME	CATEGORY	LOCATION	FIRST ACTIVE YEAR	SIZE (M)	MASS (KG)	POWER (KW)	POINTING	DATA
COMM1206	BIOLOGICAL PRODUCTION UNITS	MPS	ON SPACE STATION	1994	3.5X3.5X4	4500	20	N/A	5KBPS
COMM1208	CRYSTAL PRODUC-TION UNITS	MPS	ON SPACE STATION	1995	1X1X3	5000	32	N/A	5KBPS
COMM1213	CONTAINERLESS PRODUCTION UNITS	MPS	ON SPACE STATION	1995	1X1X3	5000	10	N/A	5KBPS
COMM1304	OMV	SERVICING	PROX OPS	1992	4D X 1L	1500	SMALL	N/A	16KBPS
COMM1309	SPACE BASED OTV	SERVICING	PROX OPS	1994	4.3D X 6L	3000	SMALL	N/A	16KBPS
COMM1312	SATELLITE SERVICING	SERVICING	ACCESSIBLE ORBITS	1992	4.3D X 6L	14000	NOT GIVEN	N/A	NOT GIVEN
COMM1318	MULTI USE PLATFORM	[14]>							

[14]> IN MISSION MODEL AS A "PLACEHOLDER". CAN BE IGNORED

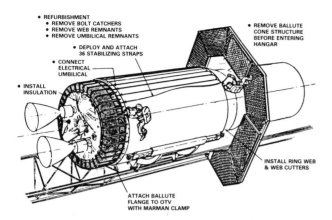

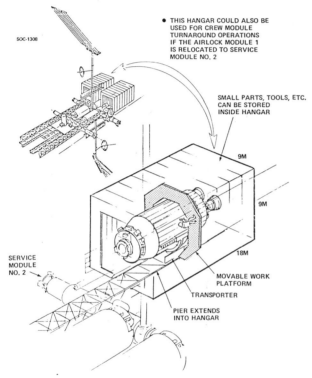

Figure 1.22 Space station hangar concepts for a space-based OTV. *Courtesy of Boeing/NASA.*

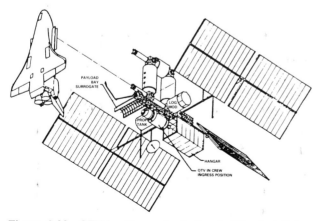

Figure 1.23 OTV handling and refueling facilities installed on a small space station. *Courtesy of Boeing.*

The large space structures missions place significant requirements on the space station for work areas and provisions, and in addition influence flight control technology in two ways. First, space station balance and inertial distributions (that impact static controllability) experience major excursions as a result of presence of large space structures. Secondly, the structural dynamics response of a space station can be driven almost entirely by the dynamics of large space structures construction projects. Planning for space station static and dynamic controllability must anticipate large space structures construction projects.

The NASA technology mission set for the initial space station is presented in Table 1.3. The benefits of crew involvement derive mainly from EVA structural assembly operations. These missions are entirely dependent on the presence of a space station for successful completion.

National Security

Space missions funded by the Department of Defense or any other agency concerned with national security are placed

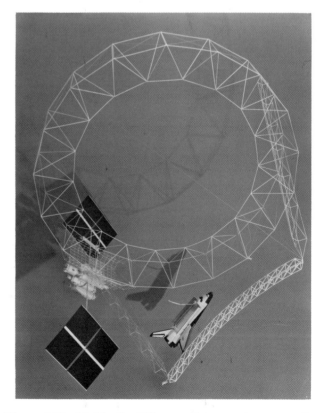

Figure 1.24 Model of a 100-meter-diameter microwave radiometer structural support ring attached to space station construction facility. *Courtesy of Boeing.*

Table 1.3 Space station mission model—technology development mission set. *Courtesy of NASA.*

NASA INDEX*	NAME	CATEGORY	LOCATION	FIRST ACTIVE YEAR	SIZE (M)	MASS (KG)	POWER (KW)	POINTING	DATA	
TDMX2010	MATERIALS PERFORMANCE TECH	MATLS TESTING	ON SPACE STATION	1991	0.2X2X3	700	< 1	SOLAR EXPOSURE	NONE	▷
TDMX2020	MATERIALS PROCESSING TECH	MPS	ON SPACE STATION	1991	–	–	–	–	–	▷
TDMX2060	DEPLOYMENT/ ASSEMBLY CONSTRUCTION	SPACE STRUCTURE	ON/AT SPACE STATION	1992	4X4X13 LARGE	9000	NOT GIVEN	N/A	10KBPS + TV	
TDMX2070	STRUCTURAL DYNAMICS	SPACE STRUCTURE	ON/AT SPACE STATION	1992	1X1X10 LARGE	4000	< 1	N/A	2KBPS	
TDMX2080	DESIGN VERIF TECHNOLOGY	SPACE STRUCTURE	ON/AT SPACE STATION	1992	2X0.2X0.2	650	< 1	N/A	2KBPS + TV	▷
TDMX2110	LARGE SOLAR CONC TECHNOLOGY	SPACE STRUCTURE	ON/AT SPACE STATION	1996	10 M DIA	4000	< 1	N/A	1KBPS + TV	
TDMX2120	LASER POWER TRANS/RECEPT	POWER	ON/NEAR SPACE STATION	1997	1X0.5X0.5	200	< 1	SOLAR	8KBPS + TV	▷
TDMX2130	WASTE HEAT REJ TECH (LIQUID DROP- LET RADIATOR)	THERMAL	ON/NEAR SPACE STATION	1995	3X3X6	1000	1	N/A	NOT GIVEN	
TDMX2150	POWER SYSTEM TECHNOLOGY	POWER	ON/NEAR SPACE STATION	1996	NOT GIVEN	200	NOT GIVEN	SOLAR	NOT GIVEN	▷
TDMX2210	ANTENNA TECH	COMMUNI- CATION	ON SPACE STATION	1993	UP TO 50 M DIA	3000	< 1	INERTIAL 360 = ARC SEC	1.5KBPS + TV	
TDMX2220	TELECOM SYSTEMS TECH	COMMUNI- CATION	ON SPACE STATION	1996	1X2X0.5	200	< 1	INERTIAL	500KBPS	

▷ NOT A WELL-DEFINED MISSION

NASA INDEX*	NAME	CATEGORY	LOCATION	FIRST ACTIVE YEAR	SIZE (M)	MASS (KG)	POWER (KW)	POINTING	DATA	
TDMX2230	SPACE INTERFER- OMETER SYST TECH	RADIO ASTRONOMY	AT/NEAR SPACE STATION	1995	4X4X3 LARGE ANT	264	< 1	INERTIAL & EARTH	750KBPS	
TDMX2260	EARTH OBS INSTR TECH	EARTH OBS	ON SPACE STATION	1992	1X1X10	5000	3	EARTH	120MBPS	
TDMX2310	FLUID MGMT TECH	FLUID PHYSICS	ON SPACE STATION	1991	4.5D X 4L	2500	1	N/A	64KBPS	
TDMX2320	LOW THRUST PROPULSION	PROPULSION	ON SPACE STATION	1994	1X1X1	25	1.5	N/A	4KBPS	
TDMX 2410	ATTITUDE CONTROL TECH	ATTITUDE CONTROL	ON SPACE STATION	1992	3X3X3	500	< 1	INERTIAL	NOT GIVEN	
TDMX2420	FIGURE CONTROL TECH	STRUCTURES/ OPTICS	ON SPACE STATION	1992	3X3X3	500	1	INERTIAL	NOT GIVEN	
TDMX2430	ADV CONTROL DEV TECH	ATTITUDE CONTROL	ON SPACE STATION	1994	NOT GIVEN	NOT GIVEN	< 1	NOT GIVEN	NOT GIVEN	▷
TDMX2460	TELEPRESENCE TECH	TELEOPER- ATION	ON SPACE STATION	1993	1.3X1.3X1.3	500	< 1	N/K	NOT GIVEN	
TDMX2470	HUMAN FACTORS TECH	HUMAN FACTORS	ON SPACE STATION	1993	1.7X0.50X1.7	450	3	N/K	2KBPS	
TDMX2510	ENVIR EFFECTS TECH	POWER	ON SPACE STATION	1991	10X1X0.3	2800	1	SOLAR	2KBPS	
TDMX2520	HABITATION TECH	HUMAN FACTORS	ON SPACE STATION	1991	0.5X0.4X0.5	40	< 1	N/A	NOT GIVEN	
TDMX2530	MEDICAL TECH	HUMAN FACTORS	ON SPACE STATION	1991	———	———	———	———	———	▷
TDMX2560	SAT SERV TECH	SERVICING	ON SPACE STATION	1991	3X1X1	3200	2.5	N/A	NOT GIVEN	▷
TDMX2570	OTV SERV TECH	TRANSP	ON SPACE STATION	1991	1X10X1	8000	1.2	N/A	4KBPS + TV	▷

▷ RESOURCES INCLUDED IN SAAX0307

in this category. They are not discussed further in this book. The DOD has, as of this writing, expressed little interest in use of a civilian space station other than perhaps for technology development. This potential application is technically similar to that described above.

Current Platform Activities

Space platforms represent a new concept of space operations. Certain initial missions and activities, however, are already being conducted.

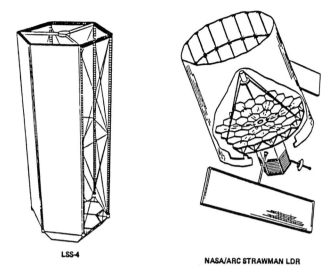

LSS-4   NASA/ARC STRAWMAN LDR

Figure 1.25 Concepts for space-assembled optical reflector instruments. *Courtesy of Boeing.*

Germany has pioneered development of a small space platform called SPAS. It flew on STS-7 and is illustrated in Figure 1.27. On later missions, SPAS may be left in orbit by the Shuttle and revisited or retrieved on a subsequent flight. The Long Duration Exposure Facility (LDEF), under development by NASA, is a simple platform. Illustrated in Figure 1.28, LDEF is to carry materials samples for exposure to the space environment. LDEF has no data, power,

or attitude control subsystems. It will be deposited in orbit by the Shuttle in a gravity-gradient stable attitude and retrieved on a subsequent flight.

ESA is developing a Shuttle-compatible platform called EURECA (*Eu*ropean *Re*coverable *Ca*rrier). An artist's concept is shown in Figure 1.29. EURECA is designed for on-orbit periods of six to nine months, with the ability to host a variety of payloads including Earth observation and materials processing. EURECA is designed for a platform payload up to 1000 kg, with 1000 watts of continuous electrical power to the payload.

Platform Missions

Allocation of missions to space platforms versus manned space stations follows a few simple criteria.

Platforms are expected to offer a more contamination-free and gravity-disturbance-free environment. Those payloads needing the greatest protection from contamination and from motion disturbances are best suited to platforms, especially if they do not need frequent manned attention.

Pointing stability of a space station can be improved by use of an instrument pointing system (IPS) like the one developed for Shuttle use by Dornier G.m.b.H. of West Germany. The Dornier IPS is illustrated in Figure 1.30. Its estimated pointing stability improvement is mapped in Figure 1.31, showing that pointing accuracies on the order of 1 arc second are expected. This is adequate for some, but not all, applications. The Space Telescope, for example, is designed to provide more than two orders of magnitude greater precision, 0.007 arc second.

A manned station offers frequent crew involvement in missions without high cost, especially if the crew involvement does not require suited extravehicular activity (EVA). Crew access to formation-flying platforms involves EVA and consequently is not "routine" in the same sense as crew involvement in missions that are carried out in a space station within the pressurized environment.

Figure 1.26 Shuttle astronaut with experimental EVA-assembled structure. *Courtesy of NASA.*

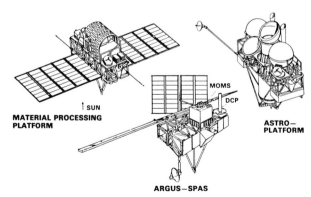

Figure 1.27 The ARGUS-SPAS and other European platforms. *Courtesy of ESA.*

Figure 1.28 Long-Duration Exposure Facility (LDEF) retrievable space platform (first launch April 1984). *Courtesy of NASA.*

Mission Accommodations

Electrical power needs of the mission set are driven by materials processing needs. These are somewhat uncertain, largely dictated by projection of commercial uses that presently enjoy investment only for technical demonstration. It is necessary to recognize these needs because failure to do so becomes a self-fulfilling prophecy: if insufficient power is available, the dependent commercial missions will not be forthcoming. Present estimates of electrical power needs for the users of an initial space station range upwards of 60 kW. Growth to twice this figure is projected by the year 2000. Clearly, provision of mission enabling power is a

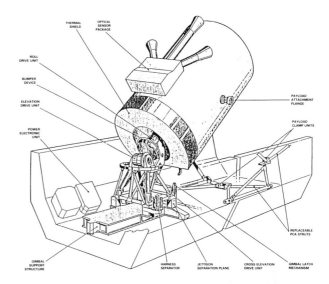

Figure 1.29 The European EURECA recoverable platform concept. *Courtesy of MBB/ERNO.*

Figure 1.30 The Dornier instrument pointing system. *Courtesy of Dornier G.m.b.H.*

IPS AND PHM STABILITY AND PAYLOAD RANGE

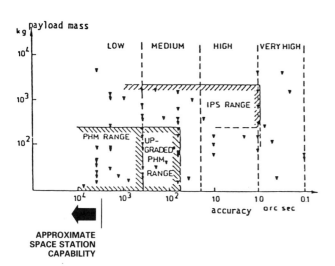

Figure 1.31 Pointing performance estimates for the Dornier instrument pointing system. *Courtesy of Dornier G.m.b.H.*

major concern for the space station designer. Space station power is a major design consideration; this requirement is discussed in later chapters.

Extravehicular, i.e., spacesuit, activities have been practiced since the early days of the Gemini program. The Apollo lunar landings employed extensive EVA, more ambitious on each successive mission. Skylab employed EVA for exchange of film and sensor equipment on mission instruments as well as for repair of the spacecraft itself, most notably in the release of the jammed solar array and deployment of a sunshade that saved the entire mission. Crew involvement needs for the space station include extensive

plans for EVA to support servicing and large space structures assembly operations as well as comprehensive crew involvements in life sciences and materials research conducted in the space station laboratories, and many operational duties involving normal day-to-day station operations as well as special operations such as control of vehicles flying in immediate proximity to the space station.

The electrical power requirements of a space station, some 75 kW or more, lead to a major requirement for thermal management. Thermal loads onboard a space station, in addition to being highly variable, will also migrate according to crew location as well as according to mission and experiment operations. Design of the thermal management system, discussed in a later chapter, must account for the special requirements of space station operations.

User needs create the primary requirement on the space station data system for flexibility and throughput. Some user missions, especially those involving Earth imaging, may need very high data rates, hundreds of megabits per second or more. Others need real-time access to mission data and real-time control of payloads. Still others are extremely sensitive to various mission parameters such as orbital state vectors, pointing attitudes, and the state of the zero-g, vacuum, or contamination environments. Influences of these needs on data system design are included in data system design considerations in a later chapter. Also described are the expected demands on the data system to support space station operations.

Definition of mission requirements on the space station design and design of practical solutions to these requirements has been an ongoing, highly volatile process. This book offers insight into the issues and options, but does not pretend any special prescience into the outcome of systems and design studies.

Chapter 2
Space Station Operations

Vehicles in the Infrastructure

The U.S. space program is entering an era of routine space operations supporting end-use missions. Routine space operations will rely upon a number of systems and operational capabilities; the term *infrastructure* refers to this aggregate. The Space Shuttle is the harbinger of the new era; the 1984 Solar Max repair mission epitomizes the emerging space operations philosophy. The space station is the logical next step by way of its utility for servicing and transportation operations. The space station offers the means to extend reusability, permanence, and routine operations to geosynchronous orbit and beyond through space-basing of reusable upper stages. It offers economies of scale in space transportation by providing a terminal in low Earth orbit for operation of heavy-lift systems—a terminal that will serve as a warehouse and staging area for payloads as well as a tank farm and refueling station for upper stages. These functions offer substantial advances in effectiveness and flexibility of space transportation operations.

This chapter describes existing and planned vehicles that will serve present and future space operations needs, and how they will operate with the space station.

Launch Systems: The Space Shuttle

The Space Shuttle, depicted in Figure 2.1, is to be the basic means of servicing the space station. NASA space station design activities are premised on the use of the Shuttle to launch, assemble, and resupply the space station.

The Shuttle is comprised of three main flight elements: the solid-propellant boosters, the external tank that carries and delivers the liquid hydrogen and oxygen propellants to the Space Shuttle main engines in the Orbiter, and the Orbiter itself.

The boosters and the main engines both operate at liftoff. The main engines, fed from the external tank, are started and brought to full power. Upon confirmation of full power, the solid rockets are ignited and the Shuttle lifts off. The solid rockets burn for about 120 seconds and are separated at about 50 km altitude and 1540 meters per second inertial velocity. The main engines continue to operate, burning

propellant from the external tank, until orbital velocity is nearly achieved. On a normal Shuttle mission the main engines shut down just short of orbital velocity. The external tank is jettisoned and enters the atmosphere approximately half an orbit later, falling into the Indian Ocean off Australia. On a "direct insertion" mission, as used for the Solar Max repair mission and planned for space station servicing, the main engines operate until the Shuttle Orbiter is driven into a transfer orbit with apogee (see Chapter 3) at the mission orbit altitude. The external tank is then jettisoned and travels most of one orbit before reentry; the impact point is near the Hawaiian Islands. Direct insertion provides Shuttle payload capability near the nominal 29.5 metric tonnes to more than 500 km altitude; without direct insertion, Shuttle's payload capability deteriorates very rapidly above about 370 km.

Figure 2.2 illustrates a representative Shuttle mission profile. Shuttle performance capabilities projected for the space

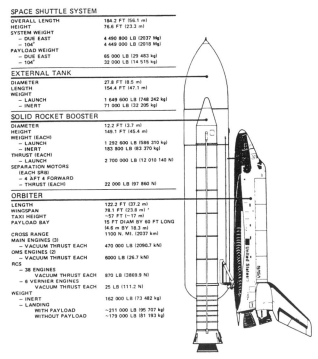

SPACE SHUTTLE SYSTEM	
OVERALL LENGTH	184.2 FT (56.1 m)
HEIGHT	76.6 FT (23.3 m)
SYSTEM WEIGHT	
– DUE EAST	4 490 800 LB (2037 Mg)
– 104°	4 449 000 LB (2018 Mg)
PAYLOAD WEIGHT	
– DUE EAST	65 000 LB (29 483 kg)
– 104°	32 000 LB (14 515 kg)
EXTERNAL TANK	
DIAMETER	27.8 FT (8.5 m)
LENGTH	154.4 FT (47.1 m)
WEIGHT	
– LAUNCH	1 649 600 LB (748 242 kg)
– INERT	71 000 LB (32 205 kg)
SOLID ROCKET BOOSTER	
DIAMETER	12.2 FT (3.7 m)
HEIGHT	149.1 FT (45.4 m)
WEIGHT (EACH)	
– LAUNCH	1 292 600 LB (586 310 kg)
– INERT	183 800 LB (83 370 kg)
THRUST (EACH)	
– LAUNCH	2 700 000 LB (12 010 140 N)
SEPARATION MOTORS	
(EACH SRB)	
– 4 AFT 4 FORWARD	
– THRUST (EACH)	22 000 LB (97 860 N)
ORBITER	
LENGTH	122.2 FT (37.2 m)
WINGSPAN	78.1 FT (23.8 m)
TAXI HEIGHT	~57 FT (~17 m)
PAYLOAD BAY	15 FT DIAM BY 60 FT LONG (4.6 m BY 18.3 m)
CROSS RANGE	1100 N. MI. (2037 km)
MAIN ENGINES (3)	
– VACUUM THRUST EACH	470 000 LB (2090.7 kN)
OMS ENGINES (2)	
– VACUUM THRUST EACH	6000 LB (26.7 kN)
RCS	
– 38 ENGINES	
VACUUM THRUST EACH	870 LB (3869.9 N)
– 6 VERNIER ENGINES	
VACUUM THRUST EACH	25 LB (111.2 N)
WEIGHT	
– INERT	162 000 LB (73 482 kg)
– LANDING	
WITH PAYLOAD	~211 000 LB (95 707 kg)
WITHOUT PAYLOAD	~179 000 LB (81 193 kg)

Figure 2.1 The Space Shuttle system. *Courtesy of NASA.*

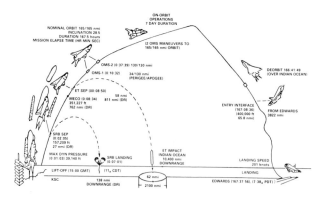

Figure 2.2 Representative Space Shuttle mission profile (STS-4 data shown). *Courtesy of NASA.*

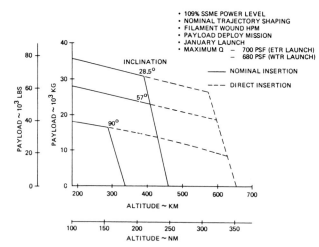

Figure 2.3 Projected Space Shuttle performance for the space station era. *Courtesy of NASA.*

station era are presented in Figure 2.3. The figures presented are gross launch (i.e., lift) capabilities. Everything chargeable to payload must be included within these capabilities, e.g. payload support equipment, extra crew, extra time on orbit. Management reserves (allowances for contingencies) are also normally applied, further reducing the net payload. The present limit on Shuttle landing payload is 14,400 kg. (32,000 lb). This value applies to payloads intended for landing. Launch payloads not intended for landing are not limited to 14,400 kg. (32,000 lb). Inasmuch as a launch emergency might require a landing, these payloads are still subject to the landing center-of-gravity (CG) limits described below.

Launch Systems: Shuttle Derivative Vehicles

The Shuttle propulsion system places more than 100 metric tonnes in orbit. Most of the mass is the Shuttle Orbiter itself, essential if a flight crew is needed in orbit or if a payload needs to be returned to Earth. If, however, a simple delivery of payload to orbit is needed, the Orbiter is somewhat superfluous (but it offers the ability to return payloads to Earth in the event of problems, a capability not offered by unmanned systems). The Shuttle propulsion system could be configured as an unmanned delivery system capable of heavy payload delivery as illustrated in Figure 2.4. One, two, or three Shuttle engines might be used on the core vehicle, depending on the desired payload. A single engine offers a modest increase over Orbiter payload capability, and two or three engines offer major increases. Shuttle derivative vehicles (SDV) performance capabilities are graphed in Figure 2.5. SDVs are under study by NASA and the Air Force; no firm development plans presently exist.

Because the SDV could fly at roughly Shuttle costs and deliver two to three times the payload, it offers significant economies at relatively little development cost where a demand exists for heavy payload delivery. This offers a major payoff for delivery to orbit of propellant for space-based

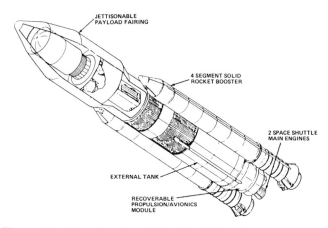

Figure 2.4 Cargo launch vehicle derived from Shuttle propulsion systems. *Courtesy of Boeing.*

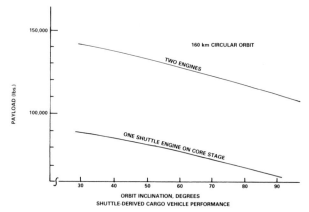

Figure 2.5 Shuttle-derived cargo vehicle performance. *Courtesy of Boeing.*

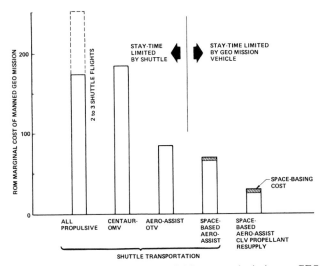

Figure 2.6 Cost reduction potential for manned missions to GEO with advancements in space transportation technology. *Courtesy of Boeing.*

upper stages. A tank farm at the space station would provide the operational buffer between launch operations and upper stage operations. The SDV would deliver propellant to the space station tank farm, from which the upper stage—the orbit transfer vehicle (OTV)—would be fueled. This operating mode offers the possibility of manned missions to geosynchronous orbit at low enough cost to make manned satellite servicing at GEO an economically viable proposition. Figure 2.6 illustrates manned geosynchronous mission cost trending from Shuttle-Centaur technology to space-based aerobraked OTVs with propellant delivery to the space station by a heavy-lift vehicle. The rapid accumulation of commercial and other space assets at GEO makes economic manned access to that orbit an exciting potential for the future of routine space operations.

Orbital Systems: Orbital Maneuvering Vehicle

Early in the Shuttle development program it was seen that a small, maneuverable propulsive vehicle could greatly enhance Shuttle operations. The Shuttle Orbiter is a massive vehicle. Its propellant consumption for a given change in velocity is, of course, proportional to its mass. Many payload delivery and retrieval operations, once the Shuttle has placed the payload in orbit, can be accomplished by a much smaller vehicle. Such a vehicle, illustrated in Figure 2.7, is at this writing in the early stages of development. This device was originally called a teleoperator maneuvering system (TMS) by NASA but is now known as the orbital maneuvering vehicle (OMV). The OMV is planned for initial service as an adjunct of the Shuttle. When the space station becomes operational, one or more OMVs will be based at the station. OMVs will deliver payloads from the Shuttle or station to more energetic orbits, retrieve payloads and

return them to the Shuttle or station for servicing or return to Earth, and perhaps conduct teleoperated servicing. (The term *teleoperated* infers human control of operations through remote control links. Typically, cameras on the OMV would relay video to the human operator, who would in turn control manipulators and other equipment to carry out the servicing operation.)

The OMV planned by NASA is to carry a propellant load of storable bipropellants (biprops) of 3175 kg (7000 lb). Cold gas thrusters for low-contamination operation near sensitive payloads may be provided. OMV delivery, retrieval, and round-trip payload performance is graphed in Figure 2.8. The OMV is planned as a reusable vehicle; all the performance data shown presume retrieval of the OMV.

The OMV by itself does not have the ability to reach geosynchronous orbit, but could be delivered there by a more powerful upper stage such as Centaur or an OTV. Depending on success in developing teleoperated servicing techniques, delivery of OMVs to GEO for servicing operations may become a useful means of extending servicing to this altitude before manned missions to GEO are implemented.

Orbital Systems: Orbit Transfer Vehicles

The term *orbit transfer vehicle* (OTV) implies a vehicle able to deliver payloads through major orbit changes such as from low Earth orbit to GEO or to lunar orbit. Delivery to and return from GEO is often used as a design reference mission.

Figure 2.7 Orbital Maneuvering Vehicle (OMV) concept with Shuttle Orbiter in background. *Courtesy of Boeing.*

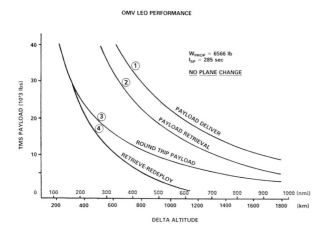

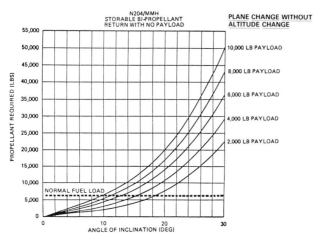

Figure 2.8 OMV performance for altitude change and plane change deliveries. *Courtesy of Boeing/NASA.*

The existing inertial upper stage (IUS) and the Centaur offer this service. Current use of the term *OTV*, however, refers to an advanced, reusable vehicle contemplated by NASA for initial service in the mid-1990s. Such a vehicle could operate either from the Shuttle or from a space station. It would very likely make use of aerodynamic drag in the upper atmosphere for transition from high-energy return transfer ellipses to low Earth orbit. A broad spectrum of OTV concepts is presently under study. A planning date for a development start has not yet been set. Figure 2.9 illustrates representative vehicle concepts.

Most OTV concepts have featured propellant capacities from 20 to 40 metric tonnes. Designs for special applications have employed both smaller and larger loads. OTV concepts have most often employed liquid oxygen and liquid hydrogen propellants, but a few studies have invoked storables or other combinations. Propellant fraction (that mass fraction of the fully fueled vehicle that is useful, i.e., impulse, propellant) is typically about 0.87 to 0.89, but less in cases where an aerobrake is employed. Aerobrakes tend toward about 10 to 20 percent of the retarded mass (vehicle inert

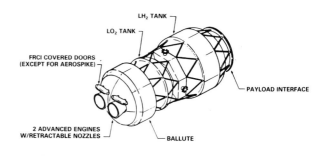

Ballute Brake Configuration

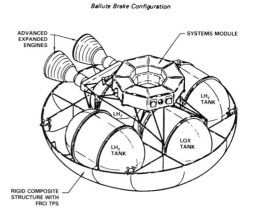

Sharped Brake Configuration

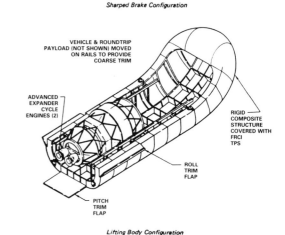

Lifting Body Configuration

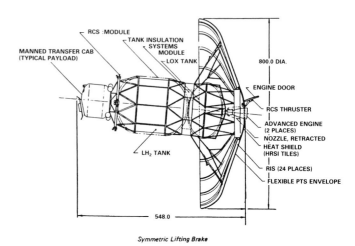

Symmetric Lifting Brake

Figure 2.9 Representative Orbit Transfer Vehicle (OTV) design concepts. *Courtesy of Boeing.*

Table 2.1 Typical Orbit Transfer Vehicle (OTV) mass summary. *Courtesy of Boeing.*

Item	Mass (kg)
Structure	1447
Thermal Control	124
Avionics	292
Electrical Power System (EPS)	234
Main Propulsion System (MPS)	691
Attitude Control System (ACS)	125
Space Maintenance Provisions	216
Weight Growth Margin	468
(Dry Weight-Less Ballute)	(3597)
Residuals	413
Reserves	332
(Burnout Weight)	(4342)
Ballute	308
Inflight Losses	382
Fuel Cell Reactant	46
Attitude Control Propellant	326
Main Impulse Propellant	32,289
(OTV Gross Weight)	(37,693)
Payload	7687
(OTV + P/L Weight)	(45,380)
OTV Mass Fraction	0.8638

**Geo Base Support
(Crew Rotation/Resupply)
7600 Kg Up, 5000 Kg Down**

plus remaining propellant plus payload masses), the lesser value for non-lifting inflatables and the greater for rigid or lifting types. Table 2.1 presents typical mass summaries from recent design studies. Table 2.2 presents representative mission profiles for all-propulsive and aerobraked missions to GEO with return of the OTV to low Earth orbit. These mission profiles were computed using a specific impulse of 460 seconds (jet velocity 4511 m/sec). Figure 2.10 shows parametric performance to GEO for several mission cases.

Transfers to and from lunar orbit demand slightly smaller velocity changes than do transfers to GEO, the one-way delta v (Δv) being about 4000 m/sec as compared to 4250 m/sec.

Vehicle Performance Estimating

Calculations of propellant consumption for rocket vehicles are usually carried out using a delta v budget and the ideal rocket equation. The delta v budget expresses the propulsion requirement for each maneuver as an equivalent ideal delta v occurring in a gravity free vacuum. The ideal delta v includes allowances for losses induced by gravity, drag, atmospheric pressure, and use of the rocket jet for attitude and directional control of the vehicle. For launch vehicles, these losses typically average 15 percent of orbital velocity in low orbits. For OTVs, the losses are ordinarily small (1 to 2 percent) compared to the delta v needed to overcome differences in orbital energy.

Table 2.2 Typical OTV mission and remaining mass sequence.

AERO-ASSISTED OTV MISSION PROFILE

Event	Delta V (m/s)	Prop Usage (kg)	Losses (kg)	Mass Remaining (kg)
Start Burn				50,830
Separate	3	72	3	50,755
Phase Inject	1,370	12,700	44	38,011
Trans Inject	1,098	7,834	19	30,157
Midcourse	15	109	20	30,027
GEO Circ	1,771	9,335	17	20,676
Orbit Trim	9	87	9	20,580
Deploy Payload	0	0	1	7,053
(13,526)				
Trans Inject	1,844	2,265	24	4,764
Midcourse	20	22	20	4,721
Aeromaneuver	0	0	201	4,520
Inject	67	63	17	4,439
LEO Circ	122	112	18	4,310
Rend and Dock	18	36	5	4,269
Reserves	137	121	0	4,128

ALL-PROPULSIVE OTV MISSION PROFILE

Event	Delta V (m/s)	Prop Usage (kg)	Losses (kg)	Mass Remaining (kg)
Start Burn				50,830
Separate	3	72	3	50,755
Phase Inject	1,370	12,700	44	38,011
Trans Inject	1,098	7,834	19	30,157
Midcourse	15	109	20	30,027
GEO Circ	1,771	9,335	17	20,676
Orbit Trim	9	87	9	20,580
Deploy Payload	0	0	1	10,593
(9,987)				
Trans Inject	1,771	3,291	24	7,295
Midcourse	20	22	20	7,253
LEO Circ	2,468	2,943	18	4,310
Rend and Dock	18	36	5	4,269
Reserves	137	121	0	4,128

Propellant consumption for an ideal delta v maneuver is determined from a momentum balance between the vehicle and the departing jet:

$$m_v dv = v_j \, dm. \qquad (2.1)$$

This differential equation is integrated to give

$$\text{(initial mass)/(final mass)} = m_o/m_f = exp(\delta v/v_j) \qquad (2.2)$$

a result first obtained by Tsiolkovskii and later, independently, by others. If the ratio of initial to final mass for a

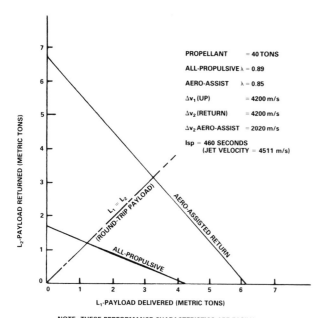

NOTE: THESE PERFORMANCE CHARACTERISTICS ARE EASILY OBTAINED FROM EQ. 2.8 AND 2.9 OR 2.11 AND 2.12. IF MISSION AND VEHICLE-SPECIFIC PARAMETERS ARE INSERTED, EQUATIONS OF THE FORM $a_1 \cdot L_1 + b_1 \cdot L_2 = m_{pi}$, i = 1, 2 ARE OBTAINED. ADDING THE EQUATIONS FOR i = 1 AND 2 YIELDS A LINEAR EXPRESSION FOR L_1 AND L_2 IN TERMS OF $m_{p1} + m_{p2}$. SINCE THE LATTER IS A CONSTANT, I.E. THE VEHICLE PROPELLANT CAPACITY, THE GRAPH OF THIS EQUATION IS THE PERFORMANCE CHARACTERISTIC.

Figure 2.10 Representative OTV performance for GEO delivery and return. Isp = (jet velocity)/g, units of sec. comes from dividing thrust lb_f by propellant flow lb_m/sec.

given delta v is expressed as μ, then the propellant used is obtained from

$$m_p = (\mu - 1)m_o. \qquad (2.3)$$

Application of this equation to mission sequences such as in Table 2.2 is readily apparent.

It is frequently desirable to use the performance estimating equations simultaneously with mass estimating relationships to size vehicles. The simplest form of this technique is for a single-stage vehicle with payload to be delivered through the entire ideal delta v. In this case, the definitions of the ideal rocket equation and the propellant fraction $\lambda = m_p/(m_i + m_p)$, where m_1 is the inert mass of the rocket stage, are easily combined to yield an expression for the ratio of initial mass to payload mass:

$$\frac{m_o}{m_L} = \frac{\mu\lambda}{1 - (1-\lambda)\mu}. \qquad (2.4)$$

Since, in a multistage vehicle, each subsequent stage is the payload for the prior stage, the above expression is simply multiplicative for multistage vehicles.

Certain applications such as delivery to GEO of one payload, with return either of a different payload (mass) or no payload, need a "split-payload" expression. This is quite simple for a fixed vehicle inert mass, but if vehicle sizing is included, it involves three equations in three unknowns.

If vehicle inert mass is expressed by m_I, the three equations are

$$m_I + m_{p2} + L_2 = \mu_2(m_I + L_2) \qquad (2.5)$$

$$m_I + m_{p1} + m_{p2} + L_1 = \mu_1(m_I + m_{p2} + L_1) \qquad (2.6)$$

$$m_I = \frac{(1-\lambda)}{\lambda}(m_{p1} + m_{p2}) \qquad (2.7)$$

where L_1 and L_2 are total payloads on legs 1 and 2 m_{p1} and m_{p2} are propellant used per leg.

A simultaneous equation routine can be readily employed to solve these. Algebraic substitution yields the following discrete formulae for propellant quantities:

$$m_{p1} = \frac{(\mu_1 - 1)\{[1 - \mu_2(1-\lambda)]L_1 + (\mu_2 - 1)L_2\}}{1 - \mu_1\mu_2(1-\lambda)} \qquad (2.8)$$

$$m_{p2} = \frac{(\mu_1 - 1)(\mu_2 - 1)(1-\lambda)L_1 + [1 - \mu_1(1-\lambda)](\mu_2 - 1)L_2}{1 - \mu_1\mu_2(1-\lambda)}. \qquad (2.9)$$

The use of propellant fraction as an estimator of vehicle inert weight, although common, suffers from inconstancy with variation in propellant capacity. Numerous design studies have shown that inert weight is more accurately estimated by a fixed quantity that includes factors such as avionics, and a quantity proportional to propellant weight representing factors such as tank weight. This trending represents inert weight as

$$m_I = a + b(m_{p1} + m_{p2}). \qquad (2.10)$$

The split-payload equation again appears as three equations in three unknowns, with eq. 2.10 replacing eq. 2.7.

This equation is resolved by substitution, yielding

$$m_{p1} = \frac{\mu_1 - 1}{1 - b(\mu_2\mu_1 - 1)}\{(L_2 + a)(\mu_2 - 1)(1 + b) + (L_1 + a)[1 - b(\mu_2 - 1)]\} \qquad (2.11)$$

$$m_{p2} = \frac{\mu_2 - 1}{1 - b(\mu_2\mu_1 - 1)}\{(L_2 + a)[1 - b(\mu_1 - 1)] + b(L_1 + a)(\mu_1 - 1)\} \qquad (2.12)$$

These expressions provide an overview means of roughly estimating vehicle performance. If the values of a and b are derived from suitably accurate preliminary design parametrics, results are entirely compatible with the accuracy usually accorded preliminary design studies.

Flying in the Shuttle

The Space Shuttle, a reusable space launch vehicle that flies not only as a rocket but also as an unpowered aircraft, poses

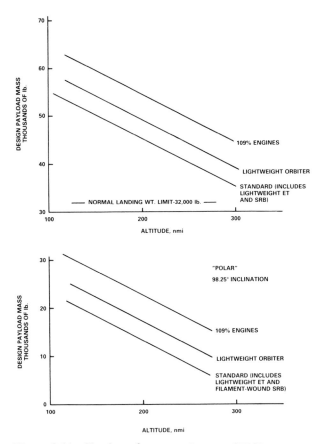

Figure 2.11 Shuttle performance. *Courtesy of NASA.*

a number of constraints for designers that do not apply to unmanned, expendable launch systems. Payload mass capabilities and size constraints are of course applicable to all launch systems. In addition, the Shuttle user must be concerned with center-of-gravity limits, safety requirements, and the location and capability of load carrying points within the payload bay. Other factors include design loads for landing as well as launch, and limitations for access to payloads while the Shuttle is in the final days and hours of the launch countdown process.

Mass and Volume Limits

Nominal Shuttle payload mass capability versus altitude for normal and direct insertion launch operations for three representative orbit inclinations were shown in Figure 2.3. Shuttle performance depends, however, on the main engine thrust level used as well as on the particular Orbiter (each has a somewhat different inert mass), the solid rocket booster, and flight envelope limits associated with the time of year. Some of these characteristics are described in Figure 2.11.

The Shuttle payload bay dimensions are 4.57 meters (15 feet) in diameter by 18.29 meters (60 feet). Payloads must be smaller than these dimensions by the amount necessary to allow for structural dynamics excursions experienced in

flight. Dynamic clearances are typically on the order of 10 cm, but must be confirmed by detailed structural dynamics analyses to ensure that loads and dynamics experienced in flight will not cause damage to Shuttle Orbiters or payloads.

Loads

Loads applicable to Shuttle payloads include launch loads as well as reentry and landing loads. Launch loads come from the accelerations imposed by the launch propulsion system, including applicable dynamic factors. Reentry loads are modest. Landing loads include those due to nominal as well as emergency landing conditions. Landing loads are applicable to all payloads whether or not normal operations would involve a landing. All payloads are subject to a "return to launch site" (RTLS) abort. Under such abort conditions, the payload will be subjected to landing loads and must not break loose or otherwise introduce damage or hazards to the Shuttle or its crew. The Shuttle launch and landing loads, in terms of "g" factors, applicable to space station and platform design, are summarized in Table 2.3.

Payloads installed in the Shuttle usually employ a structurally determinate installation loads principle. This prevents payload installations from introducing loads, e.g., due to thermal deformations, into the Shuttle other than those calculable through straightforward loads analysis. The Shuttle payload bay provides standard structural support points about every 20 centimeters at the sides of the payload bay and along the keel. The standard trunnion support at the sides is illustrated in Figure 2.12. Structural support requirements on payloads are summarized in Figure 2.13.

Center of Gravity

Because the Shuttle flies as an unpowered aircraft during normal as well as abort return to landing, all payloads carried

Table 2.3 Design limit load factors for payloads in the Shuttle payload bay. *Courtesy of NASA*; Space Transportation User Handbook, *1982.*

Condition	Load Factor in gs		
	X-axis	Y-axis	Z-axis
Liftoff	−0.2	±1.4	2.5
	−3.2	±1.4	−2.5
Ascent	−1.1	±0.4	0.25
	−3.2	±0.4	−0.59
Entry	1.01	±0.85	2.5
	−1.5	±0.85	−1.0
Landing	1.8	±1.5	4.2
	−2.0	±1.5	−1.0
Emergency	20.0	±3.3	10.0
Landing	−3.3	±3.3	−4.4

Emergency landing conditions apply only to protecting the Orbiter from damage and its crew from injury.

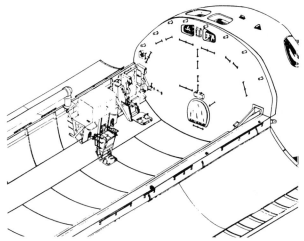

Figure 2.12 Shuttle Orbiter trunnion for payload structural support. *Courtesy of NASA.*

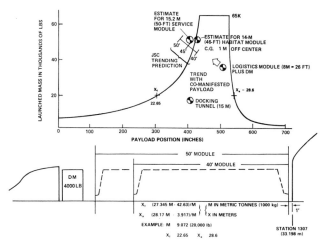

Figure 2.14 Shuttle payload bay fore-and-aft center-of-gravity limits. *Courtesy of Boeing/NASA.*

in the Shuttle must conform to center of gravity (CG) restrictions imposed by aerodynamic controllability considerations. Limits are set for x-offset (fore and aft), y-offset (athwartships), and z-offset (up and down). Ordinarily, only

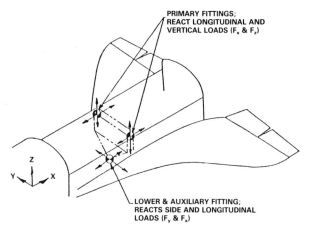

PRIMARY FITTINGS;
REACT LONGITUDINAL AND
VERTICAL LOADS (F_x & F_z)

LOWER & AUXILIARY FITTING;
REACTS SIDE AND LONGITUDINAL
LOADS (F_y & F_x)

3-POINT PAYLOAD RETENTION SYSTEM (DETERMINATE)

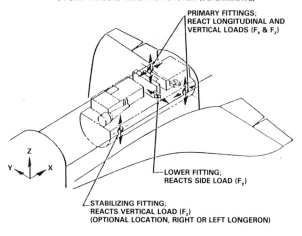

PRIMARY FITTINGS;
REACT LONGITUDINAL AND
VERTICAL LOADS (F_x & F_z)

LOWER FITTING;
REACTS SIDE LOAD (F_y)

STABILIZING FITTING;
REACTS VERTICAL LOAD (F_z)
(OPTIONAL LOCATION, RIGHT OR LEFT LONGERON)

4-POINT PAYLOAD RETNETION SYSTEM (DETERMINATE)

Figure 2.13 Structural support requirements for installation into the Shuttle payload bay. *Courtesy of NASA.*

the x limits are of concern since the center of gravity of a payload tends to be at its centroid and this is usually not a problem with respect to y and z offsets. Because the Shuttle is a modified delta-winged aircraft, the tendency of payloads toward centroid CG can be a problem. For massive payloads, the permissible center of gravity limits do not include the centroid of the payload bay, as illustrated in Figure 2.14. (The figure includes the equations for the limit curves.) Space station pressurized modules, in particular, tend to have their center of gravity at their centroid. Further, if a module delivery flight includes a requirement to dock or berth with the space station, a docking/berthing module must be installed in the front of the payload bay as illustrated in the prior figure. As also shown, the space station module length is expected to be restricted to about 13 meters (45 feet) by CG constraints. Several studies of the possibility of designing a module with asymmetric CG have shown that CG offset from the centroid is not likely to exceed 1 meter. Even this is probably optimistic for real designs.

Thermal, Electrical, and Data Utilities

The Shuttle provides limited thermal, electrical, and data utilities in the payload bay as illustrated in Figure 2.15. Use of these utilities requires a significant integration effort, especially if flight software changes are needed. A possible benefit for space station mission users is the opportunity to fly payloads inert insofar as the Shuttle is concerned, thus minimizing integration cost.

Safety

Flight in the Shuttle requires particular attention to potential hazards that could pose a risk to the Shuttle vehicle or its crew. Safety characteristics of Shuttle payloads are established and confirmed through an iterative review process that begins when a flight opportunity is first requested and ends with the flight readiness review. Safety requirements imposed on payloads flying in the Shuttle are given in NHB

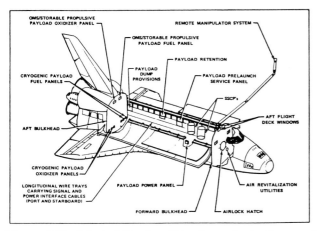

Figure 2.15 Principal Shuttle utilities for payloads. *Courtesy of NASA.*

1700.7A, "Safety Policy and Requirements for Payloads Using the Space Transportation System" (NASA). The main requirements include triply redundant valving to prevent accidental release of hazardous fluids or gases in the payload bay and similar provisions to prevent hazardous thermal conditions, and electrical or RF interference. Structural safety requirements were described earlier. Safety of operational practices such as berthing and payload removal from the payload bay as well as handling by the RMS must be established by precedent, analysis, or simulations.

This discussion has provided a brief overview of requirements and design constraints imposed on payloads to be flown in the Shuttle payload bay. Actual design of payloads for Shuttle flight relies on an extensive system of documents issued by NASA, JSC-07700 Volume XIV. In particular, Attachment 1 (ICD 2-19001) defines Shuttle Orbiter/cargo standard interfaces and should be used as a reference for payload installation design requirements.

Integrated Space Station Operations

Mature operational systems are highly complex. Each element of the operational infrastructure is tailored for a particular function or need. Operational systems for people transportation in the United States, for example, include rail, bus, air, ship, private auto, and human-powered modes such as bicycles, not to mention special applications like elevators. Systems for cargo are equally complex. By comparison, space transportation systems are very simple in operational structure, reflecting both operational immaturity and difficulties of the technology.

A space station, serving as a transportation terminal in Earth orbit, will be an important step in the maturation of space transportation operations. The space station will permit isolation of the operating constraints on Earth-to-orbit transportation from those imposed on orbit-to-orbit transportation. The implications of this are subtle, but extremely

important to advancing the state of the art of space transportation toward comparable maturity with transportation operations used on Earth.

The space station will serve as a spaceport in low Earth orbit. It will be the base for a change in operational mode, i.e., from launch to orbit-to-orbit transportation, analogous to the way a seaport serves the change from land to sea transportation. Orbit-to-orbit systems will be based, serviced, and refueled at the spaceport. Payloads will be checked out, their appendages deployed as necessary, and they will be mated to orbit-to-orbit transport systems. Launch systems will berth at the station while their cargoes are offloaded, perhaps replaced with Earth return cargoes, and while crews are exchanged according to their assignments.

Other missions of the space station including construction, spacecraft servicing, and science also have operational aspects that influence integrated operations. These are described following transportation operations.

Upper Stage Operations

The OMV and OTV upper stages will be based at the space station, the OMV initially and the OTV later. Operations for these will be similar. Both will involve storage at the station (presumably in a hangar), maintenance and checkout, launch preparations including payload mating, proximity operations (flight in the immediate vicinity of the space station where safety issues will dictate operational modes), handover to ground controllers, reacquisition for return proximity operations, and recovery.

The mission operations for OMV and OTV are different. OMV missions presently anticipated include subsatellite use, where the OMV carries an experiment that operates in cooperation with but at a distance from the space station. A second principal use is satellite servicing, either remotely controlled where the OMV itself is the servicer, or by OMV retrieval of satellites or platforms where the OMV docks to the vehicle to be serviced and returns it to the space station and redeploys it following the servicing.

The main OTV missions are delivery of spacecraft to geosynchronous orbit and transport of manned missions to the same orbit for satellite servicing. Depending on the success of developing remotely controlled servicing technology, the OTV could serve as a remote servicer at GEO.

An operations control capability for upper stage operations will be provided within the space station. Modern controls and displays technology will enable implementation of a control station with multipurpose digital displays and one or two video displays. Direct viewing of vehicles during proximity operations may be required; this issue is under debate.

The most important operations workload on the space

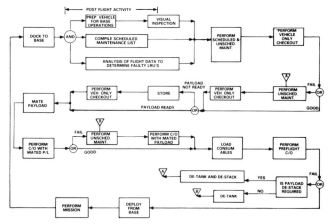

Figure 2.16 Sequence of events (functional flow) for OTV servicing at a space station. *Courtesy of Boeing.*

station for upper stages is the turnaround cycle where the upper stage is serviced, checked out, maintained as necessary, and refueled for the next mission. Figure 2.16 presents a typical operational sequence for this function. Estimates of the level of effort required vary. Through proper design of an upper stage for space servicing, it appears possible to reduce the turnaround operations workload to require two crews, one shift, for about a week.

In addition to a control station, the space station must provide hangar space for vehicle storage, protection and servicing, refueling facilities, probably quiescent power, data services for checkout and maintenance, means for transporting the upper stages and their payloads onboard the space station, e.g., from the hangar to payload mating and launch locations, holding and alignment fixtures for payload mating and demating, and launch and recovery provisions. A typical hangar concept and a concept for the OTV accommodations were illustrated in Chapter 1. Their influence on space station configuration arrangement is discussed in chapter 8.

The transportation utility of a space station is (1) as a warehouse; (2) as a facility for construction and deployment of payloads, and for mating payloads to upper stages; (3) as a servicing base for spacecraft and platforms in accessible orbits; (4) as a transportation node, a base and refueling station for upper stages, and a depot for Shuttle operations; and (5) as an operational buffer between launch systems operations and upper stage operations.

The value of the operational buffer is easily underestimated. It is probably the most valuable of all the above services. Without a space station, a Shuttle flight involving an upper stage must deliver the upper stage, fully fueled, to orbit along with the payload. The fuel load is that needed to accomplish the mission. With a space station, payloads and fuel delivery may be manifested in the most efficient manner, i.e., nearer the limit of Shuttle lift capacity, and

only the fuel for the upper stage (rather than the entire vehicle) must be delivered.

Analyses of the transportation node function have reached the following major conclusions.

1. A propellant tank farm on the space station is essential to benefit from space basing upper stages; it is the key to uncoupling launch operations from upper stage operations.

2. Efficient propellant transfer from the launch vehicle tanker to the space station tank farm is necessary to realize the potential benefits of space basing. "Efficient" may be interpreted to mean that 95 percent or more of the propellant brought up from Earth is delivered to the space station tank farm.

3. Co-manifesting of payload and propellant deliveries is beneficial, even necessary. Payloads tend toward low densities while a propellant delivery tanker is high in density. Co-manifesting is necessary to achieve a near approach to mass-limited manifesting. Co-manifesting is facilitated through use of a "mini-tanker," a propellant delivery tanker that is designed to be manifested with payloads as diagrammed in Figure 2.17. The short tanker provides a generous allowance of payload bay mass and volume for payload assignment while accommodating up to 20 tonnes (44,000 lb) or so of propellant delivery capacity. Optimization of the tanker capacity has not been conducted but a 20-tonne capacity has been shown to be much preferable to operation of dedicated tanker flights combined with dedicated payload delivery flights.

Further analysis is needed to select between a forward-mounted mini-tanker versus an aft-mounted one. The tanker and its co-manifested payload must meet the Shuttle center-of-gravity constraints whether (1) the tanker and payload are fully loaded; (2) the tanker is emptied but the payload is present (propellant has been transferred but payload must be returned to Earth to correct a malfunction); (3) the tanker is loaded but the payload is not present; and (4) tanker is emptied and payload is not present. The aft tanker appears to be preferred but the payload capacity under case (2) above may be limited by CG contraints.

Science Operations

One of the benefits of a space station is its ability to support scientific research in orbit. Science operations include operation of remote sensing instruments for investigations that need human involvement in data acquisition, as well as experimentation conducted in onboard laboratories for zero-g research. Operation of solar telescopes is an example of a remote sensing mission needing crew involvement. The conduct of research onboard a space station will permit very rapid progress compared to conducting experiments on the Shuttle with later analysis of the results on Earth. Onboard research requires the presence of laboratory instruments for

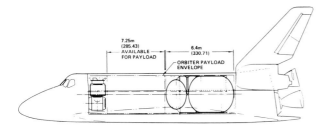

Figure 2.17 Mini-tanker concept for OTV propellant delivery. *Courtesy of Boeing.*

analysis and diagnostics on the space station in addition to those instruments used for carrying out the experiments, and will demand research time and crew talents. Other operational requirements include access to scientific reference materials, presumably by way of help from co-investigators on Earth, and on-demand real-time access to mission data streams by the onboard researchers.

Construction Operations

Construction operations at a space station will permit the creation of space systems far larger than any yet deployed in space. Construction missions have been the subject of many studies during the past several years. Although many of these studies have concentrated on the assembly of large space structures, others have examined missions for these structures and analyzed construction operations as necessary to enable specific new mission capabilities.

The design of space systems with appendages that extend beyond the payload envelope of launch systems is not new, of course. Automated deployment mechanisms have been used for many years. These are, however, limited in capability as well as expensive and not especially reliable. Design studies of construction operations have shown that launch constraints are not a limit to the size of artifacts that can be constructed, that constructed structures can be simple as well as rigid, and that construction will probably prove straightforward to carry out through astronaut EVA.

Space structures designed for space construction fall into three categories: deployable, erectable, and fabricated. Deployables designed for space construction require man-in-the-loop aids, e.g., use of an RMS or EVA crewperson, as contrasted to automatic deployables. An erectable structure is formed from members prefabricated on Earth, by assembly using some form of fasteners. The members themselves of fabricated structures are fabricated in space from raw materials, as in the ''beam machine'' depicted in Figure 2.18.

Space construction projects will create spacecraft much larger than the packaged volumes of their constituent parts. Deployable structures attain volume ratios on the order of fifty; erectables can attain a few thousands; fabricated structures may reach millions. Contemporary studies deal with

deployables and erectables. Mission applications presently in planning stages do not need the very great volume ratios attainable through fabrication of structural members on orbit. Even the use of erectables is more motivated by their design simplicity and stiffness than by the volume ratio.

Space construction operations entail a series of steps very similar to those used in Earth-bound construction. Tooling and equipment must be set up for the project at hand, the materials and parts for the spacecraft to be constructed must be delivered and warehoused, the structural assembly must be completed, subsystems and equipment must be installed and checked out, integrated testing must be completed, the finished spacecraft must be deployed or delivered to the mission orbit, and the construction setup must be dismantled or modified for the next project. Representative construction projects were described in Chapter 1 under technology development missions. The construction sequence for the large IR telescope illustrated earlier in Figure 1.25 is illustrated in Figure 2.19, the operational sequence is shown in Figure 2.20, and an estimated timeline is shown in Figure 2.21.

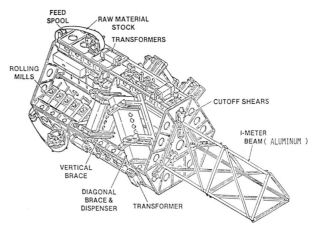

Figure 2.18 Beam-machine concept for space fabrication of triangular-section trusses. *Courtesy of Grumman Aerospace Co.*

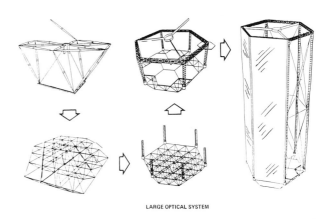

Figure 2.19 Assembly sequence for space-assembled optical reflector instrument. *Courtesy of Boeing.*

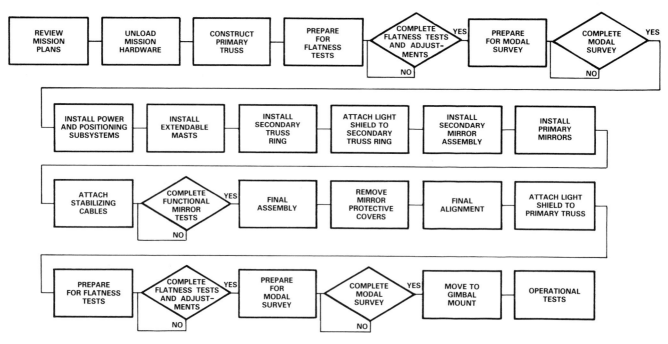

Figure 2.20 Sequence of events (functional flow) for assembly of large optical instrument. *Courtesy of Boeing.*

The timeline is based on simulation tests in the Water Immersion Facility (WIF) at MSFC and on study of EVA videotapes from early Shuttle flights.

Tooling and equipment for space construction are derived from logical Earth-based analogs. To enable suited astronauts to reach the construction work, for example, a foot restraint and work station such as illustrated in Figure 2.22 has been proposed. It would be positioned at the work by a manipulator arm such as the Shuttle arm. The obvious Earth-based analog is the ''cherry-picker'' truck used by utility companies to position workers next to overhead utility lines and equipment. Gravity provides adequate motion restraint for the worker in a cherry-picker basket. In the space application, foot restraints and perhaps a waist restraint must be used.

Logistics support for space construction is simplified by standardizing on relatively few basic tools. On the Space Telescope, a single size of wrench fits all bolts designed for EVA servicing. It appears practical to design a wide range of construction and servicing tasks to be done with a modest suite of tools and fixtures.

Planning for EVA construction and servicing operations involves four very important factors: mobility, restraint, suit limitations, and safety. Mobility provisions must facilitate moving crew, equipment, and assembly parts to the work site. EVA mobility tends to be slow. Crew provisions can include handholds and tethers, but use of an RMS appears to be more flexible and rapid. Equipment and parts must be moved from storage areas to the work site, probably by RMS. Depending on distances and size of the construction

job, a tracked (mobile) RMS may be necessary. Special fixtures for positioning and moving the construction article may be needed. A key trade is whether to move the article past the work site or to move the work site.

The lack of relative gravity force is beneficial in ease of handling massive objects, but *everything* must be restrained. One cannot put a tool down; it must be stowed or attached somewhere or it will drift away. Tethers have been used on past missions, but tethers tangle, especially if several are in use at one site. Velcro, tool caddies, or pockets may prove more effective for small objects. Positive tie-downs are probably best for large objects. Safety will dictate use of tethers for crew members unless other means are used to ensure restraint.

Task design must recognize that the space suit is an encumbrance. Arm reach is limited, especially overhead. Work should be positioned directly in front of the suited crewperson. Vision of this area is excellent, but the field of view is limited by the fact that the helmet does not move with head motion. EVA gloves are clumsy, about like ski mitts, and in addition very tiring if something is to be grasped with a closed hand for long periods. Suit technology for arms and legs is developing true constant-volume joints so that movement will not require great effort, but constant-volume fingers on EVA gloves are apparently not yet on the horizon.

Safety requirements are derived from common sense. Always provide positive restraint so that an EVA crewperson will not drift away and require rescue. Design all restraint systems so that a crewperson cannot be trapped outside.

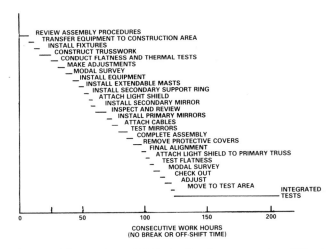

Figure 2.21 Estimated EVA timeline for construction of IR telescope.

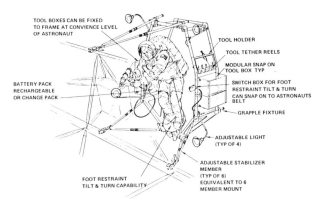

Figure 2.22 EVA workstation and foot restraint. *Courtesy of Boeing.*

Always conduct EVA on the ''buddy system'' with two crewpersons so that one can quickly aid another in trouble. Prohibit sharp or hot objects that could damage the suit; ensure safe operation of any sort of mechanical graspers, clamps, cutters, etc. Avoid situations where propulsive jets or any sort of venting or discharge can pose a risk to EVA crew. This is especially important where servicing of a fluid system could result in leakage of a corrosive or toxic fluid onto the suit. If such situations cannot be avoided, a disposable protective overgarment may be needed so that the contaminated material can be doffed before entering the airlock upon completion of the EVA.

Construction will impact on other space station operations. The presence of a large construction project is likely to so alter the space station mass properties as to require flying in a gravity-gradient stable attitude. Construction may introduce contaminants in the form of particulate matter and outgassing products. Movement of masses will create disturbances of the microgravity environment; this may be so severe as to require temporary shutdown of some microgravity research.

Crew Operations

Crew time aboard a space station is a critical resource inasmuch as the total crew hours per day are limited, probably fewer than needed for an optimal pace of operations scheduling. Crew operations are also constrained in certain ways. Planning for crew utilization must recognize these factors as well as the cost of crew time.

The cost (value) of crew time can be calculated in various ways, for example, including or not including amortization of certain research and development costs. Results obtained range from roughly $5,000 to $25,000 per crew work hour. The cost of a man-hour at the space station is expected to be at least 100 times the cost of one here on Earth. Cost-effective space station operations will not assign tasks to space crews that could be accomplished by Earthbound workers.

Humans in space, as here on Earth, cannot spend all of their time working. Time allocations for sleep and rest, eating, exercise, personal hygiene, and personal time must be provided. The time available for work is estimated as ten hours per day, six days per week. This presumes normal crew residence times for a space station, i.e., 90 days or more. For shorter missions such as the Shuttle/Spacelab flights, a crewperson can be scheduled for 12 hours per day, seven days per week.

Crew operations are constrained by physiological and psychological limits, by radiation exposure limits, by EVA work limits set by suit technology, and by skill and training considerations. Technical factors influencing these constraints are described in Chapters 4 and 6; operational considerations are summarized here.

The record for crew staytime aboard a space station is about eight months for a Soviet crew aboard Salyut 7. Various forms of physiological deconditioning in zero g, described briefly in Chapter 6, are presently believed to limit practical staytimes to about nine months. (The Soviets probably do not reveal all they have learned in their long-duration flights; what they do reveal is consistent with what the United States learned on its longest flight so far, the 85-day Skylab mission in 1974.) A nominal staytime planning figure used for several years in U.S. space station concept and design studies is 90 days. Rigorous exercise programs are necessary to maintain muscular and cardiovascular conditions on any flight that lasts more than a few days. Typical exercise regimens occupy two hours per day for each crew member.

Control of ionizing radiation exposure involves radiation shielding, operational practices, and possible limitations on crew staytime in orbit. Radiation shielding is massive; enough shielding to limit crew radiation environments in space to those of everyday experience here on Earth would amount to hundreds of tons for each space station module.

The present operational philosophy is to limit crew career exposure to about the limit levels accepted in the nuclear industry; since a career astronaut, even in the space station era, will spend at most only a few months per year in space, allowed dose rates in space can be greater than nuclear industry dose rates. If active careers are limited to a few years then the present radiation dose design levels of Table 4.1 in Chapter 4 represent reasonable career exposures. Changes to the design limits have been discussed, but the present approach is to limit the number of years that an astronaut might spend on space station active duty in favor of minimizing shielding mass design impact on the system.

The present radiation design specification for the space station requires that a one-year stay at the station not exceed astronaut radiation exposure standards. This enables long-duration zero-g research. The one-year limits are twice the 90-day limits (not four times). Thus, the present specification is more severe than that used for many earlier studies which assumed maximum 90-day crew staytimes.

Dose rates in low Earth orbit are not steady: nearly all of the exposure occurs during passages through the South Atlantic Anomaly (SAA: see Chapter 4). The number, severity, and timing of these rates vary with orbit inclination and altitude. For a space station in the (U.S.) baseline orbit at 28.5 degrees inclination, they occur on two groups of three or four orbits per day and last about 15 minutes each. A period of about 12 hours each day is free of SAA exposure, during which radiation dose rates are minimal. Operational practices can minimize crew exposures with a given amount of shielding. EVA garments provide less shielding that a space station module, so scheduling EVA around SAA passes makes sense. Crew sleep periods might be scheduled during SAA passages and sleep areas or garments provided with additional shielding. The Earth's rotation period (the SAA rotates with it) with respect to a typical space station orbit, however, is about 23.5 hours, not 24, so the space station "day" would have to be shortened slightly to maintain sleep periods synchronized with SAA passage. If a space station is operated on two-shift scheduling, only one of the shifts would benefit.

Space station crew operations must consider available skills. One could easily list dozens of desirable skills to have on board, but first-generation space stations will be crewed by 6 to 12 people. Even with cross-training, the number of skills will be limited. Certain essential skills such as EVA and knowledge of station systems will have priority. To achieve high crew productivity, we will employ onboard aids such as archived procedures and training, even "expert (computer software) systems," and rely extensively on ground personnel for consultation.

Extravehicular operations can occupy a significant share of the station's crew resource. Safety considerations require all EVAs to be conducted with two people, the "buddy system"; in addition, a third person is occupied monitoring the EVA from inside. With a six-person crew, an EVA day will consume half the crew time resource for that day. Missions that will use EVA include spacecraft servicing OMV and OTV operations, large space structures construction and related technology, and maintenance and repair of the space station itself.

Detailed planning of crew activities (timelines) has always been preplanned by operations planning people on the ground. On longer missions, the entire mission is not planned in great detail beforehand, but timelines are laid out several days in advance and radioed up to the crew. Flight crews have consistently expressed a desire to be responsible for their own detailed day-to-day timeline planning. Preparing timelines manually is far too laborious to assign to flight crews, but computer software now exists to do most of it automatically with human supervision. In the space station era, it is anticipated that such software will be provided onboard and that crews will work out their own detailed timelines, following general guidelines, objectives, and longer range mission plans devised by mission control operations on the ground.

Crew exchanges will be tied to the logistics cycle, or vice versa. Crew complements up to six are readily exchanged on a Shuttle logistics flight. The NASA STS Office prefers to use dedicated Shuttle flight crews; that is, the Shuttle pilot and copilot would not be a part of the space station crew exchange. The frequency of logistics flights will depend on the level of space station user activity. A flight every 90 days is more than sufficient for space station resupply needs and is the nominal planning number. When the space station crew grows beyond six, partial exchanges will probably be carried out, and the normal crew staytime will depend on the frequency of Shuttle visit opportunities.

Logistics Operations

Space station logistics includes the exchange of crews; the delivery of station consumables including life support and propulsion needs as well as equipment spares; return of garbage, wastes, and faulty equipment to Earth; delivery and return of mission equipment and spares; and delivery of propellant for transportation vehicles based at the space station.

The Shuttle cabin offers adequate transport capability for crew exchange for the space station presently being designed by NASA. The present design crew capacity of the cabin is seven. It has carried eight, and studies have shown that it could be increased to ten, especially for short occupancy periods. By the time the space station crew exceeds eight people, frequent Shuttle visits will probably be the rule. Initially, visits may be timed for the nominal crew staytime of 90 days.

Table 2.4 Resupply requirements for environmental control and life support.

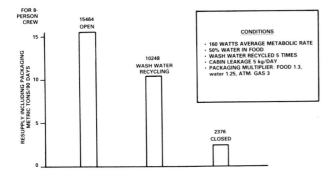

RESUPPLY IN kg/DAY PER PERSON (kg/90 DAYS WITH PACKAGING)

	OPEN	WASH WATER RECYCLE	CLOSED
FOOD	1.43 (167)	1.43 (167)	1.43 (167)
POTABLE WATER	3.4 (383)	3.4 (383)	0 (0)
WASH WATER	8.5 (956)	2.7 (304)	0 (0)
O_2	1.10 (297)	1.1 (297)	0 (0)
N_2	0.48 (130)	0.48 (130)	0.48 (130)
	14.91 (1933)	9.11 (1281)	1.91 (297)

FOR 8-PERSON CREW

15464 OPEN

10248 WASH WATER RECYCLING

2376 CLOSED

RESUPPLY INCLUDING PACKAGING METRIC TONS/90 DAYS

CONDITIONS
• 160 WATTS AVERAGE METABOLIC RATE
• 50% WATER IN FOOD
• WASH WATER RECYCLED 5 TIMES
• CABIN LEAKAGE 5 kg/DAY
• PACKAGING MULTIPLIER: FOOD 1.3, water 1.25, ATM. GAS 3

Life support resupply quantities depend on the sophistication of the life support system. The Skylab employed a non-regenerable system. Oxygen, food, and water were supplied from stores and carbon dioxide was removed by expendable lithium hydroxide (LiOH) canisters. The Soviet Salyuts employ partial water and oxygen recovery. Recent NASA studies have ranged from little to complete closure of oxygen and water systems. Partial water closure can be implemented by recycling wash water (used for showers, hand wash, and certain cleaning chores) but not drinking and cooking water. Table 2.4 compares resupply requirements for a crew of eight for systems with partial and complete water closure. The system with complete water closure also recovers oxygen from CO_2 and water; the technology for oxygen recovery is less difficult than that for purification of waste water to drinkability. Environmental control and life support technology is described in a subsequent chapter.

It is theoretically possible to grow food onboard a space station, thus reducing life support resupply to that necessary to make up for station leakage. The Soviets have experimented with food growth, enjoying some success, but do not rely on it. NASA has a low-level advanced technology activity underway; it is presently in a laboratory research stage. It is not likely that agriculture on a space station will be more than an experimental source of food before the turn of the century.

Definitive studies of spares logistics for space station and mission subsystems and equipment have not yet been accomplished. Subsystem elements are of widely varying ma-

turity; estimates of spares requirements are subject to much uncertainty. The need for onboard spares, replenishment spares (i.e., deliveries on resupply flights), and repair onboard versus return to Earth all depend on failure rates, the degree of redundancy, and the replacement level. A number of studies have assumed a high replacement level, that is, "large" boxes as orbit replaceable units (ORUs). This, however, results in much more storage volume and investment for onboard spares and higher cost for spares replenishment. Using lower level ORUs, e.g., at the circuit card level, is more like current practice for other aerospace systems. An analysis of the optimum replacement level would trade these factors against the presumably higher cost for replacement labor and diagnostics test equipment.

Those studies that have been conducted indicate that the quantity of onboard spares will not exceed 10 percent of the installed equipment volume and mass and that the 90-day replenishment quantities will be considerably less than that. The present design goal for total space station subsystems operations labor including maintenance is an average of one crewperson, one shift.

The logistics burden for missions will probably be dominated by delivery of new mission equipment and supplies and return to Earth of samples and equipment no longer needed. Estimates of this burden worthy of publication do not exist.

Propellant will be consumed by the space station to compensate for drag induced by the upper atmosphere. This subject is covered under space station propulsion in Chapter 5. In brief, propellant resupply varies with the drag frontal area which is dominated by the solar energy collection system; with the density of the upper atmosphere which varies with solar activity; and with the altitude selected for the space station orbit. Figure 2.23 summarizes these effects in a nomograph. Under certain circumstances, station attitude control can dictate propellant resupply requirements; this is discussed in Chapter 5.

Delivery of propellant for OMV operations supporting the servicing of formation-flying free flyers and platforms has been estimated as a few thousand kg per year at most. OMV missions to out-of-plane or higher altitude orbits, if necessary, will consume up to a full OMV propellant load per mission. Since the OMV propellant, contained in a suitable resupply pallet, will be a dense package, opportunities for co-manifesting with other space station resupply payloads are expected to be frequent enough that dedicated OMV resupply flights will not be needed.

Delivery of propellant for OTVs is quite another matter. Representative OTV missions need 20 to 40 tonnes of propellant each - a single OTV mission may place as much demand on resupply logistics as several months of space station consumables and onboard operations. As noted

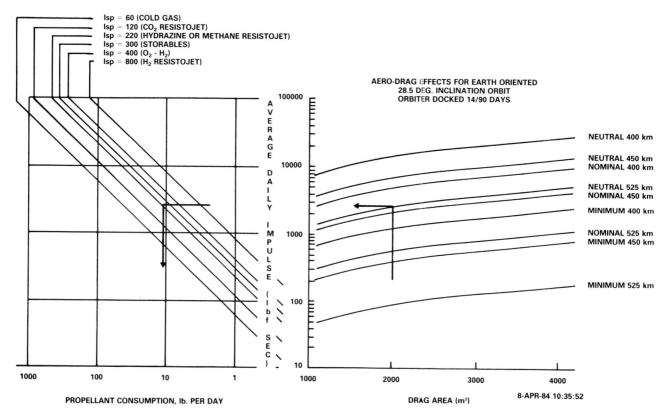

Figure 2.23 Propellant consumption for drag makeup. *Courtesy of Boeing.*

above, there are advantages to combining OTV propellant delivery with delivery of other payloads if the Shuttle is used for tanker delivery.

It is anticipated that OTV propellant tanker handling will be mostly automated, including umbilical connection of the transfer path from the tanker to the station storage tanks, fluids transfer operations, inventory control and gauging, and disconnect upon transfer completion. Transfer operations will take from a few hours to a day. The main impact on space station operations will be the significant changes in center of gravity and inertias that result from the movement of the propellant mass. The mass of OTV propellant stored at the station can approach 50 percent of the total station mass in some scenarios.

Operations Accommodations

The space station must be designed to accommodate all operations requirements together, without undue interference. This implies that the configuration must include dedicated operations and service areas for the more important operations, and that the command and control systems must serve all needs. Use of modern multifunction digital command and control systems appears mandatory. Configuration influences are discussed in Chapter 8.

As evident from the discussions in this chapter, the need for effective operations is a primary source of requirements and design considerations on space stations. The need also exists for space platforms, but is less acute.

Chapter 3

Orbital Mechanics

Keplerian Motion

The Condition of an Orbit

The flight path of an orbit is often described as free fall. The orbital condition can be quickly grasped by imagining a cannon atop a high mountain. If the cannon fires with a modest muzzle velocity, say, 1000 meters per second, the projectile will fall to Earth some distance away, depending on the height of the mountain. The downward curving of its path is greater than the curvature of the Earth, so impact is inevitable. But as the muzzle velocity of the cannon is increased, the curvature of the projectile is less and less. At a high enough muzzle velocity, the curving of the projectile path will be the same as that of the Earth's surface, and the projectile will fall *around* the Earth instead of down toward it. The condition of falling around the Earth is that of being in orbit.

The velocity of a near-Earth orbit is more than 7500 meters per second. Such high muzzle velocities have never been attained by cannon; furthermore there are no mountains high enough to place an orbit-launching gun above the atmosphere where orbital velocity can be maintained for reasonable periods of time. Consequently, rocket propulsion is the common means of attaining orbit. The rocket, launched vertically, gradually tilts toward the desired direction of the orbit, so that by the time it has climbed above the sensible atmosphere, it is accelerating horizontally to reach orbital velocity. Rockets are not limited in velocity by the energy of the propellant in the same way as guns, and can readily reach orbital velocity as is now commonplace experience.

Circular Orbits

One of the simplest ways to define the velocity needed for a circular orbit is through the balance of gravitational and centrifugal accelerations. Considering a circular path about the Earth, the gravitational acceleration (downward) is expressed as μ/r^2 where μ is the gravitational potential of the Earth's mass, 398,601 km^3/sec^2 in SI units, and r is the orbit radius from Earth's center. The centrifugal acceleration (outward) is v^2/r. When these are equal, the velocity is exactly right for the circular orbit condition. Setting them equal yields the expression $v = \sqrt{\mu/r}$, the velocity of a circular

orbit. Figure 3.1 presents values of v for orbit altitudes of 160 to 1000 km. Orbits below 160 km have very short lifetimes because of atmospheric drag, while those above 1000 km are exposed to severe radiation by the Van Allen radiation belts. Practical altitudes for manned space stations are limited to about 600 km, unless altitudes greater than 20,000 km are contemplated; the latter are above the high-intensity regions of the Van Allen belts.

The period (time to achieve one complete orbital revolution) is easily computed from the above velocity and the length of the circular path. The orbital period in seconds is given by

$$p = 2\pi\sqrt{a^3/\mu} \ . \qquad (3.1)$$

For circular orbits, the value a is equal to r, but the period expression is also valid for elliptic orbits, described below. The orbital period for typical space station and platform orbits near Earth is about an hour and a half. The period in minutes is graphed for low altitudes in Figure 3.2.

An orbit of special interest is one whose period equals that of the Earth's natural revolution. The Earth revolves 360° in about 23.93 hours. Our "day" is 24 hours because the Earth must revolve rather more than 360° to face the sun in precisely the same way, due to the Earth's motion about the sun at the rate of about 1° per day.

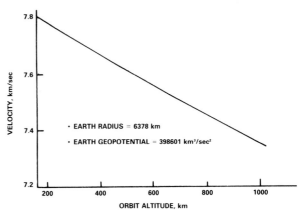

Figure 3.1 Circular orbit velocities.

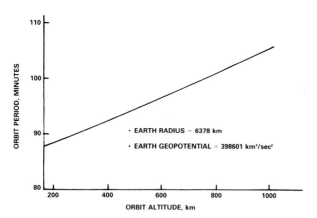

Figure 3.2 Circular orbit periods.

This special orbit is called geosynchronous, sometimes geostationary, and is often abbreviated as GEO. A satellite or space station in such an orbit, in the Earth's equatorial plane, revolves in synchronism with the Earth itself and appears motionless in the sky. Uses of the geosynchronous orbit are today predominantly for communications (antennas on Earth may be fixed, non-tracking installations), but other uses may become important in the future.

Elliptic Orbits

It is natural to ask what happens to the orbital condition if the velocity is not precisely that for a circular orbit. The answer is that a circular orbit is a special case of the general case of elliptic orbits. Orbits, in Newtonian mechanics, are conic sections. (Newtonian mechanics is adequate for all practical flight mechanics analyses, as velocities are very small compared to the speed of light, and relativistic effects are entirely negligible.)

Conic sections are depicted in Figure 3.3. The horizontal section is a circle. Sections at less than the conic half-angle are ellipses and represent elliptic orbits. Those exactly at the half-angle are parabolas and represent flight paths at exactly escape energy. Sections steeper than the half-angle are hyperbolae and represent flight paths at energies greater than escape energy.

The idea of escape energy is based on the usual physical representation of the gravitational field of a celestial body as a potential well. Although the extent of an inverse-square field such as gravity is infinite, its energy is not, and for all practical purposes the field strength becomes inconsequential beyond a certain distance. Thus one can think of an infinite flat plane of zero potential dotted here and there by horn-shaped depressions of gravity wells with a massive object at the bottom of each. In the usual physical expression of potential energy, the energy on the flat plane is taken as zero while the energy in a potential well is negative, depending on how far down into the well one's position is.

The total energy of an orbit at any point is the sum of

potential and kinetic energy. The potential energy alone is given by

$$V_{(r)} = \int_\infty^r \frac{\mu}{r^2} dr \qquad (3.2)$$

where μ/r^2 is simply the force of gravity at distance r. The potential energy integrates to $V(r) = -\mu/r$. To escape a celestial body, kinetic energy (positive) must equal the negative value of potential energy so that the sum is zero. Since kinetic energy per unit mass is $\frac{1}{2} v^2$, the kinetic velocity equivalent to freedom from the gravitational well, the escape velocity, is

$$V = \sqrt{\frac{2\mu}{r}} \qquad . \qquad (3.3)$$

For the Earth, the escape velocity from the surface radius of 6378 km is 11.18 km/sec.

The geometry of the potential well is dictated by the gravitational potential of the object at the bottom. If the object is spherically symmetric, the potential is a function only of the mass of the object, assuming that one is not inside its surface. Consequently, the potential well model is adequate for most purposes. Further, perturbational methods are adequate for most problems that must consider deviations from spherical symmetry.

Parabolic and hyperbolic orbits have open paths with trajectories that reach infinitely far from the gravitating body,

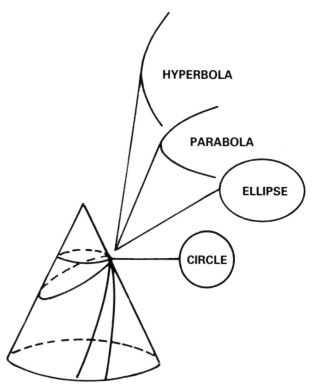

Figure 3.3 Conic sections.

as might be imagined for objects which escape from the solar system. Orbits of practical interest for space stations and platforms are elliptic. The circular orbit is a special case of the elliptic orbit; platform and station orbits will ordinarily be sufficiently near circular that the circular model is adequate.

Elliptic orbits have the gravitating body at one focus, as illustrated in Figure 3.4. Kepler discovered that the Sun's planets follow elliptic paths, and that one of the properties of these paths is that the radius vector sweeps out equal areas in equal times. Newton established that this phenomenon is a natural consequence of motion in an inverse-square-law central force field.

A mass in an elliptic orbit is analogous to a mechanical oscillator such as a pendulum, with energy periodically exchanged between kinetic and potential energy. Unless the orbit periapsis is at a low enough altitude for atmospheric drag to be significant, the elliptic orbit is a lossless oscillator, needing no addition of energy to keep it going.

Orbital mechanics analysis is customarily conducted in a polar coordinate system, with variables r and θ. The origin ($r=0$) is located at the center of the gravitating body, i.e., at one focus of the ellipse. This is different than many analytic geometry treatments of ellipses, where the coordinate origin is at the ellipse centroid. In orbital mechanics, the ellipse is described by the parameters a; the semimajor axis (half the longer dimension) and e, the eccentricity (distance between foci divided by $2a$). Since the gravity body is at one focus, the closest approach of the orbiting object occurs at the "end" of the ellipse closest to the focus as was shown in Figure 3.4. This point is designated as the periapsis. The term is sometimes body-specific; i.e., perigee (Earth), perilune (Moon), perihelion (Sun).

The geometry of the ellipse in plane polar coordinates is given by

$$r = \frac{a(1-e^2)}{1+e\cos\theta} \quad . \tag{3.4}$$

This can be readily related to the usual description of an ellipse in rectangular coordinates, namely, $x^2/a^2 + y^2/b^2 = 1$ where $x = r\cos\theta$ and $y = r\sin\theta$. (Note: if one wishes to derive one from the other, the coordinate change $x' = x - ae$ must be included since eq. 3.4 is focus-centered and the usual formula is centroid-centered.)

Referring to Figure 3.4, the semimajor axis b occurs when y is maximum. Referring to the above definition of r, y can be expressed as

$$y = \frac{a(1-e^2)\sin\theta}{1+e\cos\theta}. \tag{3.5}$$

This expression for y is readily differentiated with respect to θ and set equal to zero to find

$$y_{\max} = b = a\sqrt{1-e^2}.$$

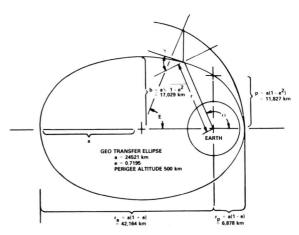

Figure 3.4 Geometry of elliptic orbits with GEO transfer ellipse as numerical example.

Also, the offset from the focus (gravitating body) to the centroid is the value of ae.

As an example, take the transfer orbit to GEO from 500 km altitude:

Periapsis radius	$r_p = 6378 + 500$	$= 6878$ km
Apoapsis radius	$r_a = 6378 + 35786$	$= 42{,}164$ km
Semimajor axis	$a = \dfrac{r_a + r_p}{2} = (42164 + 6878)/2$	$= 24{,}521$ km
Eccentricity	$e = 1 - r/a = 1 - 6878/24521$	$= 0.7195$ km
Offset of Focus	$ae = (24{,}521)(0.7195)$	$= 17{,}643$ km
Semiminor axis	$b = a\sqrt{1-e^2}$ $= 24{,}521\sqrt{1-(0.7195)^2}$	$= 17{,}029$ km.

These values can be used to draw the ellipse to scale in Cartesian coordinates.

Orbit Transfers

Orbit transfers are maneuvers that move a vehicle from one orbit to another. Often, but not always, the transfer path itself is an ellipse. Of principal interest are the velocities associated with periapsis and apoapsis. Transfers between circular orbits are concerned with the differences between these and the related circular velocities, as diagrammed in Figure 3.5.

The velocity values can be derived from the energy considerations of an orbit. The results in terms of the periapsis and apoapsis radii are

$$V_p = \sqrt{\frac{\mu}{a}\frac{r_a}{r_p}} \quad , \text{ and } V_a = \sqrt{\frac{\mu}{a}\frac{r_p}{r_a}} \quad . \tag{3.6}$$

These relations are useful for computing the delta v's for entering and leaving transfer orbits.

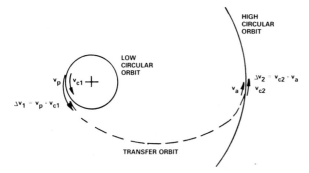

Figure 3.5 Orbit transfer velocities without plane change.

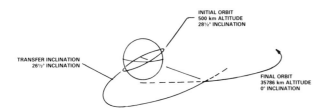

Figure 3.6 Geosynchronous orbit transfer geometry showing plane changes.

Entering and leaving may also require a plane change. The general expression for the magnitude of the difference in velocity between two velocity vectors having an angle Δp between them is

$$\Delta v = \sqrt{(v_1^2 - 2v_1v_2 \cos(\Delta p) + v_2^2)} \quad (3.7)$$

where v_1 and v_2 are the respective vector magnitudes and Δp is the included angle. A typical case is the transfer from a low Earth orbit at 28.5° inclination to a geosynchronous orbit at 0° inclination, depicted in Figure 3.6. The minimum delta v occurs when some of the plane change is made at the transfer orbit perigee and some at apogee. There is no analytical means for determining the optimum plane change split; a trial-and-error optimization finds that the perigee plane change should be about 2° as shown in Figure 3.7.

A menu of commonly useful expressions for motion in elliptic orbits is given in Table 3.1.

Orbit Geometry

An orbital object has 6 degrees of freedom; six parameters are required to fully specify the orbital condition. Two of these were described in the previous section; namely, the semimajor axis, a, and the eccentricity, e. These specify the size and shape of the orbit respectively. Three more parameters, the inclination, i, the longitude of nodes, Ω, and the argument of periapsis, ω, specify the spatial orientation of the orbit with respect to the coordinate system described by the rotation of the gravitating body about its spin axis, as shown in Figure 3.8. The final parameter, θ, specifies the location of the orbiting object along the orbital path at some particular time.

PERIGEE PLANE CHANGE	APOGEE PLANE CHANGE	V₁ km/sec	V₂ km/sec	TOTAL V km/sec	ft/sec
0°	28½°	2.378	1.820	4.198	(13.773)
1°	27½°	2.383	1.798	4.181	(13.717)
2°	26½°	2.397	1.776	4.173	(13.691)
3°	25½°	2.421	1.754	4.175	(13.698)

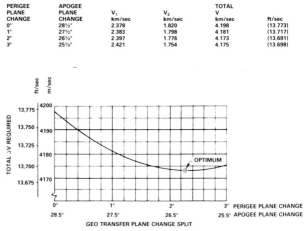

Figure 3.7 Optimizing the geosynchronous transfer plane changes. *Courtesy of Boeing.*

Analysis of orbits in three dimensions employs elementary vector arithmetic; the essentials of this are described in Appendix A. Example calculations including the determination of ground tracks are given in Appendix B.

Prediction of spacecraft motion in orbit includes the effects of various perturbations. Perturbations affect orbital motion very little in any single orbit, but their cumulative effects become important in only a few orbital revolutions.

Perturbations

Earth orbits are perturbed by gravitational effects arising from the fact that the Earth is not a perfect sphere; by aerodynamic drag; by gravitational effects of the Sun, Moon, and other bodies; and by the pressure exerted by sunlight. In nearly circular low Earth orbits, the important effects are drag and nonsphericity of the Earth. Above 1000 km or so, sunlight pressure becomes significant for low-mass, large-area spacecraft.

Earth Oblateness Effects

The Earth's gravitational field is modeled as a spherically symmetric field with perturbations due to nonsphericity. If one is interested in high-precision determination of orbital motion, a large number of spherical harmonic terms must be included in the gravitational potential. Precision orbit determination is beyond the scope of this text, but the Earth's oblateness term causes very significant long-term perturbations of orbits. This is important both in the design of space stations and platforms and to their missions.

The oblateness term is designated J2, and is equal to 0.001082 (no dimensions). It causes the plane of inclined orbits to revolve in a retrograde direction about the Earth's polar axis, and the line of apsides (the line connecting the periapsis and apoapsis of an orbit) to advance in the direction of orbital motion, except in the case of high inclinations—

Table 3.1 Useful relationships for elliptic orbits.

$$b = a\sqrt{1-e^2}$$

$$p = a(1-e^2)$$

$$r_a = a(1+e)$$

$$r_p = a(1-e)$$

$$a = \frac{\mu}{V_a^2}\left(\frac{1-e}{1+e}\right) = \frac{\mu}{V_p^2}\left(\frac{1+e}{1-e}\right)$$

$$a = \tfrac{1}{2}(r_a + r_p)$$

$$e = \frac{r_a}{a} - 1 = 1 - \frac{r_p}{a} = \frac{r_p - r_a}{2a}$$

$$r_a = \frac{r_p V_p}{V_a}$$

$$r_a = \frac{r_p}{\dfrac{2\mu}{r_p V_p^2} - 1}$$

$$r_p = \frac{r_a^2 V_a^2}{2\mu - r_a V_a^2}$$

$$V_a = \sqrt{\frac{\mu}{a}\left(\frac{1-e}{1+e}\right)} = V_p\left(\frac{1-e}{1+e}\right)$$

$$V_p = \sqrt{\frac{\mu}{a}\left(\frac{1+e}{1-e}\right)} = V_a\left(\frac{1+e}{1-e}\right)$$

$$E = \cos^{-1}\left(\frac{a-r}{ae}\right)$$

$$E = \cos^{-1}\left[\frac{e+\cos\theta}{1+e\cos\theta}\right]$$

$$r = a(1 - e\cos E)$$

$$r = \frac{a(1-e^2)}{1+e\cos\theta}$$

$$V = \sqrt{\mu\left(\frac{2}{r} - \frac{1}{a}\right)}$$

$$V = \left[\frac{\mu(1+e^2+2e\cos\theta)}{a(1-e^2)}\right]^{1/2}$$

$$\gamma = \tan^{-1}\left(\frac{e\sin\theta}{1+e\cos\theta}\right)$$

$$\theta = \cos^{-1}\left[\frac{\cos E - e}{1 - e\cos E}\right]$$

$$\theta = \cos^{-1}\left[\frac{a(1-e^2)-r}{er}\right]$$

NOMENCLATURE:

a–semimajor axis

b–semiminor axis

e–eccentricity

E–eccentric anomaly

P–semilatus rectum

r–radius at any point along
    orbit path

r_a–apoapsis radius

r_p–periapsis radius

V–velocity at any point
    along orbit path

V_a–apoapsis velocity

V_p–periapsis velocity

γ–path angle relative to
    local horizontal

θ–true anomaly

μ–gravitational potential

then the line of apsides moves slowly opposite to the direction of orbital motion.

Orbit plane regression is represented as regression of the line of nodes, and is given by

$$\Delta\Omega = -3\pi J_2\left(\frac{R_e}{p}\right)^2 \cos i \qquad (3.8)$$

in radians per revolution. R_e is Earth's mean radius and p, the semilatus rectum, is given as $p = a(1-e^2)$. The advance of the line of apsides is given by

$$\Delta\omega = 3\pi J_2\left(\frac{R_e}{p}\right)^2 \left(2 - \frac{5}{2}\sin^2 i\right) \qquad (3.9)$$

again in radians per revolution. We note that $2 - (5/2)\sin^2 i$ is zero when $\sin^2 i$ is 4/5; therefore, orbits with inclination $i = 63.4°$ do not experience apsidal advance. This characteristic has long been utilized by the Soviets in their Molniya orbits for communications satellites. Because the line of apsides does not move, the apoapsis stays put at high latitudes where it is most useful.

The rates of motion of the line of nodes and line of apsides are graphed in Figures 3.9 and 3.10. These motions amount to several degrees per day and are very significant to mission design. This is especially true of servicing missions, where a space station is viewed as a servicing base for associated free-flying spacecraft and platforms. The effects of nodal regression make it imperative that space stations and the craft they are intended to service remain at the same average altitude. Otherwise, differential nodal regression will cause large orbit plane differences to accumulate. The delta v's needed to overcome these plane differences are prohibitive.

An alternate strategy of some value is to plan on regular intervals of service when the difference in the orbital planes is small. For typical cases, the service interval is six months to two years. If the differential nodal regression, for example, is 1° per day, the orbits will line up, permitting low delta v transfer, about once per year.

Repeating Orbits

Certain missions benefit from repeating orbits. A repeating orbit is one whose ground track repeats after a certain interval which can be every day, but can also be on the order of a week. Earth observation missions benefit from repeating orbits because images taken from orbit are repetitive; this facilitates image registration, mapmaking, and change de-

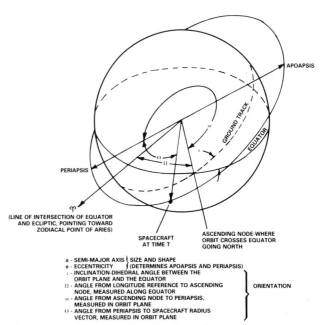

Figure 3.8 The six parameters of an orbit.

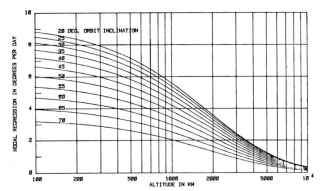

Figure 3.9 Rates of nodal regression (motion of the line of nodes in the equatorial plane). *Courtesy of Boeing*.

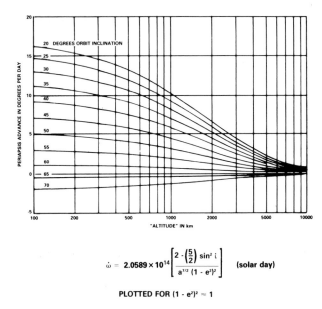

$$\dot{\omega} = 2.0589 \times 10^{14} \left[\frac{2 - \left(\frac{5}{2}\right) \sin^2 i}{a^{7/2} (1 - e^2)^2} \right] \quad \text{(solar day)}$$

PLOTTED FOR $(1 - e^2)^2 \approx 1$

Figure 3.10 Rates of periapsis motion for nearly circular orbits.

tection. If a space station is to serve as a transportation node, a repeating orbit facilitates rendezvous, inasmuch as the space station will pass over the launch site at a convenient time for rendezvous every repeat interval.

A repeating orbit must satisfy two conditions. First, the combined effects of Earth's rotation and orbit nodal regression must equal an integral number of revolutions in the repeat period. Second, an integral number of orbits, referred to the nodal period, must occur in the same period.

The repeating orbit may repeat once per day or once per number of days plus some irreducible fraction. As examples, consider 15 orbits per day, which we use as an example below, and $14\frac{1}{17}$ orbits per day, somewhat typical of a Sun-synchronous Landsat. An orbit synchronized at 15 orbits per day will repeat every day, a convenient situation if frequent launch operations to the space station are contemplated. An orbit synchronized at $14\frac{1}{17}$ orbits per day will repeat every $(14)(17) + 1 = 239$ orbits. The significance of

the latter is seen in considering Earth observation missions. If a spacecraft in a 600 km orbit is to view the whole Earth at 15 orbits per day, then each orbit must see, at the equator, 1/15 of the Earth's circumference, or $40,074/15 = 2671$ km of swath. At the edge of the swath, the elevation angle will be less than $14°$, and resolution and contrast will both be severely degraded.

With a repeat after every 239 orbits, the swath width need be only 168 km, or 200 km with a generous overlap (important for map-matching correlation techniques).

The rate of nodal regression was expressed in radians per revolution by eq. 3.8. Recognizing that there are 2π radians per revolution and expressing the inverse of the orbit period as revolutions per second from eq. 3.1, and multiplying by 86,164, the number of seconds in a sidereal day, yields

$$\dot{\Omega} = -2.0533 \times 10^{14} \left[\frac{\cos i}{a^{7/2} (1 - e^2)^2} \right] \text{ deg/day} \quad (3.10)$$

$$\dot{\Omega} = -5.7035 \times 10^{11} \left[\frac{\cos i}{a^{7/2} (1 - e^2)^2} \right] \text{ rev/day} \quad (3.11)$$

as the nodal regression rate in revolutions per (sidereal) day.

For a typical space station orbit, this rate computes to about $6.5°$ per day, or one $360°$ revolution of nodal regression in about 55 days.

Because the nodal regression is retrograde (opposite in direction to the Earth's spin) as noted under the section on "Earth Oblateness Effects," the repeat interval, analyzed on the basis of orbits per day, is less than one sidereal day. The motion is diagrammed in Figure 3.11. The daily repeat period, corrected for the nodal regression rate, can be obtained from eq. 3.11 and is given by

$$R = \frac{86,164 \ sec}{1 + \frac{5.7035 \times 10^{11} \cos i}{a^{7/2} (1 - e^2)^2}} . \quad (3.12)$$

With nodal regression and periapsis advance, the orbit period is no longer uniquely defined. One must know which periodicity is desired. The following three periods are commonly considered: (1) the sidereal period, corresponding to the time required to complete $360°$ of motion in the orbit plane about the center; (2) the nodal period, the time from one ascending node to the next (Figure 3.12), and the anomalistic period, fom one periapsis to the next. Since the line of nodes regresses while the line of apsides advances (for orbits at inclinations less than $i = 63.4°$), the nodal period is less than the sidereal period and the anomalistic period is greater.

As might be suggested by Figure 3.12, the nodal period is the one of interest for repeating orbits.

The following expression for the nodal period for N orbits

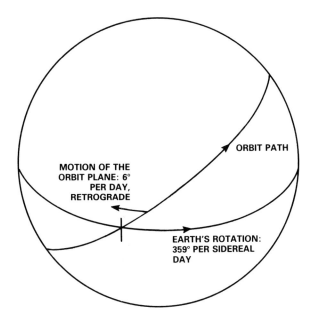

Figure 3.11 Relative motions of earth rotation and orbit nodal regression in an inertial frame.

is given by the *Orbital Flight Handbook*:

$$P' = C_t P \qquad (3.13)$$

where

$$P = 2N\pi\sqrt{a^3/\mu}$$

and N is the number of orbits per day. The correction term C_t is

$$C_t = 1 - 3J_z\left(\frac{R_e}{a}\right)^2 [(7\cos^z i - 1)/8]. \qquad (3.14)$$

Both conditions must be satisfied for a repeating orbit. These conditions are graphed for 15 orbits per day, for inclinations of 30° and 50° in Figure 3.13. The variation in semimajor axis with inclination, for 15 orbits/day, is graphed in Figure 3.14.

Sun-synchronous Orbits

If the inclination of an orbit exceeds 90° (retrograde motion), then the cosine term in eq. 3.11 becomes negative and the motion of nodal regression is in the same direction as the Earth's rotation and revolution about the Sun. Regression rates equal to the Earth's rotation are not possible, but rates equal to the Earth's rate of revolution about the Sun are quite feasible; the latter is about 1° per day, and as we have seen, regression rates exceeding 6° per day are experienced at low altitudes with low inclination. The Earth's path around the Sun averages $360/366.25 = 0.9829°$ per sidereal day. Recalling eq. 3.10, one can set

$$\cos i = -\frac{0.9829 a^{7/2}}{2.0533 \times 10^{14}} = -4.787 \times 10^{-15} a^{7/2}$$

as the defining equation for a Sun-synchronous orbit. Since

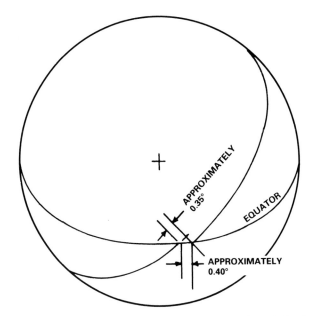

Figure 3.12 Nodal regression causes node-to-node period to be less than 360° central angle period.

the value of $\cos i$ is negative, the inclination angle i is greater than 90°, i.e., retrograde. Thus for any altitude, (up to a maximum where $\cos i = -1$) there is a retrograde orbit that maintains a constant orientation with respect to the Earth-Sun system. The relationship is graphed in Figure 3.15. The characteristic line from Figure 3.14 for 15 orbits per day is also shown. If one specifies a certain number of orbits per day and that the orbit must be Sun-synchronous, then only

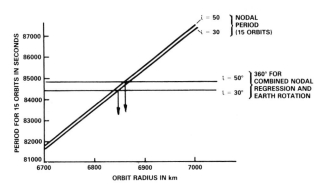

Figure 3.13 Conditions for a repeating orbit.

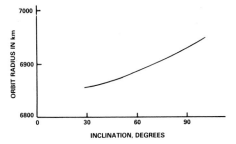

Figure 3.14 Variation in semimajor axis with inclination for 15 orbits per day.

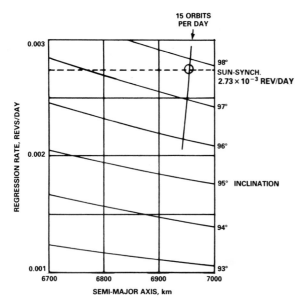

Figure 3.15 Conditions for sun-synchronous orbits.

one particular combination of inclination and altitude will satisfy the necessary conditions. This feature can be used to establish a continuously sunlit orbit and has been used, e.g., for Landsat, to establish a repeating orbit that has consistent Sun illumination of the Earth being photographed. In this case the node time (local time of day when the spacecraft crosses the equator at ascending node) is constant.

Drag

The density of the Earth's atmosphere decreases rapidly with altitude. The decrease is crudely exponential and would be almost exactly exponential if the atmosphere were isothermal and of constant composition. In a strict mathematical sense, atmospheric density never reaches zero, but at some considerable altitude it becomes no more than the very tenuous density of interplanetary space and is no longer associated with the Earth.

At altitudes typical for space stations and platforms in low Earth orbit, however, atmospheric density is not negligible. Effects of atmospheric drag must be considered, as was made plainly evident by the orbital demise of Skylab in 1980. Drag gradually removes orbital energy from an orbiting object, heating the tenuous upper atmosphere and the object by friction in the process.

It is well established that the Earth's upper atmosphere is strongly affected by solar activity. While the lower atmosphere, up to 100 km or so, is dominated by Earth's gravity and atmospheric circulations, the upper atmosphere is dominated by gravity and solar activity. At typical space station altitudes, the density of the upper atmosphere can vary more than tenfold. Upper atmosphere environments are discussed in the following chapter.

Drag effects can be expressed physically as a work term in which a force (the drag) acts over a distance (the orbital path). Equating work done by drag friction with orbital energy lost, the energy of the orbit is decreased by the amount of work done against drag forces. The total energy of a mass in a circular orbit is $\left(-\dfrac{\mu}{r}+\dfrac{\mu}{2r}\right)m=-\dfrac{\mu m}{2r}$ where the first term on the left is potential energy and the second term is equivalent to the orbital kinetic energy. The drag work per orbit is simply

$$\int_0^{2\pi r} f\,ds = 2\pi rf \qquad (3.15)$$

assuming that the drag is essentially constant over a single orbit. The drag force f is $C_d Sq$ where q, the dynamic pressure, is

$$q = \frac{1}{2}\rho v^2 = \frac{1}{2}\rho\mu/r. \qquad (3.16)$$

C_d is the drag coefficient, typically 2.2, and S is the frontal area of the orbiting object as presented to the oncoming flow of the atmosphere relative to the orbital velocity.

Therefore, the drag work in one complete orbit is $\pi C_d S\rho\mu$ and this is equal to the energy loss per unit of orbit dE/dN for the orbiting object.

The loss of energy per unit of orbit radius is $dE/dr = \mu m/2r^2$. The change in radius per orbit is dr/dN and can be evaluated from

$$(dE/dN)/(dE/dr) = \frac{-\pi C_d S\rho\mu}{\mu m/(2r^2)} = \frac{-\pi 2r^2 C_d S\rho}{m}. \qquad (3.17)$$

The time rate of altitude loss is $dr/dt = (dr/dN)(dN/dt)$ where $dN/dt = \dfrac{1}{2\pi}\sqrt{\mu/r^3}$.

Substituting, yields

$$dr/dt = \frac{-C_d S\rho\sqrt{\mu r}}{m}. \qquad (3.18)$$

Illustrating by example, let:

$$\rho = 10^{-12}\ \text{kg/m}^3$$
$$S = 1000\ \text{m}^2$$
$$C_d = 2.2$$
$$r = 6900\ \text{km} = 6.9 \times 10^6\ \text{m}$$
$$\text{mass} = 10^5\ \text{kg}$$
$$\mu = 3.98601 \times 10^{14}\ \text{m}^3/\text{sec}^2$$

The decay rate obtained from eq. 3.18 is 1.15×10^{-3} m/sec or 100 meter of altitude lost per day. This figure is quite typical for a space station or platform.

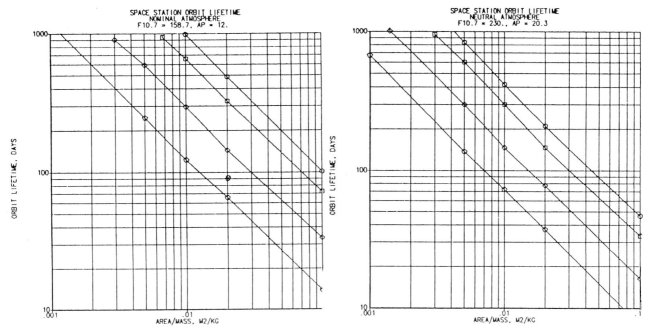

Figure 3.16   Orbital lifetimes for nominal and NASA neutral atmosphere models. *Courtesy of Boeing.*

If one models atmospheric density as an exponential function with altitude, it is possible to derive a closed-form expression for decay time from any altitude. Such expressions are nearly useless, however, because the exponential model is very poor for the upper atmosphere and the atmospheric density can vary significantly over the lifetime of an orbit. Orbital lifetime parametrics are shown in Figure 3.16 as derived by numerical integration of orbit decay.

Orbital decay rates on the order of hundreds of meters per day point to the feasibility of reboost intervals on the order of many weeks. Contemporary thinking about space station and platform operations, however, leans toward orbit makeup propulsion strategies that operate frequently enough to maintain a nearly constant orbit altitude. This is discussed in more detail in Chapter 5 under the description of space station propulsion systems.

Note that the average thrust of an orbit makeup system must equal the average drag, and that, unlike usual space propulsion problems, where space vehicle mass is an important factor, only the drag area, the atmospheric density, and the drag coefficient are involved; mass is not a factor at all. Average thrusts are small. In the example given above, the drag is 0.087 newton, only about 1/50 of a pound of force.

Differential Drag

Earlier we noted that co-orbiting objects must remain at the same average altitude in order to prevent differential nodal regression from building up large angles between orbit planes. The dihedral angle between orbit planes can be up to twice the inclination. For the planned space station orbits

at $i = 28.5°$, transfer from one object to another could require up to about 7200 m/sec delta v.

Since drag causes gradual orbit decay, and since different objects are unlikely to have equal ratios of area to mass, differential drag will cause changes in altitude that must be periodically corrected to maintain a co-orbiting condition. The maintenance of co-orbiting is sometimes called formation flying, although in a practical sense, it will not resemble formation flying of aircraft. Formation-flying spacecraft can easily be hundreds to thousands of kilometers apart while remaining mutually accessible in terms of delta v.

The rate at which distance and plane differences build up is of interest and is readily estimated. A simple, illustrative model assumes that one space vehicle has its orbit continuously maintained by thrust, acting as if it has no drag. A second space vehicle experiences orbit decay due to drag at a rate dh/dt. As its orbit radius decreases, it accelerates relative to the first vehicle at an orbital angular rate ω. If distance is measured along the path of the first object at orbital radius r_o; the acceleration can be expressed as

$$\ddot{x} = \dot{\omega} r_o = r_o \frac{\partial \omega}{\partial t} = r_o \frac{\partial \omega}{\partial h} \frac{\partial h}{\partial t} \quad . \qquad (3.19)$$

Substituting for $\partial \omega / \partial h$, we obtain $x = -\frac{3}{4} \sqrt{\frac{\mu}{r^3}} \frac{\partial h}{\partial t} T^2$. This can be integrated, and a time interval of days inserted, to obtain

$$x = 64{,}800 \sqrt{\mu/r^3} \, (dh/dt) D^2 \qquad (3.20)$$

At the dh/dt rate in the above example, 0.1 km/day, x (the

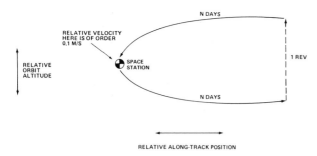

Figure 3.17 Differential drag orbit makeup strategy. *Courtesy of Boeing.*

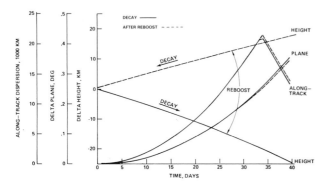

Figure 3.18 Differential drag: Correction of effects by reboost. *Courtesy of Boeing.*

along-orbit-track separation) increases to about 7.17 km in the first day, and reaches 717 km in 10 days. Thus the along-track separation builds up rapidly indeed.

A similar procedure can be applied to calculating the buildup of plane difference due to differential nodal regression, yielding

$$7.2 \times 10^{14} \, r^{-9/2} \cos i \frac{\partial r}{\partial D} D^2 \qquad (3.21)$$

in degrees, angle between lines of nodes, where r is in km, $\partial r/\partial D$ is in km/day, and D is in days.

For orbits at the same inclination, the actual dihedral angle between planes is less than the angle between the lines of nodes by a factor of $\sin i$. Thus the buildup of plane difference is quite gradual compared to the buildup of along-track separation.

Figure 3.17 illustrates a practical formation-flying strategy. The spacecraft experiencing orbit decay is periodically reboosted to an altitude greater than that of the space platform or station it is co-orbiting with. The along-track and out-of-plane deviations are corrected as shown in Figure 3.18. If continuous communications between the space vehicles are desired, the along-track separation must be kept less than the loss-of-line-of-sight distance, roughly 2000 km. If communications are not required, relatively infrequent reboosts will keep the orbits coplanar to within a fraction of a degree. Making a 1° plane change at 500 km

altitude requires 133 m/sec delta v, an acceptable figure for co-orbit access.

Proximity Operations

Spacecraft flying near one another in nearly identical orbits are said to be engaged in proximity operations. Proximity operations in the form of rendezvous and docking, or close proximity fly-arounds, were a part of the Gemini, Apollo, Skylab, Apollo-Soyuz, and Soviet Salyut programs. On STS-7, the Shuttle launched and retrieved the German SPAS platform, the first of contemporary proximity operations.

It is easy to think that proximity operations between spacecraft hurtling through space at tens of thousands of miles per hour would be difficult and risky, but every mission experience has shown that adequately trained astronauts can readily carry it off. Motions of spacecraft flying in proximity to one another are not, however, what one might intuitively expect; training is essential for effective piloting of these operations.

Relative Motion

The nature of the motion to be expected can be glimpsed by a simple derivation. In terms of the x and y components of acceleration, the differential equations for orbital motion in two dimensions are

$$\ddot{x} = -\frac{\mu x}{x^2 + y^2} \qquad (3.22)$$

$$\ddot{y} = -\frac{\mu y}{x^2 + y^2} \quad .$$

If one considers a second object in nearly the same orbit, its components of acceleration are

$$\ddot{x}' = -\frac{\mu x'}{x'^2 + y'^2} \qquad (3.23)$$

$$\ddot{y}' = -\frac{\mu y'}{x'^2 + y'^2} \quad .$$

The differential acceleration is simply the difference between these two; namely, $\ddot{x}_d = \ddot{x} - \ddot{x}'$ and $\ddot{y}_d = \ddot{y} - \ddot{y}'$. Taking these differences, and assuming that $x^2 + y^2$ is nearly equal to $x'^2 + y'^2$, we obtain

$$\ddot{x}_d = -\frac{\mu x_d}{x^2 + y^2} \qquad (3.24)$$

$$\ddot{y}_d = -\frac{\mu y_d}{x^2 + y^2} \quad .$$

Thus the equations for differential motion are similar to the equations of orbital motion. This suggests that circular or elliptic relative motion of one object about another, with a period equal to the orbital period about the parent body, should occur, and indeed it can.

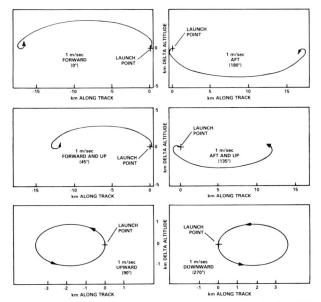

Figure 3.19   Examples of relative motions about a point in a 500-km circular Earth orbit.

To obtain this simple derivation, we assumed that $x^2 + y^2$ was equal to $x'^2 + y'^2$. This assumption suppresses secular relative motions due to differences in orbital altitude. We learned in the earlier discussion of differential drag that these are not at all trivial. Consequently eq. 3.24 is useful only in cases where the two objects have exactly the same average altitude, i.e., when one moves in an ellipse about the other as noted above. Numerical integration of the equations of Keplerian motion can provide a more general insight.

Here we confine our discussion to motion of objects launched from a space station or platform in several directions. This is a special case of more general motions and suffices to illustrate the nature of proximity relative motion.

Figure 3.19 shows relative motion in the orbit plane for objects launched along various initial relative velocity vectors.

Objects launched in the "ahead" direction gain orbital energy in the process, increasing the semimajor axis and the orbital period. Consequently, such objects actually slow down in angular rate and, although launched ahead, they fall behind. Conversely, objects launched retrograde increase in velocity and move ahead.

Docking and Berthing

One of the main purposes of proximity operations is to join together orbiting objects initially flying free of one another. Docking has been practiced since the Gemini program. In docking, two spacecraft collide with sufficient force to actuate alignment and capture mechanisms. Typical docking velocities are on the order of 0.3 m/sec (1 ft/sec). In berthing, a positive control device such as the Shuttle Remote

Manipulator System (RMS) is used to position the objects to be joined in the proper location. Latching mechanisms are then activated to complete the joining action.

Docking mechanisms are designed to accommodate position and velocity errors expected from manual piloting of the docking maneuver. Typical position errors are 15 cm and a few degrees. Velocity errors are on the order of 0.1 m/sec. Docking guides such as illustrated in Figure 3.20 serve to guide the final closing maneuver and correct the errors.

Berthing errors are thought to be much less. The only flight experience with berthing is the placement of the SPAS and some small environment sampling payloads back into the Shuttle payload bay after attachment to the RMS or free flight. This limited experience confirms that much smaller errors occur.

The advantage of docking is that the spacecraft can be flown together without special mechanisms or devices other than the docking mechanisms themselves. The disadvantages are that the energy to be dissipated by docking is significant, especially in the case of massive systems like the Shuttle and a space station, and that the mechanisms must correct substantial position and velocity errors. Most of the energy of the docking collision appears as structural dynamics energy in the space station structure. Substantial deflections are expected to occur, and some analyses have cast doubt on the structural integrity of typical space station structural elements, such as solar arrays, under docking conditions.

The advantage of berthing is that collision energies are insignificant and that position and velocity errors are roughly an order of magnitude smaller. The disadvantage is that a berthing control device such as a remote manipulator arm, e.g., the Canadian arm on the Shuttle, is needed to control the berthing operation. The Shuttle arm was not designed

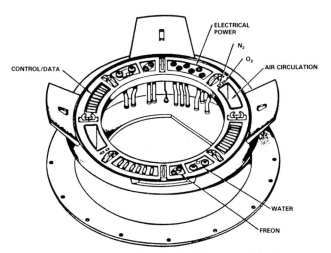

Figure 3.20   Typical docking or berthing port with alignment guides. *Courtesy of Rockwell.*

to handle masses exceeding the 29.5 metric ton Shuttle payload capability, but simulations and analyses have shown that with control software changes, the Shuttle arm can handle much greater masses, if a bit slowly.

As of this writing, berthing is generally favored as the preferred means of joining large or massive space objects to one another.

Launch and Capture Operations

One of the principal functions of a mature space station operation will be the launch and subsequent capture of high-energy upper stages flying from the space station orbit to geosynchronous orbit, the lunar vicinity, and on planetary trajectories. These stages will be for the most part unmanned and, during operations in proximity to the space station, controlled from the space station.

The relative motions described above show that if an upper stage is launched forward or aftward of the space station, even at quite low relative velocities, separations on the order of kilometers, adequate for initiation of propulsion operations for the upper stage, will occur in an orbit or two.

For capture operations, the upper stage can be placed in an approach path that results in a pass-by of the upper stage within a few meters of the space station. During the pass, which can be at small relative velocities, a station-based RMS could grapple the upper stage and retrieve it into a hangar or servicing facility. The space station is to have a proximity operations radar; terminal approaches can be monitored and the space station maneuvered to avoid a collision if necessary.

Gravity Gradient Effects

The strength of the Earth's gravitational field in low Earth orbit is nearly as great as at the Earth's surface. A space station or platform in such an orbit is not in zero-g. Its "free-fall" path about the Earth causes the net gravitational acceleration onboard to be very nearly zero. Because the gravity field of the Earth is a central force field, however, it varies in strength and direction with displacement from the center of gravity of an orbiting object. One might imagine this effect to be entirely negligible, but it is not, and in fact, can have profound influence on the design of configurations as well as flight and attitude control systems.

Torques

The variation of the gravity field about an orbiting object is plausibly called the gravity gradient. Depending on inertial properties of an orbiting object and its orientation relative to the orbit geometry, gravity gradients may exert torques on the object which must be counteracted if attitude control is to be maintained.

The gravity gradient torque on an orbiting object is given by

$$\mathbf{T} = \frac{3\mu}{r^3}\,[\mathbf{r}]^\times\,[I]\,[\mathbf{r}] \qquad (3.25)$$

where $\mathbf{T}$ is the torque vector, I is the inertia tensor of the object, and $\mathbf{r}$ is the orbit radius vector pointing from the center of the Earth through the center of mass of the orbiting object. Tensors and vectors are referenced to a coordinate system, and all must be in the same coordinate system for the above equation to be valid. Inertia tensors are described in the chapter dealing with mass properties.

Since the inertia tensor is proportional to mr^2 terms, it is clear that the magnitude of gravity gradient effects scales with the mass and with the square of dimensions of space stations and platforms. This explains why gravity gradient effects, of secondary importance for small spacecraft, become of primary importance for large, massive platforms, and indeed ultimately limit the size of objects that can be controlled in low Earth orbits.

To analyze the effects of gravity gradients, it is helpful to establish a simple but generally applicable coordinate convention, such as is diagrammed in Figure 3.21. The spacecraft is defined as flying Earth-oriented, in which case the orbit radius vector in spacecraft coordinates is fixed as

$$\begin{pmatrix} 0 \\ 0 \\ -1 \end{pmatrix}$$

or flying inertially oriented, in which case the radius vector varies as

$$\begin{pmatrix} \sin(\theta) \\ 0 \\ -\cos(\theta) \end{pmatrix}$$

in spacecraft coordinates. Calculations are carried out in spacecraft coordinates, thus directly applicable to attitude control considerations. The coordinate convention is diagrammed in the figure and stays tied to spacecraft body axes.

If the spacecraft flies *Earth-oriented*, our coordinate convention describes the radius vector as a fixed value. If the spacecraft flies *principal axis*, its inertia tensor in the selected coordinate system has no cross products, as indicated in Figure 3.22. The sequence of matrix multiplication and vector cross-product specified in eq. 3.25 always yields zero torque, as also indicated in the figure.

If the spacecraft is not principal-axis oriented, the radius vector will have components on more than one axis and net torques will result. For example, assume the radius vector is offset from the principal axis in pitch (pitch rotation is around the y-axis). If the offset is small, the vector can be

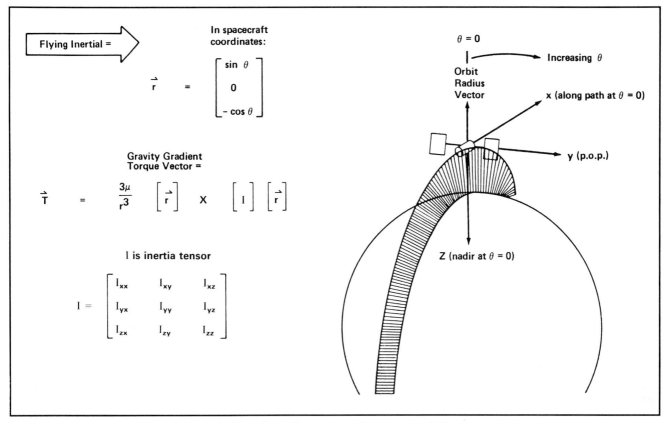

Figure 3.21   Definition of coordinate system for torques analysis. *Courtesy of Boeing.*

expressed as

$$\begin{pmatrix} \epsilon \\ 0 \\ -1 \end{pmatrix}$$

where ϵ is a very small value, and the result of eq. 3.25 is

$$T_y \, (pitch) = \epsilon(I_{xx} - I_{zz})\left(\frac{3\mu}{r^3}\right). \qquad (3.26)$$

Here the radius vector is nearly aligned with the z-axis. If $I_{xx} > I_{zz}$, the sense of the torque vector is stabilizing, i.e., it tends to restore the z-axis alignment. If $I_{zz} > I_{xx}$, the torque will try to rotate the spacecraft 90° in pitch, thus to exchange the x- and z-axes. Therefore, in Earth-oriented flight, there are fully stable and conditionally stable orientations. The fully stable orientations are designated gravity gradient stable.

Most solar-powered space station and platform design concepts fly with at least the solar array inertially oriented and the entire platform may be inertially oriented. For inertial orientation, the radius vector rotates in the x-z plane as described above. If the spacecraft has only diagonal elements in its inertia tensor, the gravity gradient torques exhibit only cyclic components as illustrated in Figure 3.23. The $\sin \theta \cos \theta$ term, by trigonometric identity, is 1/2

$\sin 2\,\theta$, and the torque passes through a full cycle in half an orbit.

The definition of a starting point in an orbit is, of course, arbitrary. If it is moved, and the spacecraft inertial attitude stays the same, the change in coordinate orientation introduces an I_{xz} term in the inertia tensor. Not surprisingly, the gravity gradient torque is still only cyclic and is given by

$$T_y = -I_{xz} \cos 2\,\tau + (I_{xx} - I_{zz}) \sin 2\,\tau. \qquad (3.27)$$

I_{xy} and I_{zy} terms in the inertia tensor represent asymmetries out of the orbit plane. The effect of these is strikingly different. Figures 3.24 and 3.25 show the effects of these terms; they generate secular torques that cause momentum to accumulate indefinitely.

The significance of cyclic versus secular torques is that the former, if they are not too large, can be handled by momentum storage devices such as inertia wheels or control moment gyros (CMGs). Secular torques will soon saturate any plausible momentum storage device and must be controlled by magnetic torquers reacting against the Earth's magnetic field or by expenditure of propellant through attitude control thrusters. Since the Earth's magnetic field is weak and expenditure of propellant is costly in terms of resupply, the minimization of secular gravity gradient torques is an important consideration in the development of space station and platform configurations. Configuration ge-

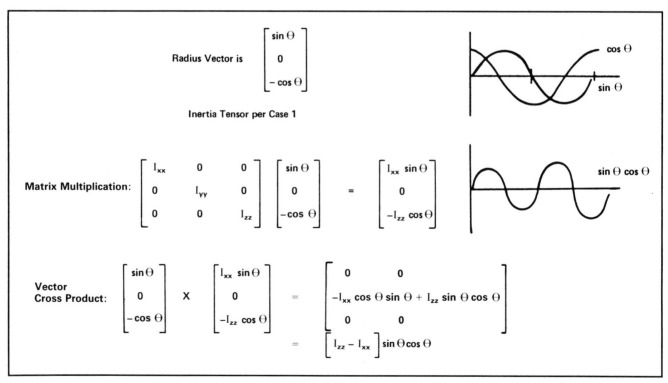

Figure 3.22 Earth-oriented, "principal-axis" flight mode yields zero gravity gradient torque. *Courtesy of Boeing.*

Figure 3.23 Gravity gradient torques for principal axes aligned to orbit plane. *Courtesy of Boeing.*

Radius Vector per Case 2

Inertia Tensor: Add i$_{xy}$ cross product

Matrix Multiplication:
$$
\begin{bmatrix} I_{xx} & I_{xy} & 0 \\ I_{xy} & I_{yy} & 0 \\ 0 & 0 & I_{zz} \end{bmatrix}
\begin{bmatrix} \sin\Theta \\ 0 \\ -\cos\Theta \end{bmatrix}
=
\begin{bmatrix} I_{xx}\sin\Theta \\ I_{yx}\sin\Theta \\ -I_{zz}\cos\Theta \end{bmatrix}
$$

Vector Cross Product:
$$
\begin{bmatrix} \sin\Theta \\ 0 \\ -\cos\Theta \end{bmatrix}
\times
\begin{bmatrix} I_{xx}\sin\Theta \\ I_{yx}\sin\Theta \\ -I_{zz}\cos\Theta \end{bmatrix}
=
\begin{bmatrix} I_{yx}\cos\Theta\sin\Theta \\ -I_{xx}\cos\Theta\sin\Theta + I_{zz}\cos\Theta\sin\Theta \\ I_{yx}\sin^2\Theta \end{bmatrix}
$$

Figure 3.24   Gravity gradient torques, I$_{xy}$ cross-product effect. *Courtesy of Boeing.*

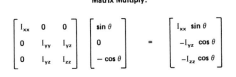
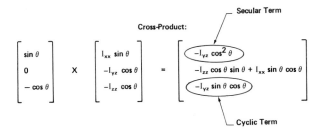

Figure 3.25 Gravity gradient torques, I$_{yz}$ cross-product effect. *Courtesy of Boeing.*

ometry influences on inertial properties is discussed in Chapter 1 under "Mass Properties."

The contributions of the inertia tensor terms to gravity gradient torques can be summed up by superposition. Table 3.2 and the embedded figure summarize the contributions to cyclic and secular torques from the inertia tensor terms. Discussion of how these terms affect flight control systems is presented in Chapter 5 under "Attitude Control."

Tethers

Tethers may be used to interconnect spacecraft elements if orbital mechanics forces will keep the tether taut. Tethered spacecraft are a special case of gravity-gradient-stable configurations, with the tether connecting spacecraft masses,

Table 3.2   Summary of gravity gradient torque effects. *Courtesy of Boeing.*

AXIS	INERTIA TERM (MILLIONS OF kg-m^2)	INTEGRAL TERM
X$_{CYCLIC}$	I$_{xy}$	CURVE, PER 1/4 ORBIT
X$_{SECULAR}$	I$_{yz}$	2π x CURVE, CUMULATIVE PER ORBIT
Y$_{CYCLIC}$	$\sqrt{(I_{xx}-I_{zz})^2 + I_{xz}{}^2}$	CURVE, PER 1/4 ORBIT
Z$_{CYCLIC}$	I$_{yz}$	CURVE, PER 1/4 ORBIT
Z$_{SECULAR}$	I$_{xy}$	2π x CURVE, CUMULATIVE PER ORBIT

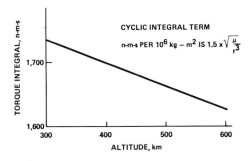

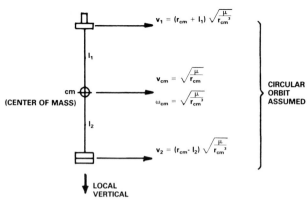

Figure 3.26 Orbital motion of a vertical tether.

usually oriented vertically referenced to local gravity. Tethers are commonly viewed as tension members having no compressional strength, needing the gravity gradient force to maintain a rigid state.

For short tethers, the tether tension (and therefore stress) is mainly dictated by the gravity forces on the end masses, and is readily calculated by differencing gravitational and centrifugal forces. For long tethers, the mass of the tether itself is significant and the design of the tether must consider the tether mass in establishing stresses and tether strength. Integral equations can be written that express tether stress; these may be used to design a constant-stress (and therefore mass-optimum) tether.

Although tethers have never been used in practical flight mechanics, they have many interesting properties and may actually serve transportation functions. As an example, consider two equal masses connected by a tether in a gravity gradient stable (vertical) orientation, as illustrated in Figure 3.26. The motion of the center of mass is given by

$$\omega_{cm} = \sqrt{\frac{\mu}{r_{cm}^3}} \quad . \tag{3.28}$$

The velocities of the upper and lower ends are

$$v_1 = (r_{cm} + l_1)\omega_{cm} \text{ and } v_2 = (r_{cm} - l_2)\,\omega_{cm}$$

respectively, assuming the center of mass is in a circular orbit. With this assumption, the upper end has excess velocity relative to a circular orbit at its altitude and the lower end has deficient velocity. Now assume the upper end is instantaneously freed. Equating the velocity for the upper end and for the perigee of a free elliptic orbit yields

$$r_a - r_p = \frac{r_p}{\frac{2\mu}{r_p v_p^2}} - 1 \quad - r_\rho = \frac{2\left(r_p - \frac{\mu}{v_p^2}\right) r_p v_p^2}{2\mu - r_p v_p^2} \quad . \tag{3.29}$$

This equation can be solved for the radius of the apogee of the free orbit, obtaining

$$r_a - r_p = \frac{2[(r_{cm} + l_1)^3 - r_{cm}^3] - (r_{cm} + l_1)}{2r_{cm}^3 - (r_{cm} + l_1)^3}. \tag{3.30}$$

With numerical substitution and assuming $r_{cm} \gg l_1$, one finds that the height of the apogee relative to the center-of-mass orbit will be about seven times the tether length from the center of mass, expressed as follows:

$$r_a - r_p \approx 6l_1 \text{ and } r_a - r_{cm} = r_a - r_p + l_1 \approx 7l_1. \tag{3.31}$$

Tethers can also be used to exchange momentum and energy. An example based on the above relations is that a space station instead of simply undocking a Shuttle Orbiter, could reel it downward on a tether. After the tether was extended 100 km or so, the Orbiter could be released. The resulting Orbiter trajectory would be on a reentry path, and the space station orbit would increase in average altitude. The space station orbit, however, would become elliptic, perhaps an undesirable situation. Furthermore, the dynamics of the tether itself must be considered; for example: would the released strain energy cause the tether to recoil and destructively wrap itself around the space station?

Tethers need not necessarily be gravity-gradient-stable. Rotating concepts have been proposed. Some years ago, the idea of a rotating tether in lunar orbit was offered as a means of simplifying lunar transportation. A tethered space platform could be placed in a lunar orbit with the center of mass at an altitude equal to the tether radius and the tether tip velocity equal to the product of the orbital angular rate and the lunar surface radius. If the Moon's surface were an ideal sphere, the ends of such a tether would come momentarily to rest at the lunar surface and a space traveler could (quickly) step on or off. Objects released at the upper part of the tether travel would be at escape velocity relative to the Moon and would, for example, return to Earth (there to arrive at a high velocity, of course).

Concepts such as these are ill-defined at present, but rotating tethers offer interesting and potentially beneficial opportunities for exchange of energy and momentum, especially for two-way transportation, and we may expect to see much more attention to these ideas in the future.

Tether dynamics is a new, inadequately explored field. Useful applications of tethers will undoubtedly be found, but the present state of knowledge is inadequate to specify exactly what these will be.

Flight Modes

A space station or platform is not simply to be placed in orbit. There are a number of attitude or flight control strategies that can be applied to how the platform is to fly. These must reconcile mission needs with the practical aspects of attitude control technology and costs.

The following discussion will employ acronyms com-

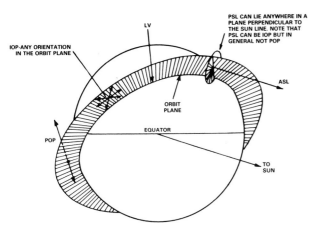

Figure 3.27 Attitude orientation terminology.

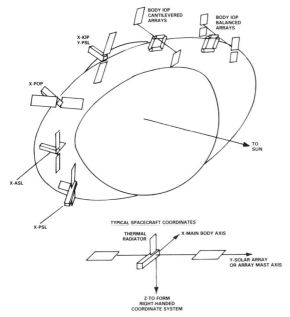

Figure 3.28 Representative attitude orientation strategies.

monly used to describe attitude strategies. These are: POP—perpendicular to the orbit plane; IOP—in the orbit plane; PSL—perpendicular to the Sun line; LV—local vertical, i.e., Earth-oriented; ASL—aligned with the Sun line. These are depicted in Figure 3.27.

A very large, even infinite number of flight mode strategies exist. Here we will describe five that are frequently considered. The first three are inertial modes and the last two are Earth-oriented modes. All are shown in Figure 3.28.

1. *x-IOP, y-PSL:*

   The spacecraft x-axis is in the orbit plane. By suitable roll about the x-axis, the y-axis is placed perpendicular to the Sun line so that a simple rotation of the solar array about the y-axis causes the array to track the Sun. Because the y-axis is not perpendicular to the orbit plane, the solar array generates a z-y product of inertia resulting in secular gravity gradient torque. A smaller x-y product may be created depending on the relationship of the x-axis to the Sun line.

2. *x-POP and y-IOP and PSL:*

   With the y-axis in the orbit plane and perpendicular to the Sun line, the only cross-product of inertia is the small one created by solar array rotation about the y-axis to track the solar beta angle.

3. *x-PSL and y-IOP:*

   This orientation permits Sun-facing of a fixed solar array. With x-PSL, x-z products will be generated. The significance of these depends on the configuration arrangement.

4. *Body Earth-oriented, array cantilevered:*

   If the solar array is to track the Sun, it is always essentially inertial. For Earth-oriented stations, the solar array assembly may be considered as despun. Arrangement (4) has a solar array mast perpendicular to the orbit plane so that a simple rotation about the mast provides Sun-tracking. The Sun line can be out of the orbit plane by as much as 52° (assuming a station orbit inclination of 28.5°; the worst case is the sum of the orbit inclination and the maximum Sun declination of 23.5°). The solar array is hinged and cantilevered about the mast end to provide beta tilt. Large secular torques result from this arrangement. The redeeming virtue of this arrangement is that the solar arrays are deployed far from the center of station activity and are not limited in size by clearance considerations.

5. *Body Earth-oriented, array balanced:*

   The balanced array configuration greatly reduces cross products of inertia. Large y-z products are replaced by much smaller x-y or y-z ones. If the array is hinged in such a way as to cause center-of-mass offsets to counter array tilt, the inertia products may be cancelled entirely (at the expense of a somewhat more complex beta tilt mechanism). Because the array panels rotate about the array mast, clearance problems not present with strategy (4) are created. It becomes necessary to know how large in area the solar array may need to become, because it sweeps out an area dependent on the ultimate array size. While inertial cross-product disturbances are reduced, the need to anticipate ultimate array size becomes much more urgent.

Summary

Flight mechanics influences on space station and platform design are numerous and complex. Characteristics of the orbit influence station or platform utility for Earth and space observations and for space transportation operations. Upper atmospheric drag and perhaps gravity gradient torques dictate selection of a space station/platform propulsion system. Drag and gravity gradient torques are principal considerations in selection of a configuration. Adoption of a tether system can influence many aspects of system design and operation. Flight modes must be selected based on the influences of orbital mechanics effects.

This chapter has provided an overview of many important orbital considerations and defined the basic tools and techniques applicable to orbital analysis.

Chapter 4

Space Environments

The Sun

Sunlight in space is considerably stronger than at the surface of the Earth because of the lack of atmospheric absorption. The increase in intensity is especially important at the shorter wavelengths, i.e., ultraviolet. Figure 4.1 compares the solar spectrum in space with a typical spectrum at the surface of the Earth.

The energy of a photon is inversely proportional to its wavelength. Ultraviolet photons are more energetic than those of visible light, enough so to be far more photochemically active. The greater intensity of solar UV in space is important to materials usage because most organic polymeric materials degrade much more rapidly in space sunlight than at the bottom of the atmosphere. The shortest-wavelength, most damaging solar ultraviolet is almost entirely absorbed by the atmosphere.

Ultraviolet damage occurs to plastics, paints, adhesives, most types of glass, and to the plastic matrix materials used in the manufacture of composite materials such as graphite epoxy. There is at present no evidence of UV damage to the graphite fibers themselves, but we are only beginning to accumulate experience in being able to examine these materials after long-term exposure in space. Research on the effects of long-duration exposure to the space environment will be much accelerated by experiments using space stations and platforms.

Ultraviolet damage is readily prevented by protection of susceptible materials. Using UV-absorbing paints, wrapping with metal foil, or wrapping with metallized plastic film such as aluminized Kapton are practical methods. Kapton itself is used because it is more damage-resistant than Mylar.

The solar flux in low Earth orbit is often taken as 1353 watts per square meter. This is in fact a minimum value used for solar array design. Because the Earth's orbit about the Sun is slightly elliptic, solar intensity varies and reaches a maximum of about 1425 W/m². Analyses concerned with heating effects of solar radiation should use the maximum value while those concerned with degradation effects should use the average of 1390 W/m².

The Earth's albedo is on the order of 0.5, i.e., the Earth typically reflects about half the solar radiation that falls on it. This value is highly variable, however, depending on weather conditions in the atmosphere below a spacecraft. Solar radiation reflected from the Earth as well as the Earth's own infrared radiation are heat sources for objects in low Earth orbit. Since the Earth's infrared is emitted from both its sunlit and dark hemispheres, the temperature extremes that spacecraft can experience in low Earth orbit are less severe than in locations where the Sun is occulted without a nearby warm planet.

Analysis of the heating effects of these radiations on spacecraft is discussed in Chapter 5 under *Thermal Control*. IR, visible, and UV radiations are the only significant environmental heat inputs to spacecraft in low Earth orbit. Atmospheric friction is not important unless the spacecraft is well along a reentry path.

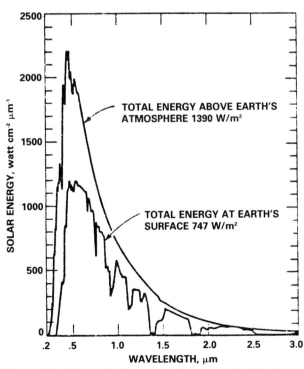

Figure 4.1 Solar radiation spectrum in space and at Earth's surface. *Courtesy of NASA.*

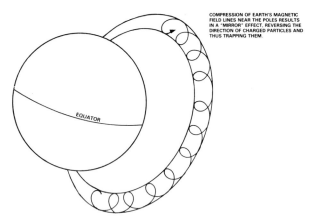

COMPRESSION OF EARTH'S MAGNETIC
FIELD LINES NEAR THE POLES RESULTS
IN A "MIRROR" EFFECT, REVERSING THE
DIRECTION OF CHARGED PARTICLES AND
THUS TRAPPING THEM.

Figure 4.2 Trapping of charged particle in Earth's geomagnetic field.

SPATIAL VARIATION OF TRAPPED ELECTRONS

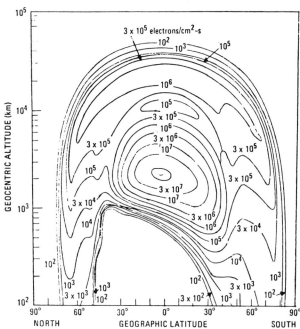

Figure 4.3 Spatial variation of trapped electrons. *Courtesy of NASA.*

Ionizing Radiations

Ionizing radiations are those that possess enough energy or charge to cause ionization of exposed materials. Sources of natural ionizing radiation in space include high-energy electrons and protons trapped in the Earth's magnetic field (the Van Allen belts), solar x-rays and high-energy particles, and cosmic rays originating outside the solar system.

Trapped Radiation

High levels of radiation trapped by the Earth's magnetic field were discovered by the first American space satellite, Explorer 1. The field lines of the geomagnetic field form a natural magnetic bottle that traps energetic charged particles as illustrated in Figure 4.2. Both protons and electrons are

so trapped. The lifetime of trapped particles is apparently years.

The Van Allen belts include inner and outer peaks of intensity as depicted in Figure 4.3. The inner belt is the one of main concern to space station design, as some exposure to the inner belt occurs at typical space station altitudes. Most of this exposure is caused by the South Atlantic Anomaly (SAA), a region of the geomagnetic field where the field lines dip anomalously low in altitude. Since the anomaly is part of the geomagnetic field, it rotates with the Earth. The approximate location of the SAA is shown in Figure 4.4. A typical space station orbit at 28.5° altitude will pass through the SAA on three or four orbits per day. At least six consecutive orbits per day (about 10 hours) will be essentially radiation-free. This is important because crew radiation exposures can be significantly reduced by restricting extravehicular activity (EVA) during passages through the SAA.

Spacecraft Charging

Spacecraft charging is a phenomenon related to trapped electron activity near geosynchronous altitudes, about 6.6 Earth radii. At this altitude, the confinement of trapped particles is weak. The particles are of relatively low energy, typically a few keV. Magnetic turbulence frequently arises from the interaction of the magnetic fields of the Sun and the Earth. During these periods, clouds of electrons driven by the turbulence can interact with an orbiting spacecraft, causing electrostatic charging of dielectric surfaces and other areas insulated from the spacecraft conducting structure. Differential charging occurs between solar illuminated surfaces which can dissipate charge by emission of photoelectrons, and unilluminated surfaces which cannot. Voltage differences can become large enough to cause arcing. The results can cause physical damage to a spacecraft or more likely, disruption of electronics due to electromagnetic interference

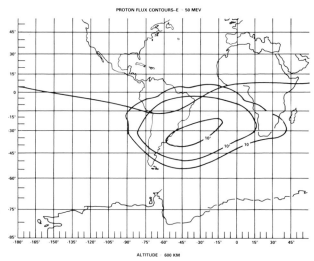

Figure 4.4 Location and extent of the South Atlantic anomaly. *Courtesy of Boeing.*

(EMI) caused by the arcing. Damage to optics is also possible.

Solar Radiation

The Sun also emits ionizing radiation. Solar x-rays have been the subject of considerable research related to solar physics. X-rays are ionizing but the solar ones are soft enough (low enough in energy) and of sufficiently low intensity as not to be of concern; even the relatively modest protection of a spacesuit will stop solar x-rays.

The Sun also emits low-energy particles, mostly protons, in a continuous flow called the solar wind. The solar wind does not penetrate the Earth's magnetic field to low orbit altitudes. Solar wind particles are very low in energy and are not a design consideration for space stations and platforms.

The Sun is very active magnetically and its magnetic phenomena include the sudden release of energy stored in magnetic fields in such a way as to accelerate charged particles to very high energies. These releases are called solar flares or solar proton events, and can engulf the Earth, as depicted schematically in Figure 4.5, in clouds of high-energy protons that are a serious radiation hazard to flight

SOLAR COSMIC RAY EARTH INTERACTION

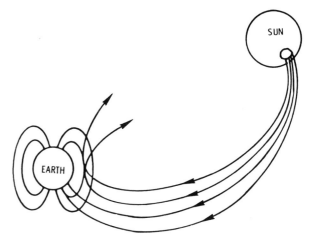

Figure 4.5 Solar flare particles interaction with Earth. *Courtesy of NASA.*

crews. These events are also the principal source of radiation degradation of solar arrays in geosynchronous orbit.

The Earth's magnetic field deflects nearly all solar flare particles from the region of space occupied by a low orbit, low inclination space station. Consequently, solar flare pro-

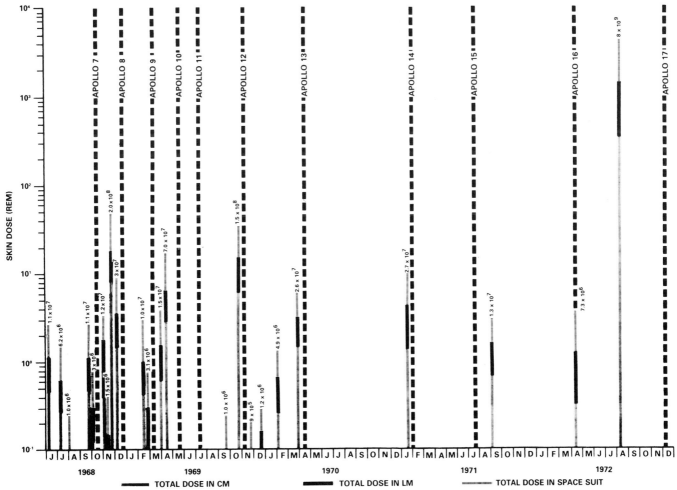

Figure 4.6 Solar flare occurrences and predicted doses during the Apollo mission period. *Courtesy of NASA.*

SOLAR ACTIVITY AND FLARE PROTON FLUENCE

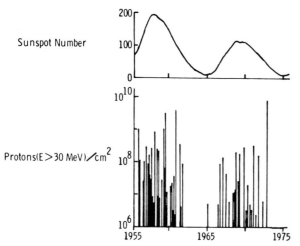

Figure 4.7 Correlation of solar flares with solar activity cycles.

Cosmic Rays

Cosmic rays are very high energy particles that originate outside the solar system. Their sources are not known but candidates include supernovae and high-energy processes associated with exotic phenomena such as neutron stars and black holes. The cosmic ray flux is far less intense than that of solar flares, or of particle fluxes in the Van Allen belts, but cosmic ray flux is continuous and shielding is impractical.

Most of the cosmic ray particles are hydrogen and helium nuclei, but heavy nuclei are also present as shown in Figure 4.9. Cosmic ray particles are bare nuclei, fully ionized. The heavy nuclei carry high charge (Z) at high energy and are often called high-LET (linear energy transfer) or HZE (high-Z, high energy) particles.

As these particles pass through the structural wall of a space station, their interaction with the wall usually causes incremental loss of energy and charge, but very few are stopped. Those that are usually create cosmic ray showers; occasional head-on collisions with atomic nuclei in the wall result in both nuclei being shattered into many smaller, but still high-energy, nuclear particles. The net result is that the radiation dose for the crew increases with shielding thickness up to a point of very thick shields. Only extremely thick shields, on the order of hundreds of grams per square centimeter, are sufficient to reduce cosmic ray doses to values similar to Earth surface background. (The Earth's atmosphere provides about 1000 g/cm^2 mass shielding.)

The Earth's magnetic field deflects cosmic rays as it does solar flare particles, but the most energetic cosmic rays are

tection is not a design requirement on a station that will operate in such an orbit. Above about 60° Earth latitude, the flare particles can stream all the way down to the atmosphere, along field lines. (Their interactions with the upper atmosphere cause the aurorae.) Spacecraft in polar orbits spend about one-third of their time above 60° latitude; their exposure to flare radiation is about one-third that of spacecraft outside the protective influence of Earth's magnetic field. Crews of space stations that might be placed in polar orbits clearly need protective measures as do those in stations or vehicles operating at geosynchronous altitudes or beyond.

The Apollo lunar vehicles operated outside the Earth's magnetic field; the risk of encountering a solar flare was a serious issue for these missions. Figure 4.6 presents a history of the Apollo missions along with the flare activity of the same time period. None of the Apollo missions encountered a significant flare. Of the events during this period, only the massive 1972 flare would have constituted a major health risk. Had an Apollo crew been on the lunar surface during the 1972 flare, they would very likely have received enough radiation to become ill. (Radiation sickness effects at an exposure level of a few hundreds of rem take hours to days to become debilitating. James Michener's description in *Space* was not accurate.)

As suggested by the previous figure, flares are random events and cannot be predicted in advance. There is a long-term correlation with the solar sunspot cycle as shown in Figure 4.7. The radiation from a flare event lasts only a few days; Figure 4.8 presents a representative radiation intensity profile. At present, the only known protective means for crews operating in regions subject to solar flare events is adequate radiation shielding or a mission abort capability that allows a retreat to within the protection of the Earth's magnetic field or atmosphere within at most a few hours. Flare radiation is isotropic and requires fully enveloping (four-pi) shielding.

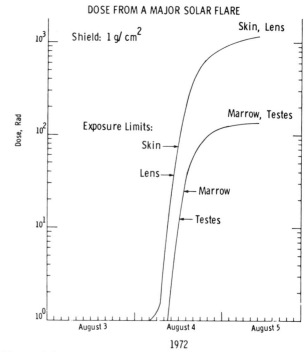

Figure 4.8 Radiation dose buildup at onset of a major solar flare. *Courtesy of NASA.*

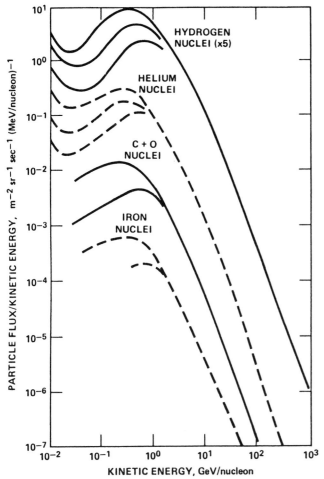

Figure 4.9 Distribution of energies of galactic cosmic rays for various nuclei. *Courtesy of NASA.*

rays contribute somewhat more. The absorption (and deceleration) of Van Allen radiation particles by a cabin wall causes secondary emission of Bremmstrahlung (a German word for braking) radiation in the form of x-rays and gamma rays. This radiation can dominate crew dose as will be seen. At high altitudes, above the Van Allen belts, solar flares contribute most of the dose with cosmic rays second. (For very thick shields, cosmic rays can be the primary contributor, but such shields are impractical for the foreseeable future.)

Crew Exposure and Shielding

Radiation exposure standards for astronaut crews were established by the National Academy of Sciences for the Apollo program. The levels set recognized the generally hazardous nature of space flights as well as the very small population at risk. Thus, while exposure standards for nuclear industry workers are about ten times higher than those for the general public, standards for astronauts are roughly ten times higher than those for nuclear industry workers. Yet, even astronaut standards are below exposure levels that would result in clinically observable acute (i.e., immediate) symptoms of radiation exposure. Thus the risk to an astronaut is mainly that associated with the cancer-causing effects of cumulative radiation exposure. Because astronauts have historically flown infrequently and for short durations, their career risk has been less than that for nuclear industry workers. In the future of space stations and platforms, that may not be true, and some consideration is now being given by NASA to adjusting the astronaut standards to lower levels.

The present astronaut exposure standards are summarized in Table 4.1. The different levels for skin, eye lens, and bone marrow/testes recognize the different severity of risk for these organs and the shielding for deeper organs provided by the body itself.

little affected. For a space station in a low altitude, low inclination orbit, Van Allen radiation contributes most of the crew dose; solar flares contribute very little, and cosmic

Table 4.1 Radiation exposure limits recommended for space flight crewmembers. *Courtesy of NASA.*

Constraint	Primary Reference Risk (Rem at 5 cm depth in tissue)	Ancillary Reference Risks			
		Bone Marrow* (Rem at 5 cm)	Skin (Rem at 0.1 mm)	Ocular Lens (Rem at 3 mm)	Testes (Rem at 3 cm)
1-year average daily dose		0.2	0.6	0.3	0.1
30-day maximum		25	75	37	13
Quarterly maximum**		34	105	52	18
Yearly maximum		75	225	112	38
Career limit	400	400	1200	600	200

*Whole body exposure.

**May be allowed for two consecutive quarters followed by 6 months of restriction from further exposure to maintain yearly limit and includes all occupational exposures.

Table adapted from *Radiation Protection Guides and Constraints for Space Mission and Vehicle-Design Studies involving Nuclear Systems*, Radiobiological Advisory Panel, Committee on Space Medicine, National Academy of Sciences, Washington, D.C., 1970.

Table 4.2 Measured radiation exposures in U.S. manned space flight programs. *Courtesy of NASA.*

Mission	Mean Dose (Rad)	Mission	Mean Dose (Rad)
Mercury 9	0.027	Apollo 10	0.480
Gemini 3	.020	Apollo 11	.180
Gemini 4	.045	Apollo 12	.580
Gemini 5	.177	Apollo 13	.240
Gemini 6	.025	Apollo 14	1.140
Gemini 7	.150	Apollo 15	.300
Gemini 8	.010	Apollo 16	.510
Gemini 9	.018	Apollo 17	.550
Gemini 10	.840	Skylab 2	1.980
Gemini 11	.025	Skylab 3	4.710
Gemini 12	.015	Skylab 4	7.810
Apollo 7	.160	STS-1	.020
Apollo 8	.160	STS-2	.015
Apollo 9	.200	STS-3	.461

From Nachtwey, 1982.

In the past, U.S. crew exposures have been small compared to these standards, as is summarized in Table 4.2.

The original unit of radiation exposure was the roentgen, defined as that amount of radiation which, when passed through 1 cubic centimeter of air at standard conditions, produces a saturation current sufficient to produce 1 electrostatic unit of electricity. This is a cumbersome unit and is little used today. The common engineering unit of dose is the rad (roentgen absorbed dose), the deposition of 100 ergs of energy per gram of exposed matter. For crew radiation exposure, the dose in rads is usually corrected by an RBE (relative biological effectiveness) to describe the dose in rem (roentgen equivalent man). The RBE for photons, i.e., x-rays, gamma rays, and Bremmstrahlung, is assumed to be 1. Proton RBE can be higher and is energy-dependent. The RBE for highly charged (HZE) cosmic ray particles is still debated, but is high, e.g., more than 10. Passage of a single HZE particle through a cell nucleus will usually kill the cell. The setting of special standards for HZE exposure has been discussed, but so far this has not occurred.

Estimated crew dose rates to the eye lens for space stations in low Earth orbits are shown in Figure 4.10 as a function of altitude, for a cabin wall shield of 2 g/cm² of aluminum equivalent. The eye lens dose is usually the design case for a low-orbit space station. The curve labeled ''Hardy'' includes an RBE factor (value unstated in the source), while the point labeled ''Stassinopoulos'' is in rads. Since the

dose under the conditions stated is mainly protons, which have an RBE from 1 to about 10, the apparent disparity in the data is not surprising. Furthermore, the environmental data are uncertain by a factor on the order of two. Since the dose rate at 500 km, multiplied by 90 days, approxi-

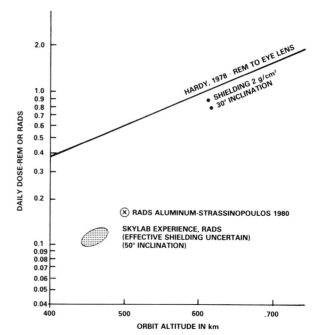

Figure 4.10 Predictions of radiation dose in low Earth orbit for 2.0 g/cm² aluminum shielding. *Courtesy of NASA.*

ORBITAL RADIATION STUDY

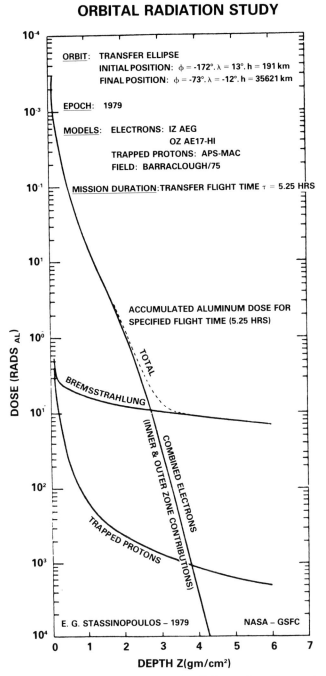

ORBIT: TRANSFER ELLIPSE
INITIAL POSITION: $\phi = -172°$. $\lambda = 13°$. h = 191 km
FINAL POSITION: $\phi = -73°$. $\lambda = -12°$. h = 35621 km

EPOCH: 1979

MODELS: ELECTRONS: IZ AEG
OZ AE17-HI
TRAPPED PROTONS: APS-MAC
FIELD: BARRACLOUGH/75

MISSION DURATION: TRANSFER FLIGHT TIME τ = 5.25 HRS

ACCUMULATED ALUMINUM DOSE FOR SPECIFIED FLIGHT TIME (5.25 HRS)

TOTAL

BREMSSTRAHLUNG

COMBINED ELECTRONS (INNER & OUTER ZONE CONTRIBUTIONS)

TRAPPED PROTONS

E. G. STASSINOPOULOS – 1979   NASA – GSFC

DOSE (RADS AL)

DEPTH Z(gm/cm²)

Figure 4.11 Radiation dose data for GEO transfer ellipse and GEO orbit—worst cases. *Courtesy of NASA and E. G. Stassinopoulos.*

ORBITAL RADIATION STUDY

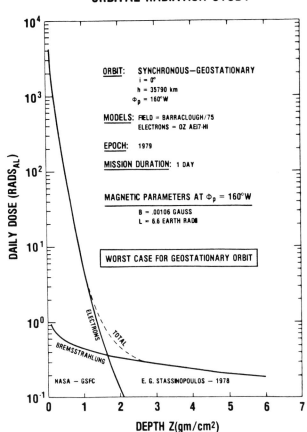

ORBIT: SYNCHRONOUS—GEOSTATIONARY
i = 0°
h = 35790 km
Φ_p = 160°W

MODELS: FIELD = BARRACLOUGH/75
ELECTRONS = OZ AEI7-HI

EPOCH: 1979

MISSION DURATION: 1 DAY

MAGNETIC PARAMETERS AT Φ_p = 160°W

B = .00106 GAUSS
L = 6.6 EARTH RADII

WORST CASE FOR GEOSTATIONARY ORBIT

ELECTRONS   TOTAL

BREMSSTRAHLUNG

NASA – GSFC   E. G. STASSINOPOULOS – 1978

DAILY DOSE (RADS AL)

DEPTH Z(gm/cm²)

Figure 4.11 Radiation dose data for GEO transfer ellipse and GEO orbit—worst cases—*Continued*

ideally something containing hydrogen, as the outer wall to stop the charged particles with a minimum of Bremmstrahlung production, and a high-Z inner wall (e.g., tantalum) for greatest effectiveness in absorbing the Bremmstrahlung. Optimum shields, even if thin such as 2 g/cm², will be about half the mass of an aluminum shield, and can be better by a factor of several if thick.

Radiation dose data in rads for representative GEO transfer orbits and for GEO orbit trapped radiation are presented in Figure 4.11. The transfer orbit data are given in total dose for 5.25-hour transfer and the GEO data are given in rads per day. The GEO data do not include a solar flare contribution. The RBE for radiation in these orbits is approximately one, so the rem dose is approximately the same. Note the rapid increase in transfer dose for thin cabin walls in the transfer orbit. (A structurally optimum OTV crew cabin would result in an intolerable total dose.) The GEO dose rates are quite similar to the 500-km orbit case. The GEO data given are the "worst case"; the best case is about a factor of two better. Uncertainties exist as is true for low orbits.

Since solar flares are infrequent and of short duration (a few days at most), the best design practice is to provide a

mately equals the present eye lens exposure standard, it may be concluded that a cabin wall equivalent of 2 g/cm² is about right for this altitude. This thickness, if used for design of the cabin pressure vessel of a typical Shuttle-launched station, is 0.75 cm, about five times that required to safely contain the internal pressure.

Crew dose rate predictions are ordinarily given for shield thicknesses of aluminum equivalent. This is the usual cabin wall material, but it is not an optimum shield. Optimum shields for these applications will use a low-Z material,

Table 4.3 Representative atmosphere constituency. *Courtesy of Boeing and Science & Engineering Associates (R. Rantanen).*

Species	Sea Level (%)	Altitude 200 km (%)	300 km (%)	800 km (%)
N_2	79	30	18	0.01
O_2	20	34	1.3	—
O	—	36	80	24
Ar	1	0.03	0.01	—
He	—	0.05	0.53	61
H	—	—	0.03	14
O^+	—	—	0.08	—
Total Number Density: per cm³	2.5×10^{19}	8.76×10^9	5.89×10^8	6.97×10^5
per m³	2.5×10^{25}	8.76×10^{15}	5.89×10^{14}	6.97×10^{11}

small emergency well-shielded area into which the GEO crew can retreat for the duration of a flare. Such areas are aptly called "storm shelters." Various investigators have recommended from 20 to 40 g/cm² of aluminum-equivalent protection in the storm shelter.

Earth's Atmosphere

Space stations and platforms in low orbits fly through Earth's tenuous upper atmosphere. In addition to drag, significant environmental effects occur.

Atmosphere Density and Atmosphere Models

In this presentation, we deal only with the upper atmosphere at altitudes for which significant orbital lifetimes are possible. This means altitudes of approximately 160 km and greater.

The pressure at any altitude in a gaseous atmosphere enveloping a gravitating body results from the effect of gravity on the mass above. This may be expressed as a very simple differential equation

$$\frac{\partial p}{\partial h} = -\rho g. \qquad (4.1)$$

Since, for an ideal gas, $p = \rho R T$, where ρ is density, R is the thermodynamic gas constant, and T is absolute temperature, the differential equation may be rewritten

$$\frac{\partial \rho}{\rho} = \frac{-g \mathfrak{M}}{R_U T} \partial h. \qquad (4.2)$$

Here we have also substituted $R_U/\mathfrak{M}$ for R, where R_U is the universal gas constant, 8314 joules per mole-°K and $\mathfrak{M}$ is the molecular weight of the gas. This differential equation has an exponential-form solution

$$\rho = \rho_o exp \left(\frac{-g \mathfrak{M} h}{R_U T} \right) \qquad (4.3)$$

where $\frac{g \mathfrak{M}}{R_U T}$ is taken as constant and ρ_o is the density at any known altitude, e.g., at the surface of the Earth.

If an atmosphere were of constant temperature and constant molecular weight, its decrease in density would be very nearly exponential, differing only with the slow change in gravitational acceleration with altitude. Real atmospheres vary in both parameters, and atmosphere modeling employs numerical integration.

The Earth's upper atmosphere is gravitationally stratified according to molecular weight of constituents. Hydrogen, for example, is almost nonexistent in the lower atmosphere but is the predominant constituent at very high altitudes. Table 4.3 shows major atmosphere constituents at four altitudes. The upper atmosphere is also strongly affected by the Sun. Photochemical dissociation occurs, e.g., $O_2 \rightarrow 2[O]$, as does substantial heating. Thus the state of the upper atmosphere is very dependent on the state of affairs on the Sun. Periods of high solar activity result in heating of the upper atmosphere and it expands upward, increasing in density at any given altitude. While atmospheric density at the surface changes moderately, variations at space station altitudes can exceed a factor of ten.

Sophisticated computer routines are available to predict the density of the upper atmosphere as it is affected by the solar activity and the day-night cycle. These are able to make reasonable forecasts of atmospheric effects such as orbital lifetimes. For most analytical purposes, however, it is sufficient to work with atmosphere models. NASA has developed a set of four models corresponding to various levels of solar activity. They are based on a relatively severe solar cycle. Figure 4.12 depicts nominal and ±2 sigma model cycles. The atmospheric models shown in Figure 4.13 correspond to a solar minimum (minimum model), an average level for the nominal cycle (nominal model), the high-

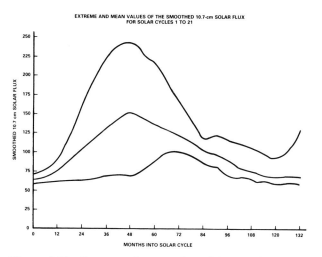

Figure 4.12 Extreme and mean values of the smoothed 10.7 cm solar flux for solar cycles 1 to 21. *Courtesy of Boeing/NASA.*

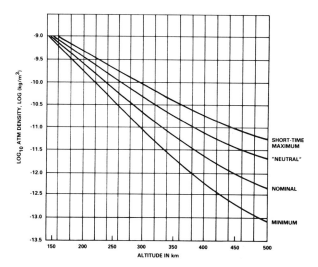

Figure 4.13 Density models for Earth's upper atmosphere.

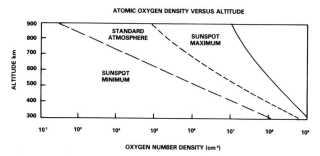

Figure 4.14 Atomic oxygen density versus altitude. *Courtesy of NASA/SEA, inc.*

est level for the +2 sigma cycle (neutral model), and the occurrence of a solar flare during a period of high solar activity (short-time maximum model).

Since the neutral model atmosphere can persist for about a year, it is usually used as a design case for orbital lifetime and orbit makeup (drag compensation) propulsion. It is well to remember, however, that this design case is much more severe than the average. The average requirement for propellant resupply, for example, is much less than that determined from the neutral atmosphere case. The short-term maximum does not last long enough to be important for orbit decay and is of principal importance for control authority calculations.

Atomic Oxygen

Atomic oxygen is an important constituent of the upper atmosphere at space station and platform altitudes. Atomic oxygen is a highly reactive oxidizer, and even though the upper atmosphere is very tenuous, a space station or platform will encounter enough oxygen atoms to cause erosion of susceptible materials. This phenomenon was not recognized as a serious matter until Shuttle flights returning to Earth brought back samples exhibiting significant atomic oxygen damage. It is now believed that previously unexplained failures of several low orbit spacecraft were in fact due to atomic oxygen damage.

The effects of atomic oxygen are proportional to the number density and the latter varies with altitude and solar activity. Estimates of atomic oxygen density with altitude are shown in Figure 4.14. The interaction of atmospheric gas with spacecraft moving through it is in the free molecular flow regime. The mean free path for collisions between gas particles is large compared to the dimensions of a space station or platform.

Molecules and atmospheric atoms stream toward the ve-

hicle at a relative orbital velocity of about 7700 m/sec. The gas particles directly impact surfaces on a line-of-sight path, and then slowly drift away. The collisions are almost completely inelastic. There is no boundary layer, no shock wave, and no continuum flow.

The erosion effects of atomic oxygen depend on the efficiency of the erosion process, i.e., what fraction of the oxygen atoms impinging on a target actually react with the surface, carrying away one or more atoms of target material. The atomic number density of a solid is

$$N = \frac{6.023 \times 10^{26} \rho}{\mathfrak{M}} \text{ (per m}^3\text{)} \qquad (4.4)$$

where 6.023×10^{26} is Avogadro's number, ρ is the solid density, and $\mathfrak{M}$ is the mean atomic weight of the solid. For hydrocarbon plastics, the mean atomic weight is on the order of 5, the density is about 1600 kg/m^3, and a typical number density is 1.927×10^{29} atoms/m^3. The volume of one atom averages about 5×10^{-24} cm^3.

The material erosion rate due to atomic oxygen is

$$r = \frac{\phi \eta}{N} \qquad (4.5)$$

Table 4.4 Representative atomic oxygen effects. *Courtesy of NASA.*

Flight	Material	Thickness Loss, μm	Fluence,* 10^{20} atom/cm²	Reaction Efficiency, 10^{-24} cm³/atom
STS-3	Osmium	4.4	2.16	2
	Kapton TV Blanket	5.5	2.16	1.5
STS-4	Kapton	1.8	0.65	2.6–2.8
	Teflon	0.07	0.65	0.1
	Mylar	1.8	0.65	2.8
STS-5	Kapton Black	1.35	0.99	1.4
	Mylar	1.5–2.8	0.99	1.5–2.2
	Tedlar	1.3	0.99	1.3
	Teflon	<0.5	0.99	<0.5

*Fluence is (Flux) × (Time)

where r is in meters per second, ϕ is the flux in m^{-2} sec^{-1}, η is the erosion efficiency, and N is the number density from eq. 4.4 above. Flux is simply given by $\phi = nV$ where n is the gas number density and V is the relative velocity. If one takes a typical mass density for atomic oxygen in the upper atmosphere as 10^{-12} kg/m , then with $V = 7700$ m/sec, $\phi = 2.9 \times 10^{17}$ particles/m²/sec. The erosion rate, if $\eta = 1$, is $2.9 \times 10^{17}/1.927 \times 10^{29} = 1.5 \times 10^{-12}$ m/sec, or roughly 1 micron every 10 days. This equates to 365 microns, or roughly a third of a millimeter, in 10 years.

Loss rates for highly susceptible materials as high as 2×10^{-24} cm³ per atom of oxygen have been reported on Shuttle flights. This equates to an erosion efficiency of roughly 40 percent. Number densities, even at 500 km, can approach ten times the value used in the sample calculation above. Erosion rates in excess of the example, up to 5 microns in five to seven days, have been experienced at 250–300 km altitude. Table 4.4 lists some results from sample exposures on recent Shuttle flights. Clearly, heavy structural members will be little affected, but thin plastic films and lightweight structural members may disappear over a period of years. Silver solar cell interconnects will be damaged unless protected. Micron-thick coatings are commonplace and can be obliterated in a few days.

Atomic oxygen is also implicated in a glow phenomenon experienced on Shuttle flights. The glow is seen in the visual and infrared (IR), brightest adjacent to vehicle surfaces facing the oncoming flow. IR photography from the ground has shown the Shuttle to be enveloped in a low-intensity glow to a distance of several meters. This glow has the potential of interfering with scientific instruments. IR, visible, and UV instruments were successfully used on Spacelab I. The targets were generally bright, and glow phenomena were seen in the data. Glow severity falls off with altitude,

another reason for selecting higher altitudes for space stations and platforms. The severity of this problem needs further assessment and is under continuing study.

Solid Matter

Near-Earth space includes two kinds of solid matter that present hazards to space stations and platforms - meteoroids and manmade debris. Meteoroids are natural bodies left over from formation of the solar system or the products of collisions between natural bodies making up the solar system. Manmade debris has arisen from the space flight activities of mankind since the beginning of the space age in 1957. It is comprised of spent stages and separation hardware, inoperative satellites, and collision and explosion products. The prediction of the hazard from both of these sources is accomplished through use of statistical models.

Meteoroids

A common feature of the "space opera" movies is an encounter with meteoroids (usually called "meteors" in the movie—but a meteor is a meteoroid that has entered Earth's atmosphere and created an incandescent trail). The ship is surrounded by swarms of moving, glowing rocks, accompanied by much noise and vibration. Real meteoroids are small, most often smaller than a grain of sand, very fast moving and hence invisible as well as unavoidable, cold, and silent unless they hit something. Microphone devices have been used to register meteoroid hits and exhibit a ping-like sound when struck. There are, of course, larger meteoroids but they are fortunately very rare. Even an object as large as the Earth is only hit by a large one occasionally.

The meteoroid flux near Earth has been estimated by visual and radar observation of meteors entering Earth's atmosphere, by meteoroid measurement satellites such as the Pegasus satellites launched in the mid-1960s, and by crater pit counts, especially in windows, for spacecraft that have returned to Earth. Additional data for very small and very large masses, respectively, are derived from observations of the zodiacal light and by counts of young craters on the Moon. Figure 4.15 shows a current flux estimate for near-Earth meteoroids. This is a cumulative model; the flux values are the total flux of all particles larger than a given mass value. Since the log slope is steeply negative the likelihood of being struck by an object much larger than a selected design value is quite small.

Manmade Debris

When the space age began, the idea that the vast reaches of outer space could, within 25 years, become polluted with manmade space junk to the point of creating a collision hazard would have seemed quite fanciful. Yet today, the North American Air Defense Command (NORAD) catalog of near-Earth artificial space objects exceeds 5000 in number, and the risk of serious damage to a space station or platform is much larger (but still small) for debris than for natural meteoroids.

Figure 4.16 shows the collision probability for a space shuttle (AREA = 250 m²) for the objects in the 1980 NORAD catalog as a function of altitude. This probability is at least an order of magnitude larger than the probability of collision with a meteoroid equal to or larger in size than the smallest objects in the catalog.

The smallest objects detectable by NORAD are a few centimeters in size and presumably a few tens of grams in mass. Radar detection, of course, determines only radar cross section and not mass. Debris objects are probably irregular in shape and, since they are parts or fragments of space vehicles, the ones large enough to be detectable are probably far from spherical. In terms of number count, the catalog is dominated by smaller objects originating as explosion fragments (Figure 4.17). Modeling of explosion and impact processes has been used to predict the flux of debris objects too small to be detected and to predict the growth in the number of debris objects in the future. Typical results are shown in Figure 4.18. Since the slope of the debris flux model is much less negative than the slope of the meteoroid flux model, collisions are predicted as more likely with debris for larger objects and more likely with meteoroids for smaller objects. The crossover for these models is at roughly 0.1 gram, but the debris models probably predict too high a flux below about 1 gram as noted below.

Most of the debris objects are in nearly circular orbit. Predictions of the flux of small debris objects usually ignore upper atmosphere drag. Nevertheless, the lifetime of objects less than 1 gram in mass at orbit altitudes of 500 km or less will be at most a few years, and during periods of high solar activity not more than a few months (refer to Figure 3.20). Thus we may expect the debris flux at 500 km to peak in

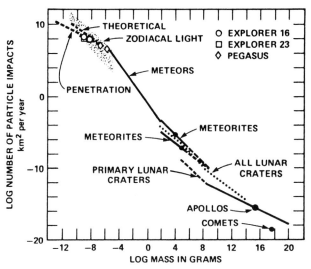

Figure 4.15 Flux rates of meteoritic material estimated by various methods. *Courtesy of NASA.*

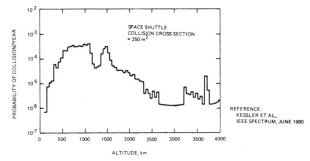

- NORAD CATALOG ITEMS HAVE APPROXIMATELY .01m² RADAR CROSS SECTION
- THE NORAD CATALOG HAS APPROXIMATELY 20% "LEAKAGE"

Figure 4.16 Probability of debris collision with Space Shuttle based on 1980 NORAD catalog. *Courtesy of NASA.*

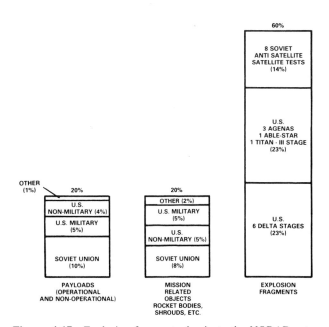

Figure 4.17 Explosion fragments dominate the NORAD catalog. *Courtesy of NASA/Kessler.*

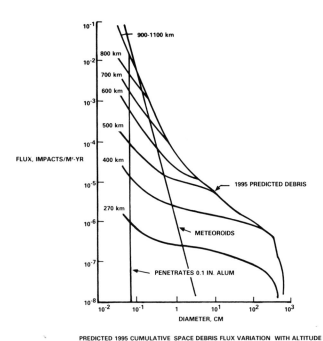

PREDICTED 1995 CUMULATIVE SPACE DEBRIS FLUX VARIATION WITH ALTITUDE

Figure 4.18 Predicted 1995 cumulative space debris flux. *Courtesy of NASA.*

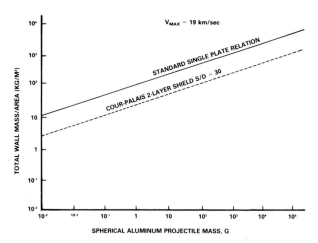

Figure 4.19 Collision shielding requirements as a function of projectile mass at 10 km/sec. *Courtesy of Boeing.*

the vicinity of 1-gram objects. The predicted flux is in the range of 10^{-6} to 10^{-5} per m^2 per year, yielding an impact probability for a representative 100 m^2 cluster of space station pressure modules of 10^{-4} to 10^{-3} per year. The probability of collision for a 2000 m^2 solar array is on the order of 0.02 per year.

Collision Prediction, Damage, and Protection

The probability of collision with an object greater in mass than m, given a flux model that predicts the flux of all such objects to be ϕ and a spacecraft projected area of A, is $p_c = \phi A \delta t$ where δt is chosen small enough that $p_c \ll 1$. For larger increments of time T, the probability is calculated as

$$p_c = 1 - e^{-\phi AT}. \qquad (4.6)$$

Collision penetration models are based on experiments with hypervelocity guns and on collision and cratering theory. Penetration depth relationships usually take the form

$$D = r^q v^n m^{1/3} f(s) f(a) \qquad (4.7)$$

where D is penetration depth, V is impact velocity, m is projectile mass, r is projectile/target density ratio, and $f(s)$ and $f(a)$ are shape and impact angle factors respectively. The power law exponents q and n have estimated values

somewhat less than 1/2 and between 1/3 and 2/3 respectively. These relationships are valid in a velocity range much higher than the speed of sound in the spacecraft wall and where the collision energy is sufficient to vaporize the incident particle. The velocities of debris objects are near or possibly below the range of validity. There has been little recent research on collision phenomena applicable to debris collisions, but NASA is conducting new work as a part of the space station program.

Debris objects have average impact velocities of about 10 km/sec while meteoroids have velocities typically 30 km/sec or greater. The density of small meteoroids is typically less than 1 g/cm^3 while most debris is believed to be metallic with densities from 2.7 to about 8 g/cm^3.

Optimal collision protection is offered by dual-wall or multi-wall shields where the outer walls serve to break up the incoming object and the inner wall absorbs the residual collision energy. Figure 4.19 compares calculated requirements for single and two-wall shields for aluminum impact objects at 19 km/sec.

Like radiation shielding, collision protection must be considered as a design criterion for space station habitat pressure vessel walls. Since the consequences of a penetration may be serious (a 1 - gram object at 20 km/sec has kinetic energy equivalent to about 50 grams of TNT), it is usual practice to select a penetration probability that is fairly small. Values as low as 10^{-4} per year have been used in studies, but values in the range 10^{-3} to 10^{-2} per year are probably more practical.

Chapter 5

Subsystems for Space Stations and Platforms

Space systems today are divided into a set of discipline-oriented *subsystems* which, taken in the aggregate, comprise the entire system. The subsystems set adopted for this book is:

- Structures and Mechanisms
- Electrical Power
- Environmental Control and Life Support (EC/LS)
- Thermal Control
- Guidance, Navigation, and Control (GN&C)
- Propulsion
- Automation, Autonomy, and Robotics
- Communications

An additional subsystem, Crew Accommodations and Crew Systems, is discussed in Chapter 6.

Structures and Mechanisms

Typical Space Station Structures

Space station structures include pressure vessels for human habitation, equipment support structures, trussworks for coverage of lengths or areas, and masts and booms for smaller units of equipment needing special supports.

Pressure vessels may be designed by any one of three criteria: (1) Structural strength to contain the interior pressure; (2) the wall thickness needed to meet protection criteria against meteoroid or orbital debris penetration; and (3) radiation shielding for protection of the flight crew. (Meteoroids, debris, and radiation environments are discussed in Chapter 4.) Because integrity of the pressure vessel is essential to crew safety, conservative designs are used. Those for permanent space stations are expected to use redundant structure similar to that used for commercial passenger aircraft cabins. Two complete structures are provided, usually one represented by the wall membrane and a second represented by the network of stiffener longerons and frames. Either structure is able to carry the pressure load, so that if one fails (for example, a crack in the membrane caused by a meteoroid), the other will pick up the load and prevent a catastrophic failure.

Space station pressure vessels are ordinarily cylindrical in shape. Figure 5.1 illustrates a representative general arrangement of a space station habitable volume pressure vessel. It may be structurally analyzed as a thin-walled cylinder. Determination of the stress in a thin-walled cylinder simply equates the (pressure) $\times$ (area) terms arising from internal pressure and internal diameter, and from wall thickness and material stress. The appropriate equation is

$$t = \frac{pD}{2\sigma} \tag{5.1}$$

where t is thickness in meters
   p is internal pressure, usually one atmosphere, $\approx 10^5$ Pascals
   D is internal diameter, usually about 4.2 meters, and
   σ is allowable stress, typically 10^8 n/m^2 for aluminum.

Except for internal pressure, the on-orbit loads on space station and platform structures are small. (Launch loads are not small and must be considered in the structural design.) Space-frame trusses are often preferred for establishing the configuration of unpressurized members that must span considerable distances or areas. They offer very high moments of inertia to resist bending and compression loads for their weight. Graphite composites can maximize this, but if thin sections are to be used, the material is likely to need atomic oxygen protection. Trusses may be designed to be deployed or assembled (the term *erectable* is often used), and can be delivered to orbit with a packaged volume only a tiny fraction of the volume to be occupied by the completed structure.

Common trusswork arrangements include triangular A-frame and pentahedral trusses, and hexahedral (box) trusses as illustrated in Figure 5.2. Compact designs for tetrahedral trusses that can be deployed into large area trussworks have been developed (see Figure 5.3). Strictly speaking, there is no such thing as a purely tetrahedral truss. The tetrahedron's geometry does not fill all space when many tetrahedrons are joined together; its facial dihedral angles do not add up to 360 degrees. "Tetrahedral" trusses use other geometric forms to interconnect the tetrahedra. Most common is the alternating use of tetrahedra and pentahedra; efficient structures result.

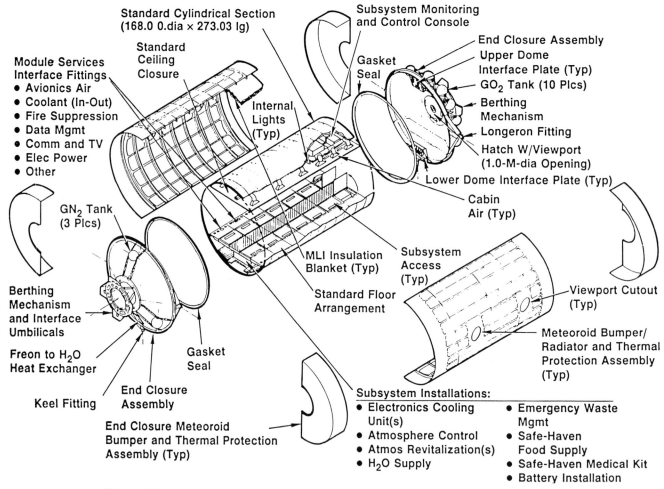

Figure 5.1   Space station pressure vessel structural concept. *Courtesy of McDonnell Douglas Corp.*

Masts and booms are ordinarily tubular structures and, like space frame trusses, are often designed to employ composites. Designs for long booms employ hinged joints for deployment. An alternate deployable mast concept uses Astromast™; Figure 5.4 illustrates this concept. It is applicable, among other things, to extension of a lightweight solar array.

The stress arising from bending of a mast or boom is calculated from

$$\sigma = \frac{mc}{I} \qquad (5.2)$$

where m is the bending moment expressed as the force multiplied by the moment arm (see Figure 5.5), c is the distance from the neutral axis, and I is the moment of inertia calculated as

$$I = \int r^2 dA. \qquad (5.3)$$

The neutral axis is located such that the stress forces acting to the left equal those acting to the right in the figure. For most simple shapes the neutral axis is at the centroid of the cross section.

Space station and platform trusses, masts, and booms will usually be designed by the required stiffness rather than by strength.

Structural Dynamics

The vibrational response of a very simple structure excited by a dynamical load can be calculated from first principles, e.g., by writing the partial differential equations for the dynamics of the structure and solving them. For complex space structures this is impractical. Complex structures can be approximated by a network of elemental structural forms, e.g., struts, beams, and plates, interconnected in a manner that closely approximated the configuration of the actual structure. This is called finite-element modeling. The dy-

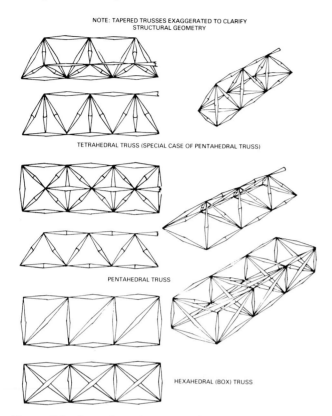

Figure 5.2 Space-frame truss concepts.

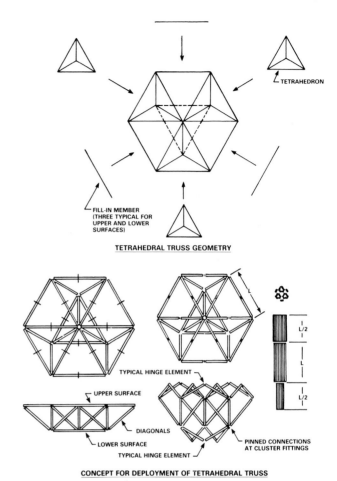

Figure 5.3 Deployable tetrahedral truss concept. *Courtesy of Boeing.*

namical differential equations of deflection and motion for each member can be written in coupled form. Simultaneous solution of these equations will then define the dynamical response of the complex structure. The solution algorithm can be reduced to the simultaneous solution of a number of algebraic equations and performed on a digital computer. This is the technique embodied in the well-known NAS-TRAN code. Figure 5.6 illustrates a typical simple NAS-TRAN structural model of a space station configuration; Figure 5.7 shows a representative mode shape (deformed shape of the structure under dynamical loading at maximum deflection). The NASTRAN solution also determines the frequency of vibration of each mode; a typical plot of modal frequency versus mode shape is shown in Figure 5.8.

From deflection analyses it is possible to obtain the stress in each member. It is also possible to represent continuous structures such as pressure vessels by a network of finite elements. Figure 5.9 shows a typical result, predicting launch loads in a space station pressurized module structure.

Finite element models are so useful that they are almost universally used for structural analyses of practical space structures. Although the numerical creation of such models was once quite tedious because of the large data base required, modern computer-aided design systems can generate finite-element models directly from the structural design data base. Figure 5.9 was produced through this technique.

Mechanisms

In addition to their use in deployable structures, mechanisms will be found in docking and berthing devices for interconnecting space station and platform elements, and in various equipment for moving things on the space station. Docking and berthing mechanisms employ a set of guides to aid positioning of the elements, and a set of latches for mechanically connecting the elements once docked or berthed. Docking implies that the two elements will fly together under control of propulsion and attitude control systems, while berthing implies that another mechanism such as a manipulator will be used to position the two elements in the berthing position. A docking mechanism thus must include means for absorbing the collision energy due to the closing velocity of docking, while for berthing it is presumed that the closing velocity is negligible and no energy absorption is needed. Figure 5.10 illustrates a representative berthing mechanism on a pressure module.

A variety of mobility mechanisms have been proposed for use on space stations and platforms. Perhaps best known of these is the Canadian Remote Manipulator System (RMS)

Figure 5.4 Deployed astromast redundant deployable lattice column. *Courtesy of Astro Research Corp.*

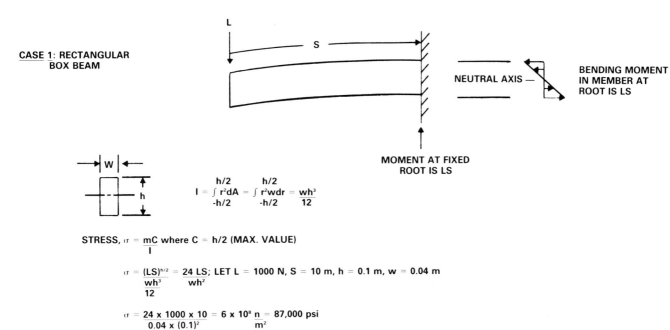

CASE 1: RECTANGULAR
    BOX BEAM

NEUTRAL AXIS —

BENDING MOMENT
IN MEMBER AT
ROOT IS LS

MOMENT AT FIXED
ROOT IS LS

$$I = \int_{-h/2}^{h/2} r^2 dA = \int_{-h/2}^{h/2} r^2 w\,dr = \frac{wh^3}{12}$$

STRESS, $\sigma = \frac{mC}{I}$ where $C = h/2$ (MAX. VALUE)

$$\sigma = \frac{(LS)^{h/2}}{\frac{wh^3}{12}} = \frac{24\,LS}{wh^2}; \text{ LET } L = 1000 \text{ N}, S = 10 \text{ m}, h = 0.1 \text{ m}, w = 0.04 \text{ m}$$

$$\sigma = \frac{24 \times 1000 \times 10}{0.04 \times (0.1)^2} = 6 \times 10^8 \, \frac{n}{m^2} = 87{,}000 \text{ psi}$$

CASE 2: TRIANGULAR TRUSS

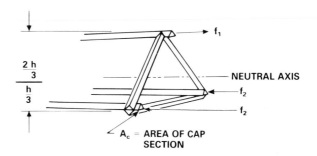

NEUTRAL AXIS IS ⅓ TRIANGLE HEIGHT
SO THAT $f_1 = 2f_2$

$$I = \left(\frac{2h}{3}\right)^2 A_c + 2\left(\frac{h}{3}\right)^2 A_c = \frac{2}{3} h^2 A_c$$

$$\sigma_{max} = \frac{m(2/3h)}{2/3h^2 A_c} = \frac{LS}{hA_c}$$

f_1

NEUTRAL AXIS

f_2

f_2

A_c = AREA OF CAP
SECTION

Figure 5.5 Representative bending stress calculations.

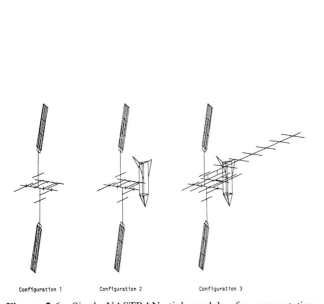

Configuration 1   Configuration 2   Configuration 3

Figure 5.6 Single NASTRAN stick models of a space station configuration. *Courtesy of Boeing.*

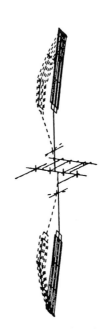

Figure 5.7 Structural dynamics mode shape depiction by NASTRAN. *Courtesy of Boeing.*

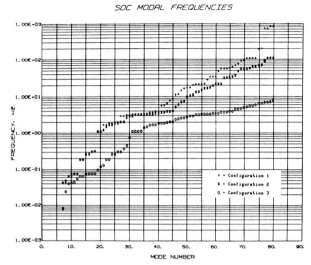

Figure 5.8 Modal frequencies for the structural models of Figure 5.6. *Courtesy of Boeing.*

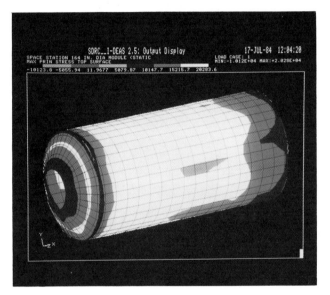

Figure 5.9 Launch stress profiles generated by computer analysis. *Courtesy of Boeing.*

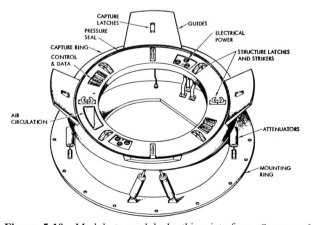

Figure 5.10 Module-to-module berthing interface. *Courtesy of Rockwell International.*

that flies on the Shuttle (see Figure 5.11). A modification of it could be used on a space station or platform. Other concepts include alternate manipulators, wheel-and-track devices, and grappling or handling devices. Some of these are illustrated in Figure 5.12.

Electrical Power

Space platforms and especially space stations will be significant consumers of electrical power. The Skylab space station flown in the 1970s had the capability to serve about 18 kW of electrical loads, making it the largest electrical power system ever to fly in space. (The Soviet Salyuts have somewhat less power.) Scientific space platforms are budgeted at a few to about 12 kW. The NASA space station is planned to have at least 75 kW initially, with some growth scenarios exceeding 200 kW by the turn of the century.

Nearly all the studies for space station power have assumed reliance on solar energy as a source, with a few studies devoted to nuclear power. Chemical fuels lead to hopeless resupply problems as do schemes relying on periodic resupply of storage devices such as batteries.

Loads Budgets

Electrical power analyses must start with requirements. Power loads on space stations and platforms fall into two categories: user loads and housekeeping loads. A third category of emergency loads is sometimes added, depending on design approach.

User loads are those that directly serve end-use missions. Instruments and scientific equipment need electrical power. Mission support activities also need power, for example, recharging EVA equipment used to serve missions, operating RMSs and other mechanical equipment, and lighting outside work areas while the space vehicle is in the Earth's shadow. Identification of support needs is important; they are unlikely to be included in housekeeping power budgets. A good rule is that all power needs devoted to serving specific missions or mission groups should be carried as user loads and all those devoted to operating the facility should be carried as housekeeping loads. For example, exterior lighting used to support construction activities is a user load, but space station position lights are a housekeeping load. Questions arise over handling laboratory loads. An entire laboratory could be considered a user load, but it is preferable to account the power needed to operate the common pressure vessel subsystems as a housekeeping load. It is clearly important to avoid double bookkeeping.

Table 5.1 presents a representative user load budget from recent space station mission requirements studies. Table 5.2 presents the complementary housekeeping load budget. Emergency needs include minimal operation of the EC/LS subsystem, emergency lighting, data processing, communications, and thermal control. Since the EC/LS subsystem

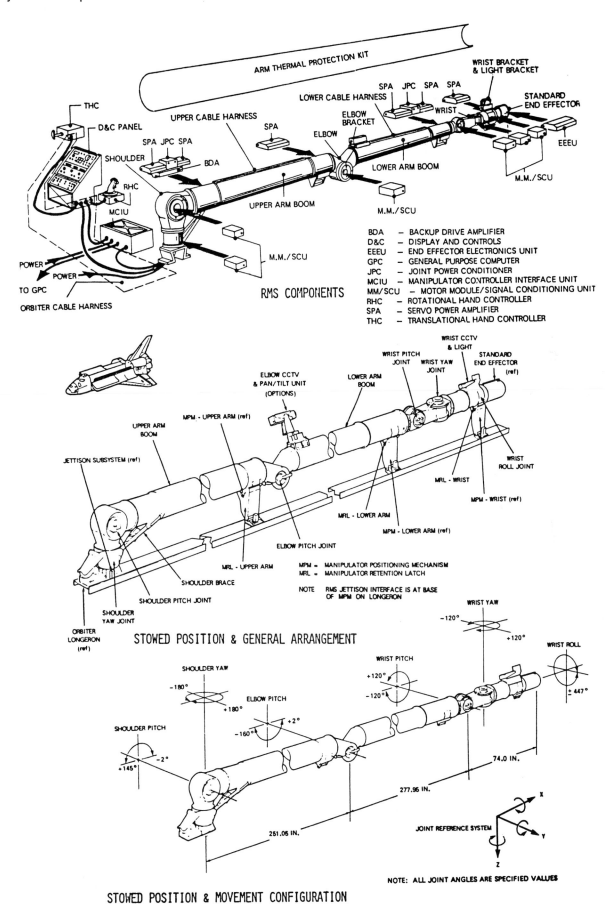

Figure 5.11 The Canadian remote manipulator system for the Space Shuttle. *Courtesy of Spar Aerospace Limited.*

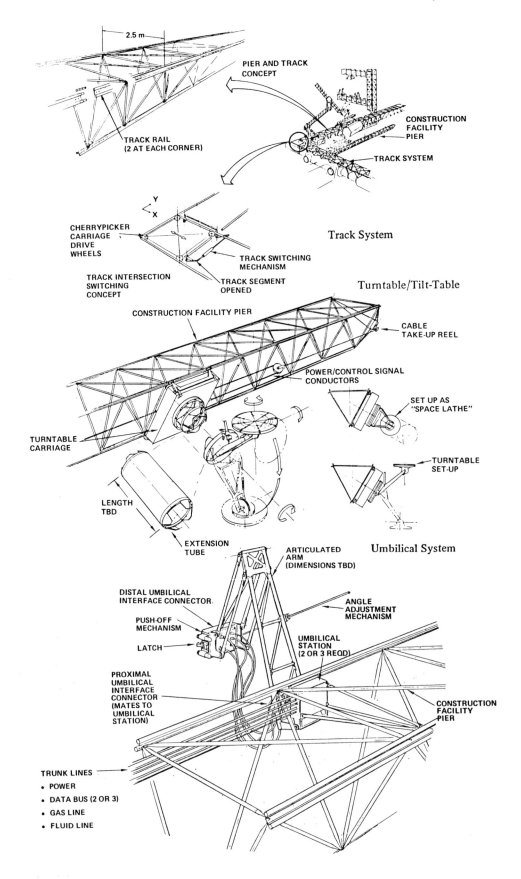

Figure 5.12 Mobility-related mechanism concepts for space station application. *Courtesy of Boeing.*

Table 5.1 Representative space station user loads.

Materials Processing Lab (Experiments and Equipment)	16 kW
Life Sciences Lab (Experiments and Equipment)	9 kW
Commercial Prototype Payloads	
Electrophoresis	10 kW
Crystal Growth	20 kW
OMV Housekeeping and Hangar Lights	1 kW
Science Payloads	5 kW
Total	61 kW

Table 5.2 Representative space station housekeeping loads.

Each Module	
ECLS Water Processing and O_2 Recovery	1.6 kW
Fans and Pumps	1.5 kW
Main Interior Lights	0.25kW
Auxiliary Interior Lights	0.25kW
Cooking, Refrigerator, and Freezer	1.5 kW
Data System and Instrumentation Elex	1.0 kW
Controls and Displays	0.5 kW
RF and Communications	0.3 kW
Power Processing and Control Losses	0.4 kW
Total	7.3 kW
4 Modules = 4×7.3	29.2 kW
Misc. External Heaters	2.0 kW
Exterior Lights	1.5 kW
Mobile RMS	0.5 kW
Reserve for Power Tools and Misc.	2.0 kW
Housekeeping Total	35.2 kW

is a substantial power user, emergency strategies usually operate EC/LS in an open mode, drawing down reserve supplies of oxygen and water. CO_2 must be removed from the atmosphere and fans must be operated to continue air circulation in the cabin (there is no convection, of course). Estimates of emergency power needs range from 5 to 10 kW for a crew of eight until a rescue can be effected. The present estimate of the maximum duration the system must operate on emergency power is 28 days. Unlike Skylab and the Salyuts, the present NASA plans for the space station do not include emergency Earth return vehicles; the system will depend on Shuttle rescue in the event of emergencies that cannot be handled onboard.

Power Generation

Low Earth orbits presently planned for space stations and platforms fly through the Earth's shadow each orbit. Consequently, solar power systems must provide for loads from storage during the shadow period. Analysis of solar generation systems begins with estimating the amount of solar input available. Determining the fraction of an orbit that is in shadow is a geometry problem. The methods of vector analysis and coordinate transforms described in Chapter 3 may be employed to derive an equation for the conditions of entry into and exit from the shadow in terms of the orbit radius, orbit inclination, angle between the orbit line of nodes and the sun line, and the sun declination. The problem is depicted in Figure 5.13. The expression for the angle θ is

$$\tan\theta = \frac{ab - cd \pm \sqrt{(ab-cd)^2 - \left[b^2 + d^2 - \left(\frac{r_e}{r}\right)^2\right]\left[a^2 + c^2 - \left(\frac{r_e}{r}\right)^2\right]}}{b^2 + d^2 - \left(\frac{r_e}{r}\right)^2}$$

(5.4)

where $a = \cos\Omega$, $b = \sin\Omega\cos i$, $c = \sin z \sin\Omega$, and $d = \sin z \cos\Omega\cos i - \cos z \sin i$. In these expressions, i is the orbital inclination, z is the sun declination and Ω is the position of the orbit line of nodes. This equation determines a total of four values for ϕ. Recognizing that the occultation is less than half an orbit permits selection of the correct pair.

The solar input power is usually taken as 1353 watts/m². This is a minimum value, based on the Earth's greatest distance from the sun.

Solar generator options include conventional silicon planar arrays of the type used on all spacecraft to date, advanced gallium arsenide concentrator arrays now in technology development, and solar thermal cycle systems using solar concentrators to focus sunlight into an absorber so as to generate temperatures needed to operate an efficient thermal cycle.

Solar cells are solid-state devices that utilize the properties of semiconductors to convert sunlight photons directly into electricity. Photons enter the (photovoltaic) semiconductor material and expend their energy by ejecting an electron (energy-wise upward) into the conduction band where it delivers its energy by crossing the semiconductor junction. Thus a solar cell has a maximum available voltage related to the junction potential and a maximum available current related to the number of photons it collects. For these reasons the solar cell characteristic curve shown in Figure 5.14 is hardly surprising. Solar cells are rather inefficient because (1) most solar photons, being of the wrong energy, do not couple efficiently into the semiconductor material, and (2) losses occur within the material. Gallium arsenide is a little more efficient than silicon because its junction band gap is better matched to the solar spectrum. Future developments in photovoltaics may use sandwiches of materials with different band gaps to better use the solar spectrum.

Concentration of sunlight on a solar cell introduces high temperatures unless special cooling techniques are em-

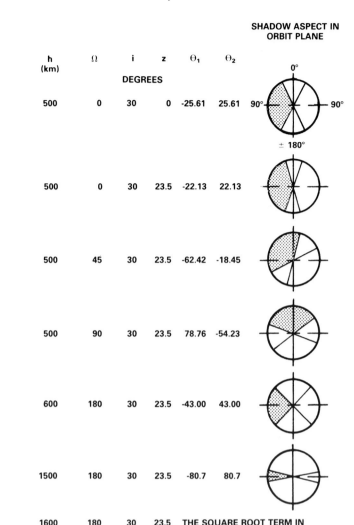

| SHADOW ASPECT IN ORBIT PLANE |
h (km)	Ω	i	z	Θ_1	Θ_2
		DEGREES			
500	0	30	0	-25.61	25.61
500	0	30	23.5	-22.13	22.13
500	45	30	23.5	-62.42	-18.45
500	90	30	23.5	78.76	-54.23
600	180	30	23.5	-43.00	43.00
1500	180	30	23.5	-80.7	80.7
1600	180	30	23.5	THE SQUARE ROOT TERM IN EQUATION 5.4 IS NEGATIVE INDICATING THAT THE ORBIT IS NOT SHADOWED	

SHADOW CIRCLE
DEFINED BY $x^2 + z^2 = r_e^2$

ORBIT PATH

EQUATOR

TO SUN

OCCULTED PORTION OF ORBIT

OCCULTATION GEOMETRY

EQUATION 5.4 IS DEFINED
BY PROJECTING THE ORBIT
RADIUS VECTOR ONTO THE
SHADOW CIRCLE AND SETTING
THE CONDITION WHERE THE
RADIUS VECTOR IS COINCIDENT
WITH THE SHADOW CIRCLE
BOUNDARY

Figure 5.13   Solar occultation in low Earth orbit; representative solutions.

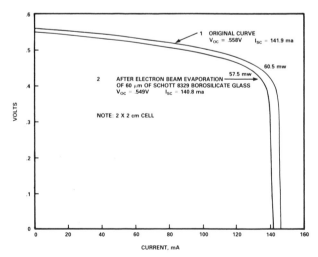

Figure 5.14   Typical voltage-current characteristics for a planar silicon solar cell.

ployed. Active thermal loops are excessively massive because of the low temperatures, i.e., near room temperature, needed for efficient silicon solar cell operation. Schemes that use very small concentrators, a few centimeters in size, with gallium arsenide cells and conductive fin coolers, are promising. A typical concept is shown in Figure 5.15. With a projected 20 percent gallium arsenide cell efficiency and 80 percent optical efficiency, a net of 16 percent may be obtained, compared with 12 percent or so for silicon. Because the sunlight concentration ratio is 100 or greater, the area of GaAs cells needed is relatively small.

Thermal cycles employ technology familiar to the Earth-based energy generation scene, typically Brayton (gas), Rankine (vapor), or Stirling (gas) cycles. These utilize thermodynamic principles to convert heat energy, derived from concentration of sunlight, first into mechanical (typically rotating) energy and then into electrical energy through an

Cassegrainian Concentrator
Solar Array

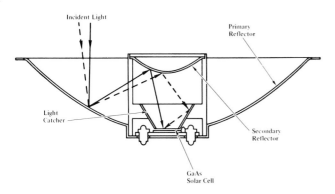

Figure 5.15 Cassegrain concentrator gallium arsenide solar generator element concept. *Photo courtesy of TRW E&D.*

alternator. Thermal cycles are subject to the efficiency principle enunciated by Carnot and involve complex cycle analyses to arrive at optimal cycle state parameters.

A glimpse of this is offered by a simplified Brayton analysis based on the use of an ideal gas in the cycle. Actual closed thermal cycles are likely to use noble gases or mixtures thereof and the ideal gas approximation is a good one. The recuperated (also called regenerative) Brayton cycle is shown in Figure 5.16. Recuperation is used to cause the cycle to approach the Carnot ideal. Approaching the Carnot ideal through recuperation involves approaching process singularities; practical limits exist, having to do with pressure drop and machinery weight. The equation for cycle performance with pressure drop and imperfect recuperation is

$$\eta_c = 1 - \left[\frac{(r_{pc}^{\varsigma} - 1)/\eta_b + \Delta T_r/T_o}{(T_3/T_o)\ \eta_T\ [1 - (G/r_{pc})^{\varsigma}] + \Delta T_r/T_o} \right] \quad (5.5)$$

where r_{pc} = compressor pressure ratio (>1)

   η_b = compressor efficiency

   ΔT_r = temperature difference across recuperator $(T_4 - T_2$ in cycle diagram)

   T_o = cycle lower limit temperature

   T_3 = cycle peak temperature

   η_T = turbine efficiency

   ς = specific heat factor, $(\gamma - 1)/\gamma = 0.4$ for $\gamma = 1.67$ as for helium.

   G = the product of the four pressure drop factors, $(P_1/P_2)\ (P_2/P_3)\ (P_4/P_5)\ (P_5/P_0)$.

It is clear from Figure 5.17 that recuperated cycle performance is sensitive to pressure drop and that if low pressure drop can be attained, the recuperated cycle is much more efficient than an open cycle.

The large values of the mass flow parameter (Figure 5.18) associated with low pressure ratio dictate avoidance of trying too hard to achieve theoretical ideals.

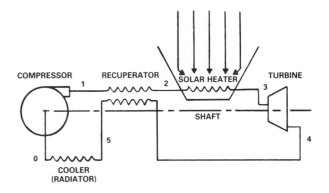

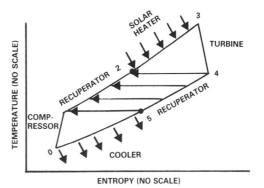

Figure 5.16 Closed-cycle Brayton schematic diagram and cycle diagram.

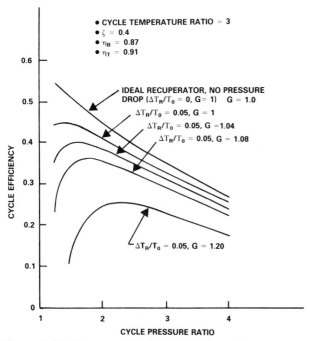

Figure 5.17 Representative Brayton cycle performance parametrics.

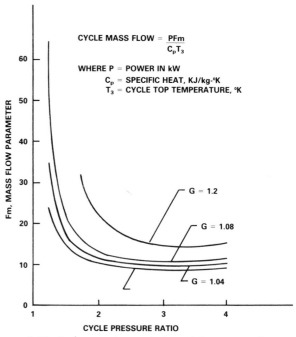

Figure 5.18 Representative variation of Brayton cycle mass flow parameter.

SPACE STATION NUCLEAR OPTIONS

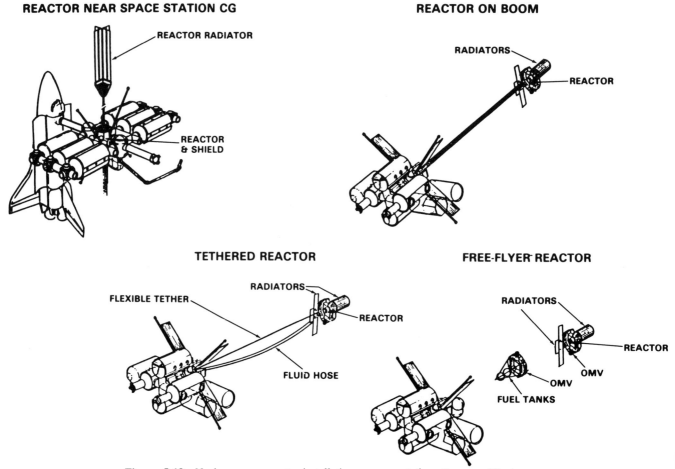

Figure 5.19 Nuclear power reactor installation on space station. *Courtesy of Boeing.*

Nuclear generation is a possibility for a space station or platform. Radioisotope thermoelectric generators (RTGs) were used on the Apollo ALSEP scientific instrument packages left on the Moon by the astronauts, on the outer planet Voyagers, and on certain other spacecraft. The United States flew an experimental nuclear reactor in the 1960s and the Soviets use reactors regularly for certain of their military satellites. For a space station, the power needs are too high for RTGs; a reactor is the only plausible solution. Nuclear reactors produce thermal power that must be converted into electrical power. Unlike solar systems, the size of a reactor is insensitive to the amount of thermal power produced; efficiency of the conversion system is not a major issue. One of the major benefits of a reactor is that an energy storage system is not needed since the reactor is not dependent on sunlight for its power generation. A reactor concept installed on a space station is illustrated in Figure 5.19.

In the power range of interest, up to a few hundred kilowatts, a reactor system, encumbered by enough radiation shielding to make it an acceptable neighbor for a manned space facility, will be somewhat more massive than a system based on solar cells. But it will not have the large collector areas of a solar powered system. Therefore the space station will have less drag and over a period of years, the mass difference will be "paid back" through less resupply. However, reactor systems must reject heat through thermal radiators. Radiators dedicated to the power system will be used and will operate at high enough temperatures to create a degree of thermal pollution.

Because of the relatively low operating altitude for space stations, special precautions to prevent inadvertent early reentry of a space station power reactor will be necessary. A typical approach would employ placement of a spent reactor at a higher altitude. Present policy requires that reactors be placed in an orbit with at least a 300 year lifetime to avoid problems associated with public exposure to radioactive materials that might survive reentry.

Energy Storage Systems

Solar energy systems will require energy storage systems for supply of electrical power to a space station or platform while in the Earth's shadow. Existing spacecraft use batteries, either nickel-cadmium or nickel-hydrogen. Future technology alternatives include regenerable fuel cells and flywheels. Thermal cycle systems will most likely use thermal storage in the solar energy absorber; thermal storage will serve to operate the thermal cycle machines during solar occultation. Thermal storage is *before* electricity generation while battery storage is *after* it in the cycle flow.

Use of the storage system is a key factor in sizing the solar energy collection system. Important storage system performance parameters are energy density, e.g., kWh per kg, and storage efficiency. More energy must be input to a storage system than can be withdrawn from it. Typical electrical energy storage efficiency is 60 percent; thermal storage

systems may approach 90 percent if thermal reradiation from the absorber is inhibited during occultation periods. From the standpoint of system sizing, the relevant efficiency is the ratio of (energy delivered from storage)/(energy available for charging). Batteries are often rated in terms of (energy delivered)/(energy input by charging), but energy available that cannot be used is an efficiency loss insofar as system sizing is concerned.

The two key storage system performance evaluation parameters are the storage system efficiency described by energy out divided by energy in and the storage system mass per unit energy stored. Storage technologies differ in the depth of discharge (the fraction of total energy stored that may be routinely delivered from storage and then recharged without unduly detracting from the life of the storage system). Storage systems are usually compared on the basis of routine operation but emergency operation, i.e., occasional use of full depth of discharge, may be an important comparison parameter. The relative performance of various storage systems is compared in Figure 5.20.

Computation of solar collector or array sizes based on

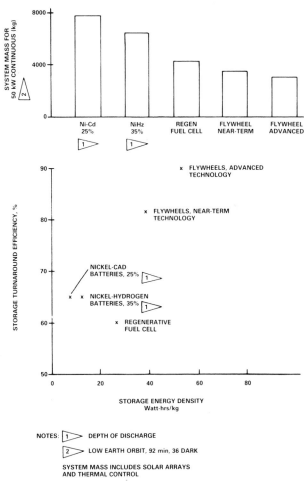

Figure 5.20 Comparison of space station storage options. *Courtesy of Boeing.*

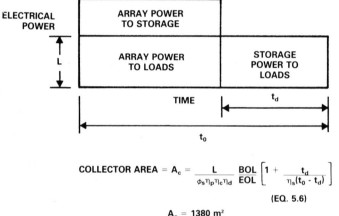
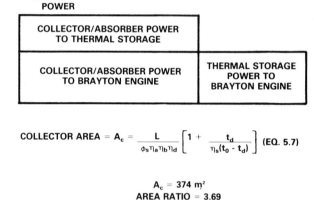

SILICON PLANAR PHOTOVOLTAIC

TYPICAL VALUES

SOLAR FLUX $= \phi_s = 1.353$ kW/m^2

PHOTOVOLTAIC EFFICIENCY $= \eta_p = 0.12$

COLLECTION EFFICIENCY $= \eta_c = 0.9$

POWER PROCESSING &
    DISTRIBUTION EFFICIENCY $= \eta_d = 0.9$

STORAGE EFFICIENCY $= \eta_s = 0.6$

DEGRADATION $= \left(\dfrac{BOL}{EOL}\right) = 1.2$

ORBIT PERIOD $= t_0 = 95$ min.

DARK PERIOD $= t_d = 36$ min.

LOAD $= L = 75$ kW

BRAYTON THERMAL CYCLE

TYPICAL VALUES

COLLECTION EFFICIENCY $= \eta_c = 0.8$

THERMAL ABSORBER
    EFFICIENCY $= \eta_a = 0.8$

BRAYTON CYCLE EFFICIENCY $= \eta_b = 0.4$

THERMAL STORAGE
    EFFICIENCY $= \eta_s = 0.95$

(OTHER TERMS SAME
AS FOR PHOTOVOLTAIC)

ELECTRICAL POWER

| ARRAY POWER TO STORAGE | |
| ARRAY POWER TO LOADS | STORAGE POWER TO LOADS |

$$\text{COLLECTOR AREA} = A_c = \frac{L}{\phi_s \eta_p \eta_c \eta_d}\,\frac{BOL}{EOL}\left[1 + \frac{t_d}{\eta_s(t_0 - t_d)}\right] \quad \text{(EQ. 5.6)}$$

$$A_c = 1380 \text{ m}^2$$

THERMAL POWER

| COLLECTOR/ABSORBER POWER TO THERMAL STORAGE | |
| COLLECTOR/ABSORBER POWER TO BRAYTON ENGINE | THERMAL STORAGE POWER TO BRAYTON ENGINE |

$$\text{COLLECTOR AREA} = A_c = \frac{L}{\phi_s \eta_a \eta_b \eta_d}\left[1 + \frac{t_d}{\eta_s(t_0 - t_d)}\right] \quad \text{(EQ. 5.7)}$$

$$A_c = 374 \text{ m}^2$$
AREA RATIO = 3.69
VARIOUS SOURCES ESTIMATE 2 TO 5

Figure 5.21 Collector area sizing equations for power systems.

storage system performance is illustrated in Figure 5.21. Results of such computations for photovoltaic electrical systems are shown parametrically in Figure 5.22. One may note from the figure that array power will normally be in excess of twice the delivered load power.

Power Processing

Solar arrays deliver electric power at low to moderate voltages. Although solar cell strings can be arranged in series to deliver arbitrarily high voltages, plasma effects in the space environment limit practical operating voltages in low Earth orbit to something like 200 volts. Also, voltage delivered by a solar array varies with the power load while many of the space station electrical loads need their power supplied with accurately controlled voltage. Further, power controls are needed to provide load power from the solar source when available, from storage otherwise, and also to isolate and correct electrical faults such as short circuits without completely shutting down the power system.

Power processing systems use high-speed switching to synthesize alternating current from the direct currents supplied by solar arrays (solar dynamic systems will probably

produce alternating current directly), thus to supply transformer/switching systems that condition power and manage loads. Power processing systems operate at efficiencies on the order of 95 percent; this loss must be considered in sizing solar source and storage systems.

System Schematics and System Sizing

Solar power systems include power generation, energy storage, power processing and distribution, and power conditioning to serve specific loads. Figure 5.23 illustrates a representative photovoltaic system schematic and Table 5.3 presents useful system sizing parameters for masses and areas.

Environmental Control and Life Support

Environmental control and life support (EC/LS) systems provide the clean water and air needed for crew health and well-being. Food systems, also required, are described in the next chapter. Since these systems are devoted to support of people in orbit, they clearly do not apply to unmanned platforms.

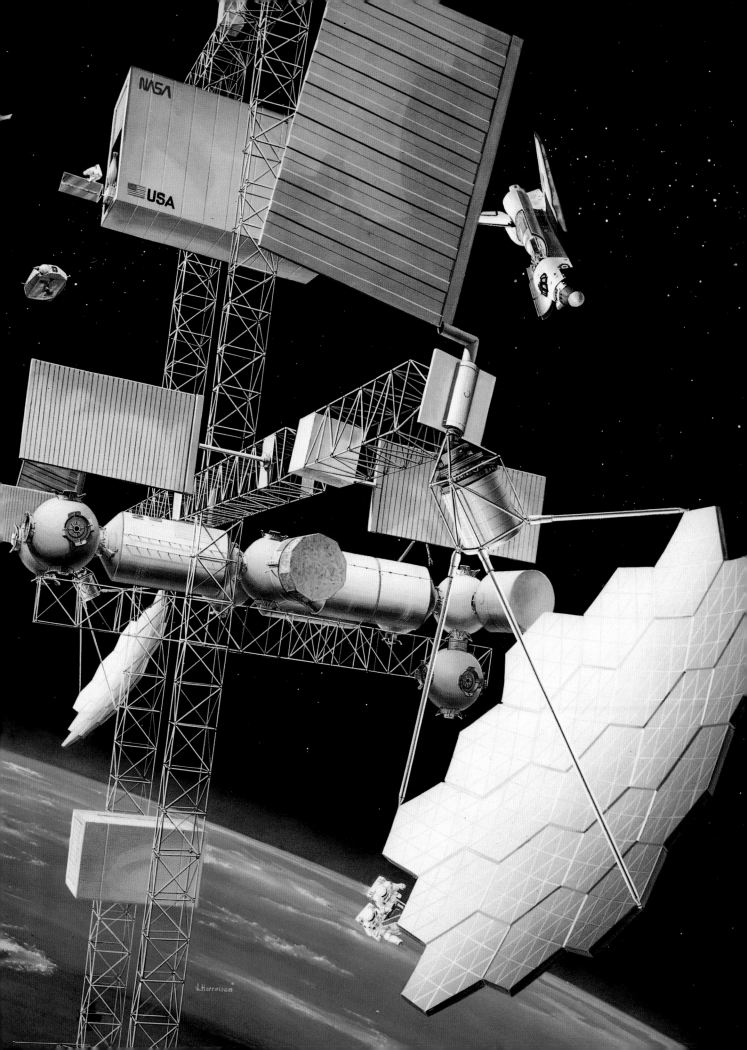

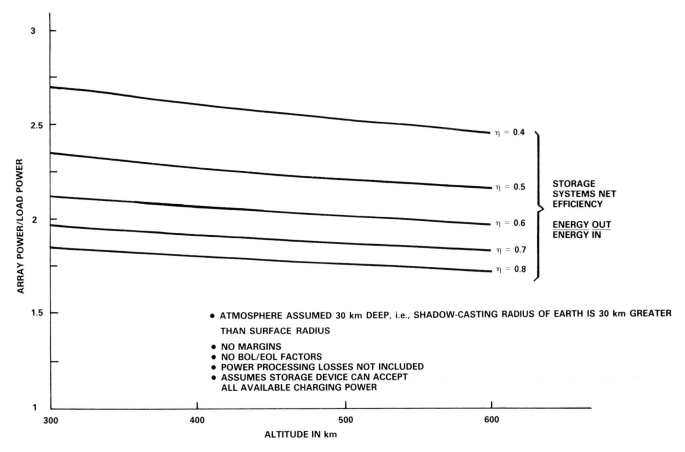

Figure 5.22 Solar array power sizing factor for energy storage.

All American manned spacecraft to date, including the Space Shuttle, have used relatively simple EC/LS systems. Mercury, Gemini, Apollo, and Skylab employed pure oxygen air systems at about 34 kN (5 psia). Oxygen was replenished from storage systems, while metabolic CO_2 was removed by expendable absorbent canisters of lithium hydroxide (LiOH), often called ''lye-oh'' by space engineers. Skylab used regenerable molecular sieves for CO_2 removal. The CO_2, concentrated in the molecular sieves, was periodically vented to vacuum. Humidity was removed by the cabin air thermal control heat exchangers and drinking water came from fuel cells (Gemini, Apollo, Shuttle) or from storage (Mercury, Skylab). (Fuel cells synthesize pure water from its constituent hydrogen and oxygen in the process of generating electricity.) Skylab had a shower; its water also came from storage. The Shuttle differs from the others in using a two-gas (oxygen and nitrogen) atmosphere at 10^5 N/m^2 (14.7 psia) pressure, but like the others, does not regenerate oxygen or water.

Experimental systems that do regenerate oxygen and water have been tested in laboratories and simulations for years. The payoff for regeneration, however, is important only for long-duration systems and none of those described above were long enough in duration to motivate flight-qualifying the more complex regenerative systems.

Space stations can benefit substantially from air and water regeneration as shown in Figure 5.24. The greatest payoff comes from recycling wash water with successively less, but still significant payoff from recycling potable (drinkably pure) water and regenerating oxygen from metabolic water and CO_2.

With regeneration, the EC/LS system divides nicely into four sub-subsystems: cabin ventilation and temperature control; air revitalization (humidity, CO_2, trace contaminant and odor removal and oxygen regeneration); potable water purification; and wash water recycling. Some concepts do not distinguish between the last two; all water is processed to potable quality regardless of end use. Further EC/LS development will likely reveal the importance of a fifth item: waste and sludge handling.

The human crewperson is an integral part of EC/LS analysis and design. The human may be considered a ''black box'' that has needs for thermal control and for serving certain inputs and outputs. These are summarized in Figure 5.25 for a nominal human metabolic thermal rate of 136 watts (117 Kcal/hr; 466 Btu/hr). About 35 percent of the heat given off by a human is in latent heat of water vapor and the balance is sensible heat. It is important to recognize that these are nominal figures. A human sleeping has about

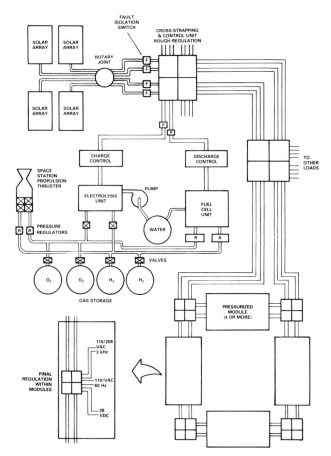

Figure 5.23 Typical electrical system schematic.

half this metabolic output; a human exercising with moderate vigor, e.g., jogging or exercising on space station exercise equipment, has three to five times this output. The inputs and outputs shown in the figure are roughly propor-

Table 5.3 Electrical power system sizing relationships.

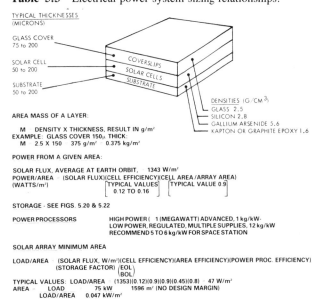

TYPICAL THICKNESSES
(MICRONS)

GLASS COVER
75 to 200

SOLAR CELL
50 to 200

SUBSTRATE
50 to 200

DENSITIES (G./CM.³)
GLASS 2.5
SILICON 2.8
GALLIUM ARSENIDE 5.6
KAPTON OR GRAPHITE EPOXY 1.6

AREA MASS OF A LAYER:

M = DENSITY X THICKNESS, RESULT IN g/m²
EXAMPLE: GLASS COVER 150μ THICK:
M = 2.5 X 150 = 375 g/m² = 0.375 kg/m²

POWER FROM A GIVEN AREA:

SOLAR FLUX, AVERAGE AT EARTH ORBIT, = 1343 W/m²
POWER/AREA = (SOLAR FLUX)(CELL EFFICIENCY)(CELL AREA/ARRAY AREA)
(WATTS/m²)   [TYPICAL VALUES]   [TYPICAL VALUE 0.9]
                              [0.12 TO 0.16]

STORAGE - SEE FIGS. 5.20 & 5.22

POWER PROCESSORS   HIGH POWER (~1 MEGAWATT) ADVANCED, 1 kg/kW-
                          LOW POWER, REGULATED, MULTIPLE SUPPLIES, 12 kg/kW
                          RECOMMEND 5 TO 6 kg/kW FOR SPACE STATION

SOLAR ARRAY MINIMUM AREA

LOAD/AREA = (SOLAR FLUX, W/m²)(CELL EFFICIENCY)(AREA EFFICIENCY)(POWER PROC. EFFICIENCY)
            (STORAGE FACTOR) (EOL)
                             (BOL)
TYPICAL VALUES: LOAD/AREA = (1353)(0.12)(0.9)(0.9)(0.45)(0.8) = 47 W/m²
AREA = LOAD = 75 kW = 1596 m² (NO DESIGN MARGIN)
       LOAD/AREA   0.047 kW/m²

tional to metabolic thermal output. No two humans are identical in metabolic output or balances; human individvals also vary with time. Analyses of EC/LS operation must include these uncertainties.

Cabin Ventilation and Temperature Control

In the zero g of a space station cabin, forced convection must be used to prevent the occurrence of "dead spots" where air humidity and CO_2 concentration could build up to uncomfortable values. Convection also aids the normal body process of heat rejection by evaporation of water vapor from the skin. The specifics of any convection scheme depend on the interior arrangements of the cabin, but the concept depicted in Figure 5.26, devised for the Space Operations Center (SOC) cabin concept, is typical. Air which must be circulated through heat exchangers by fans for thermal control is also directed through the cabin through

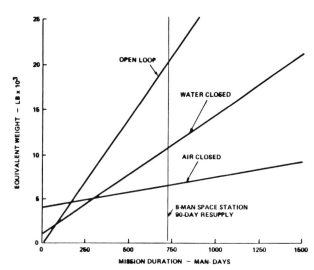

Figure 5.24 Benefits of EC/LS air and water supply cycle closure. *Courtesy of Boeing.*

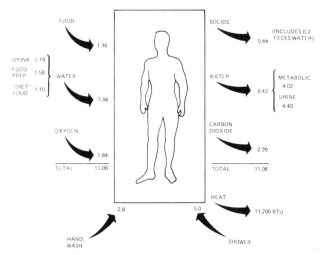

Figure 5.25 Nominal human metabolic requirements. *Courtesy of Boeing.*

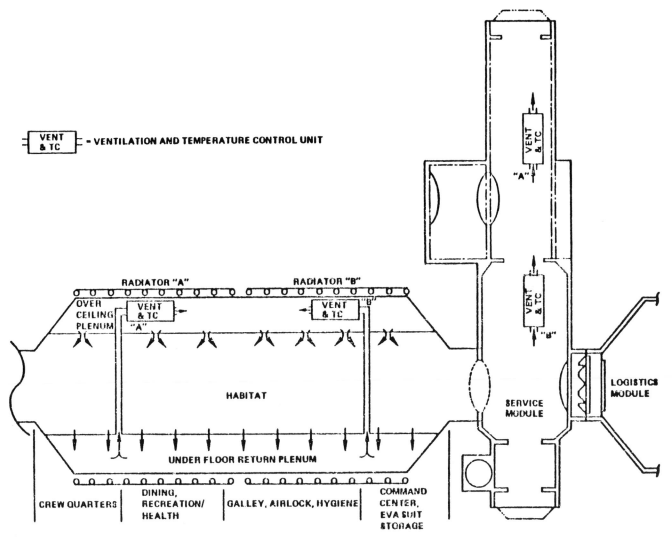

Figure 5.26 Cabin ventilation concept as proposed for Space Operations Center (SOC). *Courtesy of Boeing and Hamilton Standard.*

pneumostats (aspirators) to create the forced convection. The pneumostats cause the entrainment of additional cabin air in the circulation pattern, enhancing the convection process.

Air flow rates of about 7.5 meters/min (12 cm/sec) are considered about right. Astronauts have indicated a desire to have the flow rate locally adjustable, especially in sleeping quarters and exercise areas, in a manner similar to that used on commercial aircraft.

The cabin thermal control and ventilation equipment will be a simple fan-heat exchanger installation such as that illustrated in Figure 5.27. Fan systems used in early spacecraft have typically been designed for efficiency and are hence noisy. In a space station, it will be important to keep noise down. Less efficient but quiet fans such as squirrel-cages should be considered. Fan power is not inconsequential, but is a few kW at most for an 8-to-12 person space station.

Air Revitalization

Air revitalization includes humidity control; CO_2, trace contaminant, and odor removal; and oxygen regeneration or makeup. Humidity control could be allocated to cabin thermal control, but there are strong reasons to separate it. At a standard cabin condition of 20 °C and 50 percent humidity, and assuming control bands of 2 °C and 10 percent humidity, then the heat exchanger airflow to maintain temperature control is over two times that required for humidity control (Table 5.4). Further, the temperature of the humidity removal heat exchanger must be about 8 °C, implying considerably greater radiator area than that for thermal control at 20 °C. It is important to minimize the amount of heat rejected at low temperatures.

One regenerable means of CO_2 removal has been demonstrated in flight (molecular sieve; Skylab) and two regenerable means of CO_2 removal have been proposed and

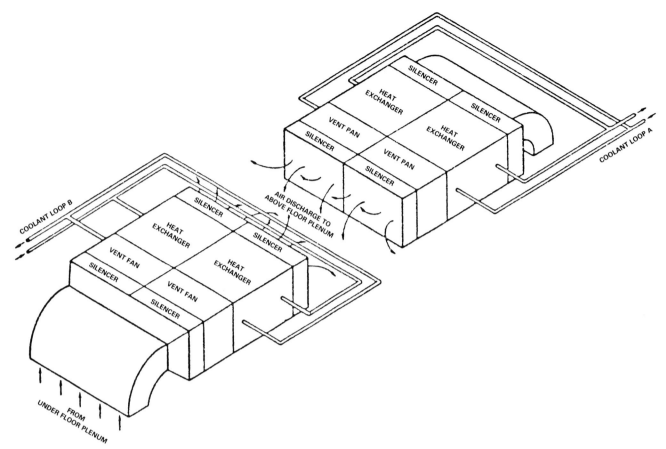

Figure 5.27 Cabin ventilation and temperature control equipment installation concept. *Courtesy of Boeing and Hamilton Standard.*

demonstrated in laboratory tests: a solid amine system and an electrochemical cell. The solid amine system is cyclic in operation; cabin airflow through the solid amine particle bed results in CO_2 absorption until the bed is saturated. Flushing hot steam through the saturated bed drives off the CO_2 for collection or disposal. When the bed is desorbed by hot steam it may be returned to CO_2 absorption service. Because the steam is driven out of the bed during normal use, it becomes a latent heat load on the humidity control heat exchangers.

The second CO_2 removal system uses fuel-cell technology to cause the CO_2 to be removed from the air stream and concentrated by an electrochemical reactor. Since the reaction is exothermic, some electricity is produced. The reactor must be fed by hydrogen produced by water electrolysis, so electrical power is consumed in the overall cycle. This system is continuous in operation.

The Soviets apparently use either sodium or lithium superoxide, NaO_2 or LiO_2. Upon contact with humid air, these compounds release oxygen and convert to hydroxides which then absorb CO_2. Sodium superoxide has been used in the United States for emergency breathing apparatus for use in mines. Superoxides are, of course, unsafe for underwater use.

Oxygen consumed by human metabolism oxidizes hydrogen and carbon in foods to release water and CO_2. Regeneration of oxygen thus must recover it from water and CO_2. Oxygen recovery from water will be accomplished through electrolysis, releasing hydrogen in the process. The hydrogen will then be reacted with CO_2 to form water and CH_4. This is done by the Sabatier process; an alternative Bosch process reduces CO_2 all the way to elemental carbon but is less well proven. Sabatier and Bosch reactors use catalysts at elevated temperatures.

Trace contaminant control will employ a catalytic oxidizer; most trace contaminants are organic and oxidizable to CO_2 and H_2O. In addition, activated charcoal beds will be used for odor control. The charcoal beds are not regenerable.

Figure 5.28 shows a schematic diagram of an air revitalization system. The system shown is fully regenerative. Since it uses a Sabatier reactor, CH_4 is a waste product. Depending on the amount of water in the food supplied, the system balance can be hydrogen-rich or hydrogen-poor. If the latter, not all the CO_2 can be reduced and some will be discharged overboard or compressed into liquid and stored for return to Earth as a waste product.

Table 5.4 Humidity control data.

SATURATED WATER VAPOR

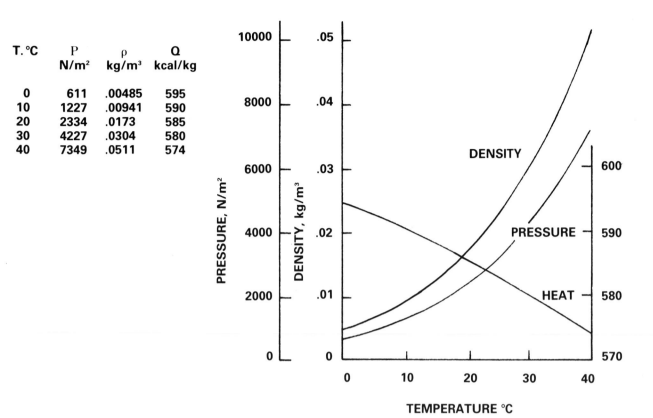

T. °C	P N/m²	ρ kg/m³	Q kcal/kg
0	611	.00485	595
10	1227	.00941	590
20	2334	.0173	585
30	4227	.0304	580
40	7349	.0511	574

AT 20°C A 10% CHANGE IN HUMIDITY $= (0.1)(0.0173 \text{kg/m}^2)$
(293K)   AND HEAT CONTENT IS $0.00173 \text{ kg/m}^3 \times 585 \text{ kcal/kg}$
$= 1.01 \text{ kcal/m}^3$ FOR 10% Δ HUMIDITY

$$\text{AIR DENSITY} = \frac{pM}{R_uT} = \frac{101{,}342 \text{ N/m}^2 \times 29 \text{ kg/mol}}{\dfrac{8314 \text{ N-m}}{°\text{K-mol}} \times 293°\text{K}}$$

$$= 1.206 \text{ kg/m}^3$$

$$\text{AIR SPECIFIC HEAT} = \frac{0.24 \text{ kcal}}{\text{kg/°K}}$$

AND AIR HEAT CONTENT IS $0.29 \text{ kcal/m}^3\text{-°K}$

Figure 5.29 illustrates a typical conceptual installation of air revitalization equipment, again assuming solid amine CO_2 absorption and Sabatier CO_2 reduction.

Potable Water

If potable water is recycled, it must be recovered from humidity condensate as well as from human wastes such as urine. The Soviets have recycled condensate for some time, but without purification it is not very palatable (condensers tend to collect dust and other matter in the air). Further, the system balance is such that condensate is not enough to make up potable water; some waste water must be processed as well.

Astronauts have consistently expressed extreme reluctance to drink water containing reprocessed urine. This is in part psychological and in part because urinal waste water contains volatiles such as ammonia that carry over through a distillation process and contaminate the "purified" water. Pre- and post-distillation treatment processes are being developed to avoid pathogen contamination of processed water and eliminate malodorous carry-over. Water distillation concepts designed to minimize distillation heat load and operate in zero g include a "vapor compression distillation" (VCD) machine and a "thermal integrated membrane evaporator system" (TIMES) system. The VCD machine uses a rotating-drum evaporator and heat regenerator (Figure

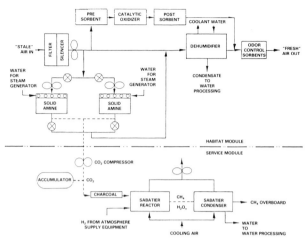

Figure 5.28 Schematic diagram for air revitalization system.
Courtesy of Boeing and Hamilton Standard.

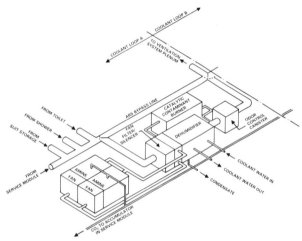

Figure 5.29 Air revitalization equipment installation concept.
Courtesy of Boeing and Hamilton Standard.

5.30) and the TIMES unit uses permeable membranes operating at modestly elevated temperatures for evaporation.

To avoid the issues related to drinking reprocessed water, it has been suggested that all potable water be processed through electrolysis and reconstitution via fuel cell. This would certainly remove concern about contaminant carryover and astronauts are used to drinking fuel cell water. Whether VCD or TIMES water would contaminate fuel cells remains to be established. Losses due to inefficiency of electrolysis/fuel cell processing would increase electrical power input to the EC/LS subsystem by about 300 watts per crewperson.

The potable water system must include hot and cold water processing for the various uses of potable water including drinking and food preparation use. Processing of all water to potable quality has been proposed and has certain advantages including the fact that most wash water is less contaminated than human waste water. As above, there are power and equipment cost penalties with this nicety.

Wash Water

Wash water includes that designated for hand wash, showering, and dish and clothes washing. Wash water, once used, will be contaminated with detergents and dirt. Studies and tests have indicated that wash water can be reused after hyperfiltration, which removes most of its contaminants. Hyperfiltration employs filters that screen out contaminant particles and molecules significantly larger than water molecules, e.g., soap and organics.

All water recycling creates sludge, i.e., water containing highly concentrated waste products. Sludge cannot go beyond a certain concentration or it becomes difficult to process. Sludge must be returned to the resupply module for return to Earth. Accumulation of concentrated and solidified sludge in sludge handling plumbing is a concern that must be addressed by analyses and tests.

Figure 5.31 shows a typical schematic for a potable and wash water handling system and Figure 5.32 illustrates an installation concept as developed for the SOC space station design.

The technical maturity of water processing systems is a developmental issue for space stations. The main concern relates to the practical service life of the hardware, given

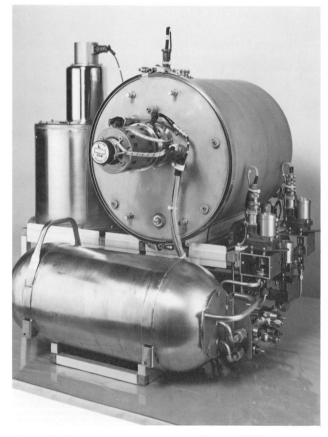

Figure 5.30 Vapor compression distillation (VCD) machine.
Courtesy of Life Systems, Inc.

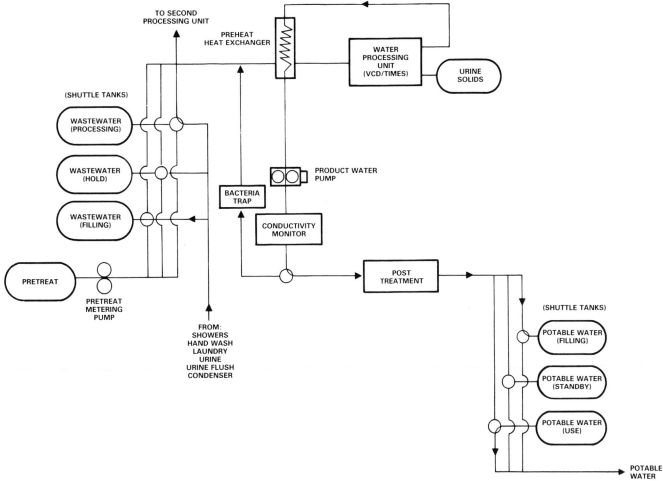

Figure 5.31 Water system schematic diagram. *Courtesy of Boeing and Hamilton Standard.*

that no such systems have ever been used in flight space-craft. Consequently, an initial space station may use partially open-loop water systems, e.g., processing only of wash water with delivery of potable water from resupplied storage. If potable water is resupplied, then it is likely that oxygen will also be resupplied rather than recovered from water and CO_2. These concepts for partially open systems represent interim solutions; there is no argument as to the benefit and eventual certainty of incorporation of complete recycling of water and oxygen.

EC/LS Systems Analyses

The elements of the EC/LS subsystem are coupled in operation through the need to satisfy performance requirements and through interchange of mass and energy. Current NASA performance requirements for EC/LS operation are summarized in Table 5.5. The values specified for normal operation are used in calculation of nominal systems performance; the others are used where EC/LS performance is degraded by failures, by equipment out of service for maintenance, or because a temporary abnormal load condition, such as the entire crew present in one module, exists.

Figure 5.33 presents a schematic for the entire EC/LS system for normal operating conditions. The space station will see extensive use of EVA. EVA crew members will have a metabolic rate on the order of twice the nominal given above while EVA. Their air and water balances will be loads on the portable life support system (PLSS) of the extravehicular mobility unit (EMU), i.e., space suit. Analysis of the effect of EVA on EC/LS balances must consider differences in EMU EC/LS technology as well as the removal of loads from the main system, If the EMU employs a water evaporator for heat rejection as does the present Shuttle unit, major alterations in water balance will occur because of the loss of the cooling water.

Appendix C presents a summary of EC/LS balance calculation algorithms.

Thermal Control

Heat inputs to space stations and platforms come from the Sun, the Earth, and internal sources usually dominated by waste heat related to electrical power use. Although space

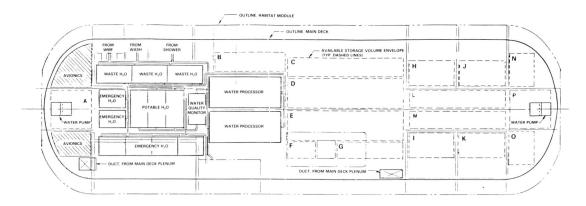

GENERAL ARRANGEMENT UNDER MAIN DECK

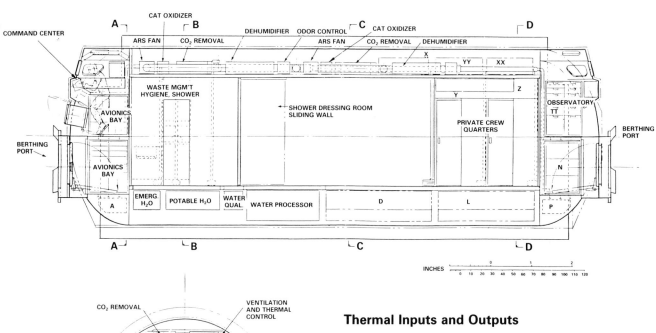

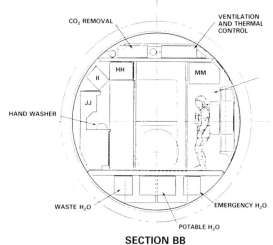

SECTION BB

Figure 5.32 EC/LS system installation in space station module. *Courtesy of Boeing.*

is popularly thought of as "cold," it is not so at all to the space platform designer. Adequate control of system and equipment temperatures is an important design problem.

Thermal Inputs and Outputs

The Sun as a source of thermal radiation was described in Chapter 4, with an energy flux maximum of 1393 watts/m^2 in Earth orbit. The only other significant external source in Earth orbit is the Earth itself. The Earth reflects about half the solar radiation that falls on it, on the average. The worst case (from the standpoint of heat input) is about 75 percent, representing bright clouds or snow beneath the orbit path. In addition, the Earth radiates thermal energy due to its own temperature, typically 240 K. Solar reflection occurs only when the Earth beneath a spacecraft is sunlit, but thermal radiation occurs on both the light and dark sides of the Earth. The nature of these thermal sources is diagrammed and plotted in Figure 5.34.

Space stations and platforms will have significant electrical power sources as described above. In addition, space stations incur thermal loads because of crew metabolism, roughly 135 watts thermal per person. All electrical power entering a system from solar arrays turns into heat that must

Table 5.5 NASA EC/LS performance requirements. *Courtesy of NASA.*

RESPIRABLE ATMOSPHERE/WATER REQUIREMENTS
(CUSTOMARY UNITS)

Parameter	Units	Operational	90-day Degraded (1)	22-day Emergency
CO_2 Partial Press	mmHg	3.0 max	7.6 max	12 max
Temperature	deg F	65–75	60–85	60–90
Dew Point (2)	deg F	40–60	35–70	35–70
Potable Water	lb/man-day	6.8–8.1	6.8 (3)	6.8 (3)
Hygiene Water	lb/man-day	12 (3)	6 (3)	3 (3)
Wash Water	lb/man-day	28 (3)	14 (3)	0
Ventilation	ft/min	15–40	10–100	5–200
O_2 Partial Pressure (4)	psia	2.7–3.2	2.4–3.8	2.3–3.9
Total Pressure (5)	psia	10.2 or 14.7	10.2 or 14.7	10.2 or 14.7
Dilute Gas	—	N_2	N_2	N_2
Trace Contam-inants (8)	mg/m³	TBD	TBD	TBD
Micro-organisms	CFU/m³ (6)	500 (7)	750 (7)	1000 (7)

RESPIRABLE ATMOSPHERE/WATER REQUIREMENTS
(SI UNITS)

Parameter	Units	Operational	90-day Degraded (1)	22-day Emergency
CO_2 Partial Press	N/m²	400 max	1013 max	1600 max
Temperature	°K	291.5–297.1	288.8–302.6	288.8–305.4
Dew Point (2)	°K	277.6–288.8	273.9–294.3	273.9–294.3
Potable Water	kg/man-day	3.1–3.7	3.1 (3)	3.1 (3)
Hygiene Water	kg/man-day	5.44 (3)	2.72 (3)	1.36 (3)
Wash Water	kg/man-day	12.7 (3)	6.35 (3)	0
Ventilation	m/sec	.076–.203	.051–.508	.025–1.016
O_2 Partial Pressure (4)	N/m² × 10³	18.6–22.1	16.5–26.2	15.0–26.9
Total Pressure (5)	N/m²;10³	70.3–101.4	70.3–101.4	70.3–101.4
Dilute Gas	—	N_2	N_2	N_2
Trace Contam-inants (8)	mg/m³	TBD	TBD	TBD
Micro-organisms	CFU/m³ (6)	500 (7)	750 (7)	1000 (7)

Notes:

(1) Degraded levels meet "fail operational" criteria.

(2) Relative humidity shall be within the range of 25–75 percent.

(3) Minimum.

(4) In no case shall the O_2 partial pressure be below 2.3 psia, or the O_2 concentration exceed 25.9 percent of the total pressure at 14.7 psia or 30 percent of the total pressure at 10.2.

(5) All systems shall be compatible with both 10.2 and 14.7 psia total pressure.

(6) CFU-Colony forming units.

(7) These values reflect a limit base. No widely sanctioned standards are available.

(8) Based on NHB 8060. lb, (J8400003).

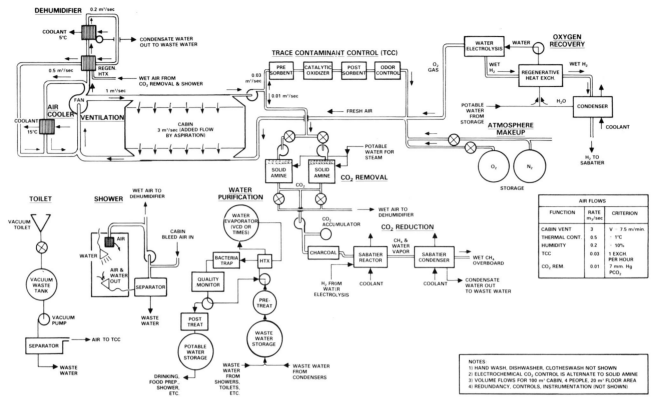

Figure 5.33 Typical EC/LS schematic diagram.

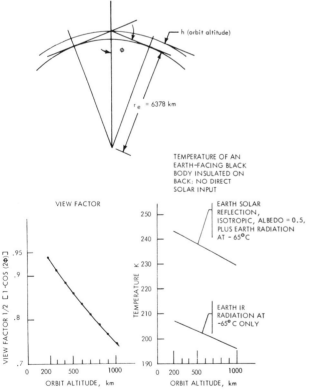

Figure 5.34 Sun and Earth thermal sources.

be rejected except for small amounts of electrical energy converted to radio frequency (RF) energy. The latter is no more than a few tens of watts for space stations and platforms and may be neglected.

Heat can leave a space vehicle only as enthalpy of an effluent (negligible for cases of interest) or as thermal radiation. The latter is emitted by all objects above absolute zero temperature in accordance with the Stefan-Boltzmann law:

$$Q = \sigma\epsilon T^4 \qquad (5.6)$$

where Q is radiation from a surface in kW/m², σ is the Stefan-Boltzmann constant, 5.6697×10^{-11} kW/m²$-(K)^4$, ϵ is emissivity, defined as 1.0 for an ideal "black body," and T is temperature in kelvins. Since energy absorbed from solar radiation is 1.353α kW/m² where α is absorptivity, and since $\alpha = \epsilon$ for most materials, a flat plate normal to the sun's radiation and radiating thermally from one side, will reach a temperature defined by

$$\sigma T^4 = 1.353; \; T = 393K = 120°C. \qquad (5.7)$$

Even radiating from both sides, the flat plate will equilibrate at 57 °C. Simply handling the Sun's heat can be challenging.

Simple Radiators and Selective Coatings

A thin flat plate in orbit, such as a solar panel, will receive solar input on the Sun-facing side and Earth input (solar reflection and IR radiation) on the side facing the Earth. Large variations in equilibrium temperature result as illustrated in Figure 5.35.

Because there is a great temperature difference between the solar spectrum, approximately a black body at 6000 K, and a space station radiator at about 300 K, it is possible

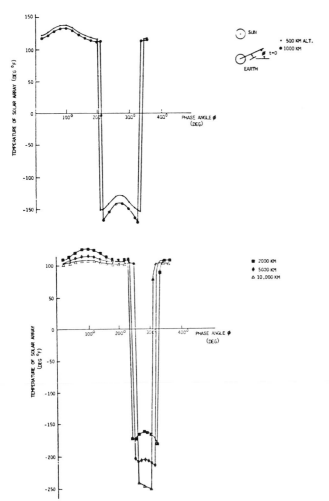

Figure 5.35 Thermal effects on flat-plate solar array in Earth orbit. *Courtesy of Boeing.*

tors on the surfaces of pressurized modules and flat-panel radiators for rejection of the excess heat that cannot be handled by the module radiators. Space platforms will use primarily the flat panel radiators.

Flat panel radiators on a Sun-oriented platform can be placed in a shaded area or oriented edge-on to the Sun's rays and will not be degraded in performance by solar input. Panels on an Earth-oriented space station will have varied solar input unless continually moved to maintain an edge-on orientation. Studies have examined ways of keeping the orientation motion simple, especially avoiding continuous rotations that would require sealing of fluid swivel joints. One of the best solutions is the "beta-track" concept shown in Figure 5.37. The radiator panel is edge-on to the flight path, eliminating drag, and is tilted so that when the spacecraft is over the noon meridian on the Earth below, the radiator is also edge-on to the Sun. The beta tilt is a slow cyclic motion that can be accommodated by a low-power actuator and flexible couplings. The performance of this radiator is poorest when the beta angle is maximum, e.g., 52° for a 28.50°-inclined orbit. In an orbit coordinate system with the x-axis at the noon meridian location, the Sun vector is

$$\begin{pmatrix} \cos \beta \\ 0 \\ \sin \beta \end{pmatrix}.$$

A vector normal to the radiator plane is

$$\begin{pmatrix} -\sin \beta \cos \theta \\ -\sin \beta \sin \theta \\ \cos \beta \end{pmatrix}.$$

The angle between the Sun vector and the radiator plane

to treat thermal control surfaces to absorb little of the solar spectrum while emitting thermal radiation efficiently at the lower temperature. Such surfaces have been used for spacecraft thermal control for decades; the coatings are called selective coatings. Emissivities better than 0.8 for thermal radiation and solar absorptivities less than 0.1 are possible. Special white paints are often used, but the highest performance coatings employ second-surface (back-coated) mirrors. The mirror substrate is transparent to sunlight but emits efficiently in the infrared. The back-surface coating reflects sunlight efficiently.

Unfortunately, selective coatings degrade with time. For a typical spacecraft lifetime of 5 years, the degradation is moderate, with the absorptivity reaching values on the order of 0.2 to 0.3, as shown in Figure 5.36 (emissivity changes very little). For a long-lived facility such as a space station or platform, the degradation is predicted to be so severe that selective coatings may be of little value. Means of periodically restoring or replacing such coatings are presently under study.

Space station thermal control systems will include radia-

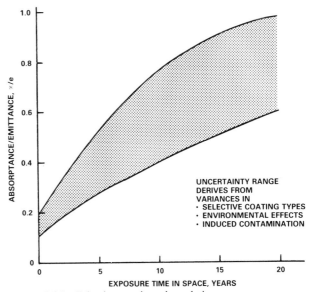

Figure 5.36 Selective coatings degradation.

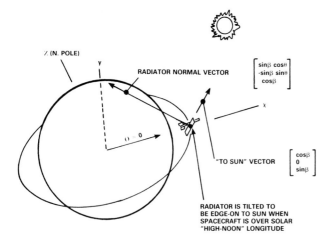

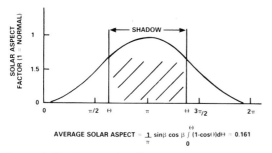

Figure 5.37 Beta-track radiator concept.

is given by

$$\sin \delta = \sin \beta \cos \beta (1 - \cos \theta) \ . \qquad (5.8)$$

The solar input is proportional to $\sin(\delta)$; this value was plotted in Figure 5.37. Without selective coatings, the average radiator temperature, defined as the temperature at which the net output over an orbit would be zero, is -20 °C compared to $+20$ °C for a Sun-facing radiator. Given a typical radiator average temperature of 30 °C, the beta-tracked radiator has a factor of four improvement in heat rejection capability per unit area.

Since space radiators can have highly variable heat rejection capability over an orbit, use of thermal storage technology has great potential. This is now being explored for application to space stations and platforms.

Thermal Transport Loops

Since heat loads in a large spacecraft occur at a distance from practical locations for thermal radiators, heat transport systems are necessary. Conduction through solids is useless except for small loads moved through short distances; fluid loops are used. Past practice has been to use single-phase liquid-pumped fluid loops for large and complex systems, with heat pipes applied to smaller simpler systems.

Single-phase fluids must change temperature to absorb or deliver heat. Two-phase systems in which boiling and condensing occur can absorb and deliver heat by phase change at a fixed temperature. For example, a water loop with a 20 °C temperature difference requires a flow of 430 kg/hr to absorb/reject 10 kW of heat. The same water loop, with complete phase change from liquid to vapor and back, would require only about 16 kg/hr.

A heat pipe is a simple two-phase loop in which the pump work is accomplished by surface-tension forces. Figure 5.38 illustrates the heat pipe principle; Figure 5.39 is a section of an experimental heat pipe with internal capillary grooves.

Estimation of heat pipe performance is usually carried out using numerical computer programs or semiempirical methods relying heavily on test data. The performance of a heat pipe depends greatly on details of the wick, because surface tension pumping and the liquid pressure drop in the wick are both important. Coupling of the heat pipe to the heat source and sink also has significant effect. Heat pipes are normally operated under conditions where the wick liquid flow pressure drop limits the heat transport, but vapor pressure drop can be the limiting condition. This is especially true when temperatures are low; the vapor pressure can become so low that the pressure ratio created by wick pumping gives rise to sonic velocities and hence "choked" flow in the vapor passage.

Except at high temperatures, the mass of a radiator can dominate the mass of a heat rejection system. This is especially true if the radiator area exceeds a few tens of square meters and if long life is desired. Under these design conditions, the radiator must be armored to prevent meteoroid or debris impact damage which can result in loss of fluid. The damage risk can be mitigated by use of large numbers of heat pipes to couple the main fluid plumbing to the radiator fins; under these conditions penetration of one heat pipe does not affect the operation of others.

There have been continuing efforts to increase the thermal transport capability of heat pipes. One technique is the use of dedicated liquid arteries. Other techniques include low-power pump assists. Boeing has developed an electrostatic "ion-drag" pump usable in dielectric fluids. Although this device produces little pumping power, it is significant compared to surface tension pumping. The present state of the art in heat pipe design achieves, for one heat pipe, up to 50 to 100 kW-m, i.e., the product of heat flow and distance over which heat is transported. Heat pipes to several meters in length have been flown on spacecraft. In summary, heat pipes provide a simple, reliable means of heat transport over moderate distances.

Liquid Droplet Radiator

A novel concept for obtaining a large radiator area at light weight is the liquid droplet radiator. The idea is literally to

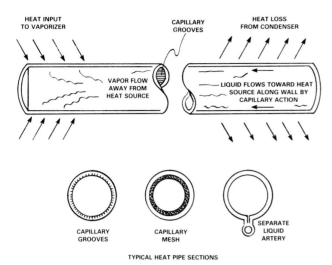

Figure 5.38 Heat pipe principle.

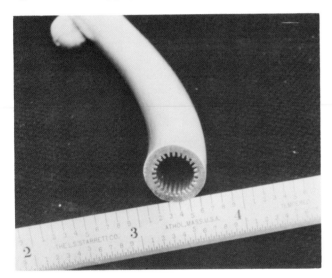

Figure 5.39 Heat pipe radiator element.

get rid of radiator plumbing almost entirely. Certain liquids, for example tin and some silicone oils, have very low vapor pressures at the lower end of their liquid temperature range. Droplets of these liquids have a relatively long lifetime in space vacuum because of their very low vapor pressure. It is proposed, for the liquid droplet radiator, to create directed sheet streams of liquid drops, controlled in size and velocity. These droplet streams, transporting the excess waste heat, would be emitted into space, traverse a distance as necessary to radiate their heat to space, and be collected by a collection device. Analytical studies have indicated a radiator mass as little as 10 percent that of a conventional radiator. Experimental studies in test chambers have demonstrated the principles of forming and directing droplets in a vacuum. There have as yet been no experiments in space, but NASA and other agencies have expressed considerable interest in such experiments and it is likely that they will occur in the future. The concept needs extensive testing before it can be routinel used in the design of practical heat rejection systems.

Radiators With Temperature Difference

Large thermal radiators used for main thermal rejection will be a part of fluid loops. If the loops are single-phase, the temperature of the radiator will change as the fluid loses heat, and the heat rejection from the radiator will vary with the temperature change.

Figure 5.40 illustrates an element of a radiator with fluid flow and thermal radiation. The heat loss per unit time per unit area is

$$\dot{q} = \frac{d^2 q}{dt\, dA} \ . \tag{5.9}$$

This can be equated to the Stefan-Boltzmann expression as follows:

$$\frac{d^2 q}{dt\, dA} = \sigma \epsilon T^4 = \frac{d^2 q}{dt\, dx} \text{ for unit width.} \tag{5.10}$$

Also, the heat transported past any point by the radiator fluid is $dq/dt = mC_p T$ and differentiating with respect to x yields

$$\frac{d^2 q}{dt\, dx} = \dot{m}\, C_p\, \frac{dT}{dx} \ . \tag{5.11}$$

Combining, we can write an equation for numerical integration, namely,

$$dx = \frac{mC_p\, dT}{\sigma \epsilon\, T^4} \ . \tag{5.12}$$

For the simple case where the radiative input to the radiator is zero, an average radiator temperature can be defined as

$$\bar{T} = \left[\frac{3T_1^3\, T_2^3}{T_1^2 + T_1 T_2 + T_2^2} \right]^{1/4} \tag{5.13}$$

where T_1 and T_2 are inlet and outlet temperatures. This is the temperature of a constant-temperature radiator that will reject the same amount heat.

Cylindrical module radiators cannot be oriented independently of the module orientation; the latter is usually dictated by configuration considerations. A typical problem

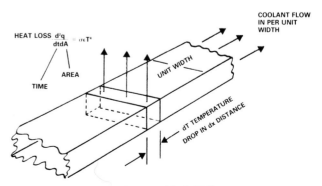

Figure 5.40 Radiator element with fluid flow.

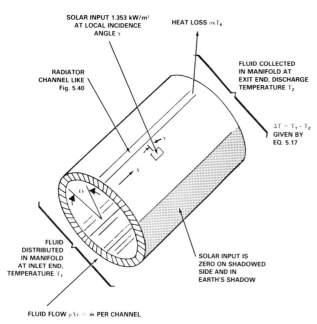

Figure 5.41 Cylindrical radiator module.

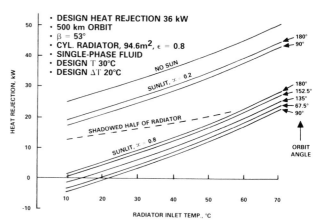

Figure 5.42 Thermal analysis results for cylindrical module radiator.

is illustrated in Figure 5.41. The solar input to any sunlit element of the radiator is, as before, proportional to sin(γ). The entire radiator is shadowed by the Earth for a portion of the orbit; in sunlight half of the radiator is on the shadowed half of the module. Radiator performance is estimated by a numerical integration of the form

$$AT = \int_0^{2\pi} \int_0^L \left[\frac{q_s \sin\left[\gamma(\theta)\right]\alpha - \sigma\epsilon \, T^4(x)}{\rho A v \, C_p} \right] dx d\theta \quad (5.14)$$

where

L is fluid channel length	α is solar absorptivity
q_s is solar input, kw/m²	T is temperature, varies with
γ is local solar elevation	x according to eq. 5.12
angle, varies with θ	ρAv is mass flow per channel
θ is radial angle around	C_p is fluid specific heat
the module	

and eq. 5.12 is used along the flow path. Figure 5.42 shows representative results. Each flow path along the radiator will have a different temperature output because of different thermal conditions. For Figure 5.42 it was assumed that all fluid is mixed in the output manifold.

The design thermal rejection was 36 kW with no Sun input, and inlet and outlet temperatures of 40 °C and 20 °C respectively. The delta T is proportional to the actual heat rejection. Radiator performance varies around the orbit as Sun aspect changes.

Radiator performance is only modestly degraded by Sun input with a good selective coating ($\alpha = 0.2$), but is severely degraded without one. Without a selective coating, one would be better off to use only the shaded half of the radiator. As the location of the shadow on the cylinder surface

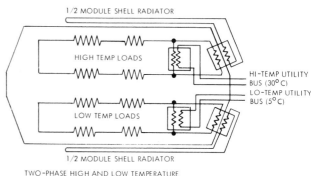

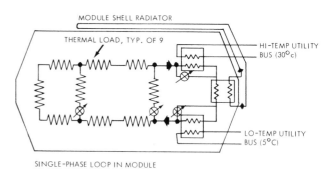

Figure 5.43 Thermal utility schematic diagram.

changes around the orbit, an "intelligent" control system would be needed.

Systems

Thermal control systems for space stations and platforms involve multiple variable loads, multiple loops, and multiple radiators. Ideally, one would like to utilize any radiator to contribute to handling any load. This implies a sophisticated "thermal utility" similar in topology to electric power or data systems. Figure 5.43 presents such a concept.

Pressurized modules use two thermal loops. Inside the module, the thermal fluid must be non-toxic and water is generally used. The radiator outside the module will at times experience temperatures below 0 °C and water would freeze. Hence a second fluid is used, usually a freon.

Heat exchangers are used between loops so that a leak in one loop will not cause loss of fluid except in that loop. Redundant loops are used for the pressurized modules. These loops share radiator panel area, so that either loop can reject nearly as much heat as both together in the event one fails or is shut down for maintenance. Single or two-phase loops may be used. Single-phase loops are simpler but require ordering of loads to match the temperature rise of the coolant fluid as heat is added. This complicates design and operations.

Guidance, Navigation, and Control

Guidance and navigation for a space station or platform is usually not a major challenge. The vehicle is in a stable orbit about the Earth and many tracking aids, including NORAD, TDRSS, and GPS, are available. For most purposes, high precision in orbit determination is not needed (there are exceptions for certain radar altimeter applications such as the planned TOPEX mission).

Control is another matter. The planned NASA space station will be more massive and much larger and more flexible than any spacecraft yet flown. Compensating for gravity gradients is a worry, as is attitude control of the large flexible structure.

Orbital Navigation and Guidance

Orbital parameters, formation flying, and ground tracks were discussed in Chapter 3. The problem of orbital navigation for a space station or platform is to determine the actual orbit path and its deviation from the planned or desired orbital path. Disturbing factors include higher-order Earth gravitational terms, effects of the Sun and Moon, and atmospheric drag.

The first-order secular orbit perturbations introduced by the oblateness of the Earth are considered a planned effect. Attempts to counter these effects (nodal regression, and advance of periapsis if the orbit is elliptical) would result in unacceptable propellant consumption. Continuous negation of nodal regression, for example, would accumulate a delta v equal to the orbital velocity in about three weeks.

Higher-order Earth gravitational effects and Sun-Moon effects cause perturbations mostly cyclic in nature. Drag, as discussed in Chapter 3, causes a monotonic orbital decay. The combined effects of these on orbital altitude are shown in Figure 5.44. It is important that an orbital guidance system not attempt to counteract the cyclic component of these effects; again, excess propellant consumption would occur. A guidance algorithm may either (1) employ an error band larger than the cyclic amplitude; (2) include simulation of the cyclic component so that it does not generate an error

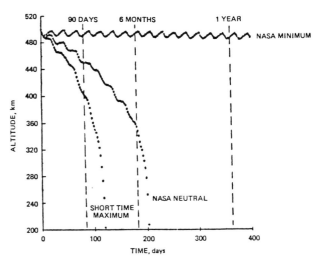

Figure 5.44 Orbit decay predictions showing effects of higher-order gravitational terms. *Courtesy of Boeing.*

signal; or (3) inhibit thrusting except when it is directed so as to increase the orbital energy.

Relative navigation will be needed to maintain a formation of free flyers, if that is required. Effects of differential drag were briefly discussed in Chapter 3. Formation flying may require sufficient precision to maintain a distance less than a certain amount between a space station and associated vehicles, as in cases where line-of-sight communications or rapid access from one to another, e.g., for service, is needed. Line-of-sight communications distance as a function of orbital altitude is shown in Figure 5.45. Access relative motion of 100 km per orbit (about 60 km per hour) is attainable at low enough delta v to be considered reasonable for an OMV. Access by an astronaut using an extravehicular maneuvering unit (EMU) as discussed in Chapter 6 will require relative distances on the order of a kilometer or less. Formation flying may need only to maintain accessibility delta v at low levels. When access time is not a critical factor, plane change dominates delta v; a representative requirement is to maintain the differential nodal angle less than 1°. As shown in Figure 5.46, the formation flying correction intervals will be on the order of months. The cyclic form of the along-track separation curves in the figure results from one spacecraft lapping the other by complete revolutions about the Earth. The space station will need onboard navigational capability to warn of collision hazards between co-orbiting objects, but much of the relative navigation workload can be delegated to ground support operations.

Attitude Control

Spacecraft body motions are described in terms of pitch, roll, and yaw motions as is the case for aircraft. If the spacecraft is Earth-oriented, the designation of pitch, roll, and yaw axes is based on the direction of flight along the

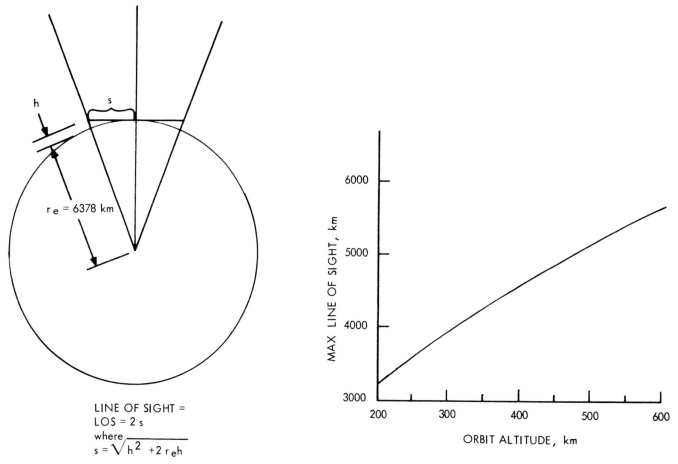

Figure 5.45 Line-of-sight distance.

orbit path, again like an aircraft, as shown in Figure 5.47. If the spacecraft is inertially or otherwise oriented, there is no fixed relation to the flight path and axis designations are selected on another basis, frequently designer's choice.

Conventional flight attitude strategies were discussed in Chapter 3. From the standpoint of the control engineer, the principal distinction is between inertial and Earth-oriented strategies. The inertial strategy for easiest control places two of the three spacecraft principal axes of inertia in the orbit plane with the third therefore perpendicular to the orbit plane (see Chapter 8 for a discussion of inertial properties). With the inertial axes so oriented, all the gravity gradient torques on the vehicle are cyclic in nature and can be counteracted by momentum storage devices. If less than two inertial axes are in the orbit plane, the vehicle will experience secular torques about the roll or yaw axes (or both), and dissipative devices such as thrusters or magnetic torquers will be required to counter the torques. Momentum storage devices may still be used up to their limit of storage capacity, but they must then be desaturated by a thruster or magnetic torquer.

Space stations are in a new regime of inertial properties magnitudes compared with earlier spacecraft because of

their large size and because inertial properties include length-squared terms. A "reasonably well-balanced" space station will have differences of inertias among the three axes of a few millions of kg-m, and if the principal axes of inertia are not aligned with the geometric axes, inertial cross products also of a million or more. (Torque equations were given in Chapter 3.) The largest available momentum storage devices are improvements of control moment gyros developed for the Skylab space station program. They have a capacity of about 4000 N-m-sec per axis. The acceptability of inertial imbalance and control requirements can be evaluated by how many such devices are needed to control a vehicle.

Figure 5.48 shows the number of momentum management devices (MMDs) per axis needed to control cyclic torques as a function of inertial differences, for inertial orientation. Secular torques, as mentioned, require desaturation and the key parameter is the frequency of desaturation; this is shown shown in Figure 5.49.

Aerodynamic drag also creates torques if the center of aerodynamic drag pressure is not aligned with the center of gravity along the orbit path. (There is no lift force in orbit regardless of shape or orientation.) Drag torques tend to be

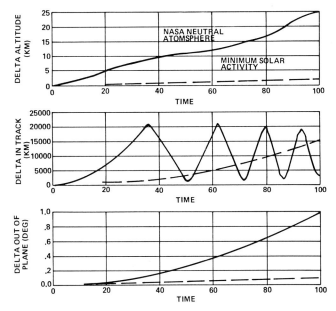

Figure 5.46 Relative motion due to differential orbit decay for platform and space station. *Courtesy of Boeing.*

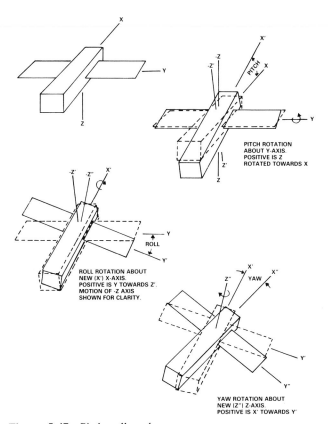

Figure 5.47 Pitch, roll, and yaw axes.

small compared to gravity gradient torques. Drag torques are cyclic for inertially oriented vehicles but can have a secular pitch component for Earth-oriented ones. A practical Earth-oriented flight strategy is one that offsets drag pitch torque with a pitch attitude bias that generates a gravity

gradient torque that compensates the average drag torque. Because the drag torque is not constant due to day-night air density differences, MMDs must be used to average out the peak values.

Flight in an Earth-oriented mode usually employs a zero average torque strategy such as alluded to above. Attitude bias compensates for configuration asymmetries to maintain two of the principal axes in the orbit plane; the third is either vertical or biased as noted to counter aero torque.

Figure 5.50 summarizes attitude control strategies for inertially and Earth-oriented vehicles. The figure also illustrates a representative configuration asymmetry and its resulting inertial imbalance.

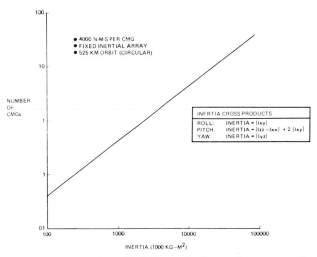

Figure 5.48 Number of MMDs required per axis due to cyclic gravity gradient torque. *Courtesy of Boeing.*

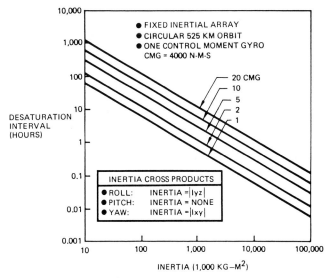

Figure 5.49 Desaturation interval per axis due to gravity gradient torques resulting in secular momenta. *Courtesy of Boeing.*

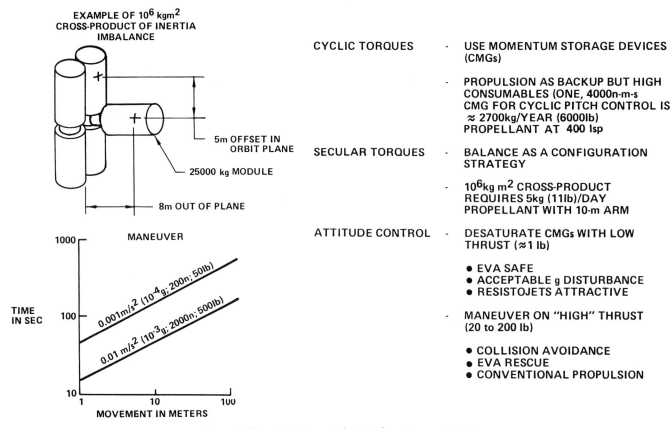

Figure 5.50 Attitude control strategies. *Courtesy of Boeing.*

Control Devices

Control devices include (angular) momentum management devices (MMDs), magnetic torquers, and thrusters. Momentum management devices are rotating wheels that store angular momentum. The exchange of momentum between the wheel(s) and the space vehicle is achieved by changes in wheel speed (inertia wheel) or by changing the angle between the spin axes of a pair of wheels—the control moment gyro (CMG). Figure 5.51 illustrates a typically large CMG.

Magnetic torquers are made in a range of sizes. They interact with the Earth's magnetic field to generate a net attitude torque and have been used as a primary means of spacecraft control for years. Some spacecraft have had no other means of attitude control. Figure 5.52 shows a few representative magnetic torquer sizes. The largest ones presently available are able to exert a torque slightly less than 0.1 N-m.

Control Laws

Attitude control devices must be commanded by a control system. The control system senses attitude error and sends commands to the control devices to correct the error. Rough attitude sensing can be accomplished in Earth orbit by horizon sensors and Sun sensors that report the angular location of the Earth's horizon and the Sun relative to the spacecraft

attitude. The precision is a modest fraction of a degree (the horizon is indistinct and the Sun subtends an angle of about half a degree), but this is adequate for many purposes. More accurate sensing is accomplished by star scanners or mappers, usually in concert with inertial measurement units (IMUs) employing gyro devices.

The simplest imaginable control system is one which senses attitude error and generates a correcting force proportional to the error. The differential equation for such a system, however, is second order without damping and the system will act as an oscillator. This can be prevented by adding rate damping, sensing the rate of attitude motion and adding a proportional correction term that opposes it. The system will be stable, but if there is a perturbing force on the system, this law will result in a residual error proportional to the perturbing force divided by the system gain. A further term that generates a correction by integrating on the residual error will suppress it. If the perturbing force is variable, more complex laws may be necessary.

Control/Structural Dynamics

The above description of simple control laws assumes that the system to be controlled has no internal dynamics. Space stations and platforms, however, are large flexible structures with numerous internal dynamic modes. These can interact with control system dynamics to cause divergent control system instabilities.

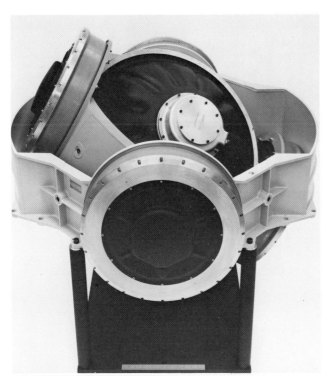

Figure 5.51 Large control moment gyro (CMG).

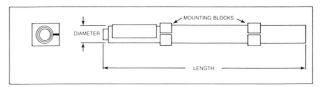

Dipole Moment [Am²]		Size [cm]		Weight [kg]	Power* [w]	
Linearity				Includes mounting	Linearity	
1%	20%	Length	Diameter	blocks†	1%	20%
10	15	40	1.8	0.4†	0.6	1.0
15	20	45	1.8	0.5†	0.6	1.5
20	30	49	1.9	0.6†	0.7	1.7
30	50	56	2.1	0.9†	0.7	1.8
60	85	64	2.6	1.7†	0.8	2.0
100	150	72	3.6	2.8	1.1	2.7
150	250	84	3.8	3.2	1.3	3.5
250	350	104	4.3	6.2	1.8	4.4
350	500	115	4.7	8.3	2.1	5.0
500	700	130	5.0	11.1	2.3	5.5
1,250	1,750	200	5.3	18.5	3.3	7.6
2,900	4,000	250	7.6	49.9	6.0	16.0

1 Ampere meter²   1000 p-cm   *When a single winding is used, power doubles

Figure 5.52 Typical torque rod sizing information. *Courtesy of Ithaco, Inc.*

Traditional aerospace experience with this problem comes from rocket vehicle practice. In these vehicles, the attitude sensor package is typically in the nose and the attitude control actuator is typically the rocket propulsion system aft.

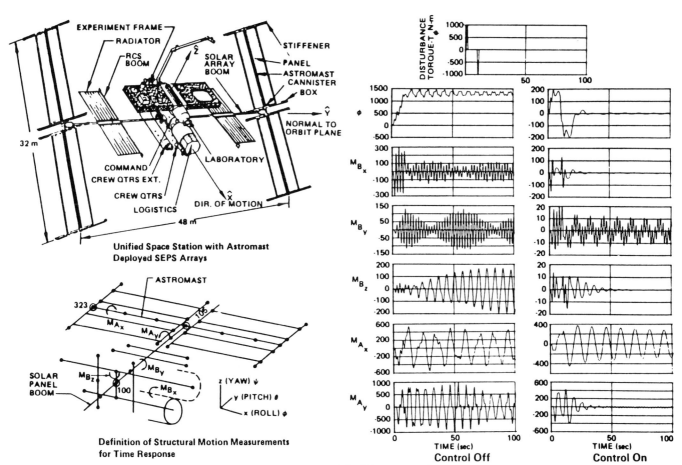

Figure 5.53 Structures/dynamic simulation of flexible space station structure. *Courtesy of Boeing.*

All the structural dynamics of the vehicle are interposed between the sensors and the actuators. If the control system can respond in the dynamic frequency range of the structure, instability is almost sure to occur.

A space station may be designed with the sensors, e.g., an IMU, and the actuators, e.g., CMGs, structurally coupled very tightly so that the flexible body dynamics are outside the control loops. Such systems are stable. Simulations of flexible space stations as shown in Figure 5.53 have demonstrated that most of the dynamic modes introduced by disturbances can be controlled. In a typical complex structural situation, some of the modes will be weakly coupled to the control system, and as illustrated in the figure, will be poorly damped. If the system includes control effectors such as thrusters that are on extremities and thus not tightly coupled to the attitude sensors, due caution must be applied.

Propulsion

Space stations and platforms need propulsion to maintain orbital altitude unless some other means is to be used, such as reboost with a separate vehicle like an OMV or the Shuttle itself. Orbit lifetime can range from a few months for periods of high solar activity to a few years for low activity. The Skylab had no reboost propulsion and its orbit decayed in 1980 after seven years despite efforts to fly it in a minimum-drag attitude. The Space Telescope, a free flyer, has no propulsion and present plans are to reboost it with the Space Shuttle until the OMV becomes available, eventually evolving to reboost by a space station-based OMV. Recent space station design studies have uniformly included a propulsion system for orbit reboost and for attitude control system desaturation. Requirements have also been identified for limited maneuver capability. Loss of control of a nearby free flyer or vehicle could cause it to be on a collision course. In such an event, the space station needs collision avoidance capability. Since motions of nearby vehicles will always be at low relative velocities, many minutes would be available for avoidance and the thrust levels needed are similar to those derived for other space station uses. Some scenarios also involve maneuvering the entire space station for EVA rescue in the event of a broken tether or other failure.

Propulsion Requirements

Two basic options, "high" and "low" thrust, exist for space station propulsion. The high thrust option is low by almost any other standard, but infers enough thrust that the time needed for reboost and desaturation is very short compared to space station operations, i.e., a duty cycle less than 10 percent. High thrust also infers enough acceleration to disrupt certain space station missions, i.e., more than 10^{-5} g; low thrust is taken to mean accelerations less than this. Since a typical space station mass is on the order of 100,000 kg, the distinction between low and high thrust is usually made at about 10 newtons (2 lbf). Accelerations for

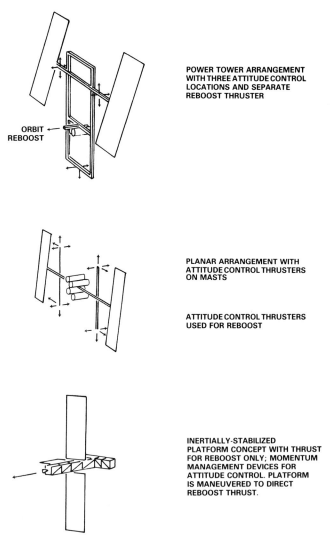

POWER TOWER ARRANGEMENT WITH THREE ATTITUDE CONTROL LOCATIONS AND SEPARATE REBOOST THRUSTER

ORBIT REBOOST

PLANAR ARRANGEMENT WITH ATTITUDE CONTROL THRUSTERS ON MASTS

ATTITUDE CONTROL THRUSTERS USED FOR REBOOST

INERTIALLY-STABILIZED PLATFORM CONCEPT WITH THRUST FOR REBOOST ONLY; MOMENTUM MANAGEMENT DEVICES FOR ATTITUDE CONTROL. PLATFORM IS MANEUVERED TO DIRECT REBOOST THRUST.

Figure 5.54 Typical space station propulsion installations. *Courtesy of Boeing.*

maneuver are typically 10^{-3} g, requiring about 10^3 newtons (200 lbf) thrust. End-of-life disposal of a space station by controlled reentry has been imposed as a requirement in some studies. Depending on the allowed Earth impact footprint, thrust up to 5000 newtons (1000 lbf) might be needed.

Desaturation of momentum management devices requires thrusters to be offset from the space station center of gravity (CG) in order to provide a moment arm for application of torques. Typical offsets are illustrated in Figure 5.54, and provide pitch, roll, and yaw torque couples. By applying thrust from suitably located thrusters in the posigrade (path of flight) direction only, attitude control thrust can be used for simultaneous reboost. Since desaturation must be accomplished on frequent intervals (Figure 5.49, previous section), combined reboost and desaturation demands use of low thrust to avoid frequent disruption of space station missions. The impulse requirements for these two purposes are similar as illustrated in Figure 5.55, thus combining the functions offers the potential for reducing total propellant

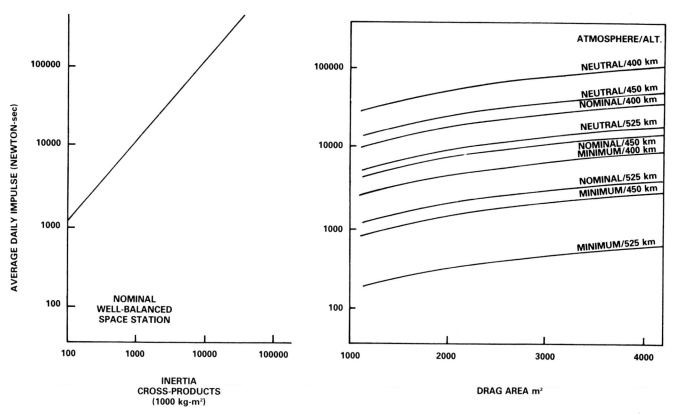

Figure 5.55 Impulse requirements for drag and desaturation.

consumption while simplifying control system logic as compared with the use of magnetic torquers for desaturation. Most of the reboost propulsion effort, in this case, will be applied by low thrust propulsion. The needed duty cycle will operate thrusters for hundreds to thousands of hours per year, raising a thruster lifetime issue.

Present indications are that both high and low thrust capabilities are needed for space stations. The maneuver requirements that dictate high thrust capability for space stations do not appear to apply to platforms, thus low thrust systems are likely to suffice. Propulsion requirements as presently understood are summarized in Table 5.6. Although the requirements are somewhat diverse, the same types of propulsion systems seem applicable to all.

Examination of space station and platform servicing strategies reveals little in the way of special propulsion requirements. The normal servicing strategy for a space station is simply to fly the Space Shuttle to the space station, exchange a resupply (logistics) module carrying supplies, and exchange crew members as required. If the space station is at greater than about 370 km altitude, the Shuttle's direct insertion flight mode must be used, but this presents no identified difficulties.

Alternative strategies include flying the space station down to a servicing altitude compatible with Shuttle normal insertion operations or using an OMV to deliver the resupply module from Shuttle altitude to the space station altitude.

Space station fly-down can be accomplished in less than one day, assuming the space station has an acceleration capability of 10^{-3} g or greater, but will consume thousands of kilograms of propellant otherwise not needed. The OMV mode requires that the resupply module be habitable for crew exchange. A degree of habitability may be imposed on this module for other reasons, depending on the crew safe-haven design approach selected. The OMV mode is also operationally more complex; at present there is no evident reason to select either of these alternative strategies.

Servicing of co-orbiting platforms from a space station requires that they fly formation with the space station as previously discussed. Analyses of servicing operations have not identified any unique requirements on propulsion systems.

Propulsion Systems

A wide variety of propulsion systems could be applied to space stations and platforms, ranging from cold gas jetted through nozzles to exotic electric systems. Table 5.7 presents a summary of applicable and inapplicable systems with rationale for excluding the inapplicable. Propellant resupply requirements are of course inversely proportional to specific impulse, but as shown in Figure 5.56, the resupply requirement over multiyear periods is in any case modest, and striving for very high I_{sp} to reduce resupply requirements is not warranted.

Table 5.6 Propulsion requirements and design considerations. *Courtesy of Boeing.*

ITEM	SPACE STATION	FREE FLYERS	SCIENCE PLATFORMS		COM'L PLATFORMS
CONFIGURATION	HIGHLY VARIABLE WITH TIME	FIXED	SOME VARIATION		FIXED
POWER LEVEL	>100 kWe	<10kWe	10-20 kWe		~ 50 kWe; MISSION DEPENDENT
M/CdA (kg/m²)	50	100-200	100		25
LIFETIME @ 500 km (NASA NEUTRAL)	200 DAYS	300-500 DAYS	300 DAYS		150 DAYS
EC/LS BYPRODUCTS	AVAILABLE	NOT AVAILABLE	NOT AVAILABLE		NOT AVAILABLE
EFFLUENT CONTAMINATION SENSITIVITY	HIGH	VERY HIGH	HIGH TO VERY HIGH		MODERATE
ORBIT	28½°/500 km	28½°/500 km	28½°/500 km	97°/600-900 km	28½°/500 km
FLIGHT MODE	EARTH OR INERTIAL	INERTIAL/POINT	INERTIAL	EARTH	DON'T CARE
G DISTURBANCE TOLERANCE	INFREQUENT	FREQUENT OK IF SHORT DURATION	FREQUENT/ SHORT	TRIMMED ORBIT	INFREQUENT
SERVICE MODE	SELF	RETURN TO STATION	RETURN TO STATION	SHUTTLE/OMV	STATION/OMV OR RETURN TO EARTH
THRUST LEVEL	HI + LOW	HIGH OR NONE	HIGH OR NONE	LOW	LOW
PROP. INST'L	DISTRIBUTED	CENTRAL OR NONE	CENTRAL OR NONE	CENTRAL	CENTRAL

Table 5.7 Space station propulsion options. *Courtesy of Boeing.*

Included:

Cold Gas:	H_2; N_2; CO_2
Monopropellant:	N_2H_4 (Hydrazine)
Resistojet:	N_2H_4 (Post-Heat); H_2 (Cold Gas Optional Mode); NH_3; CO_2
Arcjets:	CO_2; N_2H_4; H_2: NH_3
Biopropellants:	N_2O_4/MMH; N_2O_4/N_2H_4; O_2/H_2 (Gas Supply); O_2/H_2 (Cryo Supply, Gas Feed)
Compressors:	Assumed where needed

Not Included:

Solid Propellants:	Too Inflexible
Turbopumped Systems:	Complex, High Risk, High Cost, Little Benefit
Ion/Plasma Propulsion:	High Power, No Need For Such High Isp
Electrodynamic Tether:	Insufficient Data But Needs Future Evaluation
Nuclear Propulsion:	Radiation Problems and Complexity Outweigh Any Potential Benefits

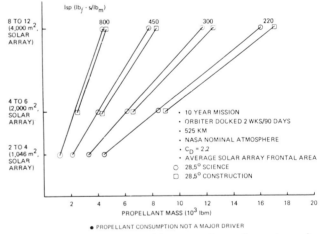

Figure 5.56 Ten-year propulsion resupply requirements resulting from aerodynamic drag. *Courtesy of Boeing.*

When pressurization options are combined with system options and various propellants, many possibilities result. Table 5.8 summarizes characteristics for 36 possible sys-

tems. These were analyzed for space station application in a recent study.

Figures of merit for selection include resupply mass, resupply volume, state of technology, and factors such as safety, reliability, and lifetime. Calculation of resupply mass and volume can be carried out as indicated in Figure 5.57. These calculations presume resupply is included in Shuttle operations for space station logistics; methods given for mass and volume calculations are applicable to estimating Shuttle payload charges. Results of such calculations

Table 5.8 Summary of propulsion options surveyed for space station application.

System Type	Pressurization Type	Fuel	Fuel Density kg/m³	Oxidizer	Oxidizer Density kg/m³	ISP (Sec)	Mixture Ratio O/F
Cold Gas	Gas Stor	H_2 Gas				228	
Cold Gas	Gas Stor	N_2 Gas				60	
Cold Gas	LV Press	CO_2 Liq	770.			49	
Monoprop	Blowdown	Hydrazin	1008.			230	
Monoprop	HE Press	Hydrazin	1008.			230	
Biprop	Gas Stor	H_2 Gas		O_2 Gas		400	5.0
Biprop	Gas Stor	H_2 Gas		O_2 Gas		380	7.0
Biprop	Cryogen	H_2 Liq	70.	O_2 Liq	1140.	400	5.0
Biprop	Cryogen	H_2 Liq	70.	O_2 Liq	1140.	380	7.0
Biprop	HE Press	MMH	876.	N_2O_4	1446.	285	2.2
Biprop	Blowdown	MMH	876.	N_2O_4	1446.	285	2.2
Res.-Jet	Cryogen	H_2 Liq	70.			800	
Res.-Jet	Gas Stor	H_2 Gas				800	
Res.-Jet	HE Press	Ammonia	618.			280	
Res.-Jet	LV Press	Ammonia	618.			280	
Res.-Jet	Blowdown	Ammonia	618.			280	
Res.-Jet	Gas Stor	Methane	372.			285	
Res.-Jet	Cryogen	Methane	372.			285	
Res.-Jet	HE Press	Hydrazin	1008.			280	
Res.-Jet	Blowdown	Hydrazin	1008.			280	
Res.-Jet	HE Press	CO_2 Liq	770.			120	
Res.-Jet	LV Press	CO_2 Liq	770.			120	
Res.-Jet	Blowdown	CO_2 Liq	770.			120	
Res.-Jet	HE Press	Water	1000.			350	
Res.-Jet	Blowdown	Water	1000.			350	
Arcjet	Cryogen	H_2 Liq	70.			1200	
Arcjet	Gas Stor	H_2 Gas				1200	
Arcjet	HE Press	Ammonia	618.			450	
Arcjet	LV Press	Ammonia	618.			450	
Arcjet	Blowdown	Ammonia	618.			450	
Arcjet	Gas Stor	Methane	372.			500	
Arcjet	Cryogen	Methane	372.			500	
Arcjet	HE Press	Hydrazin	1008.			450	
Arcjet	Blowdown	Hydrazin	1008.			450	
Arcjet	HE Press	Water	1000.			400	
Arcjet	Blowdown	Water	1000.			400	

HE = Helium
LV = Liquid Vapor Pressure

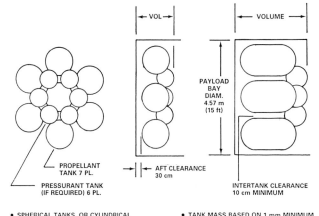

- SPHERICAL TANKS, OR CYLINDRICAL TANKS WITH SPHERICAL ENDS IF ADDITIONAL VOLUME REQUIRED
- PRESSURANT TANKS FOR HELIUM PRESSURIZED CASES ONLY
- GASEOUS PROPELLANTS USE 100% OF TANK VOLUME: CRYOGENICS, HELIUM PRESSURIZED AND LIQUID CO_2, 90%; BLOWDOWN, 50%

- TANK MASS BASED ON 1 mm MINIMUM GAUGE, OR STRENGTH DESIGN, WHICHEVER IS HEAVIEST, + 20% FOR PLUMBING
- SUPPORT STRUCTURE ASSUMED 20% OF LOADED TANKS MASS

Figure 5.57 Method for calculating masses and volumes.

communications satellite use; the resistojet electric heater is used to increase the temperature of the decomposition product gas exiting from the catalyst bed, thus raising the I_{sp} from about 225 to about 280 seconds.

Bipropellants such as hydrogen-oxygen present a thruster lifetime problem in a low-thrust mode. The state of the art for lifetime is 5 to 15 hours, compared to hundreds of hours required. Longer life may be obtained by operating at lower pressure, through sacrificing performance, or perhaps through novel design. Hydrazine thrusters and hydrogen resistojets have been operated experimentally for hundreds of hours; neither device has been flight qualified for such durations.

Representative propulsion system schematics are depicted in Figure 5.59. Thruster sizing relations are presented in Figure 5.60. Thrusters for space stations and platforms will be small, not exhibiting significant mass or configuration impact.

The resupply of cryogenic systems will probably employ cryogenic tankage installed on the resupply module, connected in orbit to the propulsion feed system through umbilicals. Because hydrazine and N_2O_4 require temperature control within strict limits, systems employing these propellants will probably be resupplied through exchangeable modules. These modules will be installed at each location where thrust is required and will consist of complete propulsion units including propellant supply, control valves, thermal control, and thrusters. This approach for the latter systems is facilitated by their relatively small volume.

Data Management

Data management is a term applied to all digital processing of data on a space station or platform from digital handling

are presented in Figure 5.58 in bar chart form, for a daily impulse requirement of 50,000 N-sec (about 11,200 lbf-sec). This is as large a requirement as likely. Those systems with so large a storage volume as to incur a Shuttle payload charge for volume rather than mass are indicated. It is clear that the resupply requirements for a variety of rather conventional propulsion systems are reasonable.

Selection of propulsion systems for space stations is presently concentrating on hydrazine monopropellant, oxygen-hydrogen bipropellant with cryogenic storage, and resistojets. A cold gas system for low-contamination operation may also be selected. Hydrogen-oxygen systems can operate in a hydrogen cold or warm gas mode and in a resistojet mode. Hydrazine resistojets have been flight qualified for

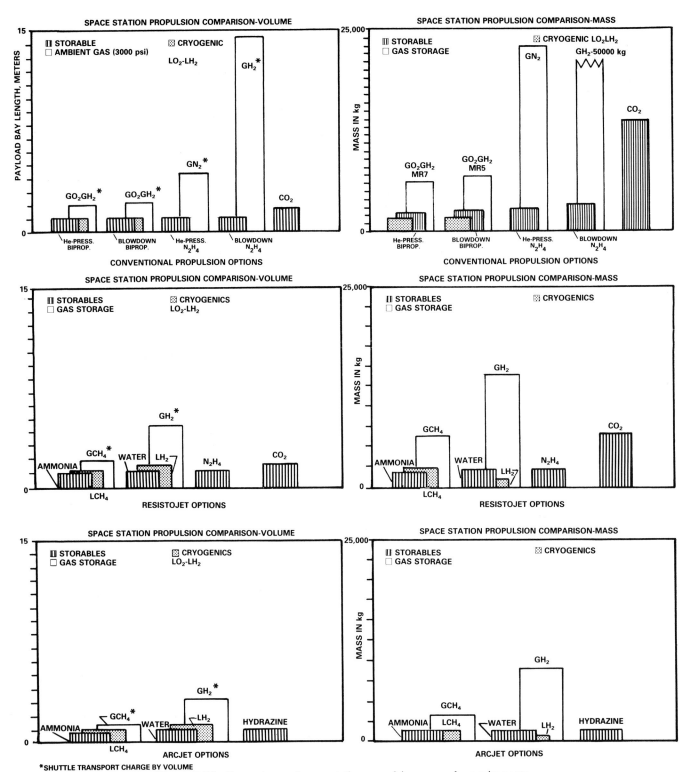

Figure 5.58 Comparisons of space station propulsion, resupply requirements.

of mission data to the application of automation, artificial intelligence, and robotics to space station operations. Data management includes both hardware, e.g., computers, and software. The two principal functions are (1) acquiring and handling of mission data and (2) data processing and computing associated with managing and operating the space

station or platform itself. The latter function includes all operator/system interfaces (OSIs) such as controls and displays for crew use. The former is driven by the need to throughput high data rates and to tag, partition, protect, record, and distribute user data in accordance with diverse user needs, while the latter is driven by multiple complex

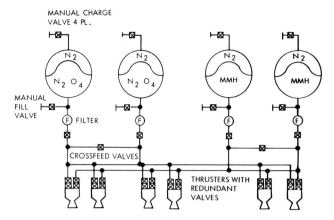

BIPROPELLANT BLOWDOWN SYSTEM. DESIGNED AS MODULAR UNITS TO BE INSTALLED AT EACH PROPULSION LOCATION. EACH THRUSTER PAIR PROVIDES REDUNDANCY. MODULES MAY USE UP TO FIVE THRUSTER PAIRS.

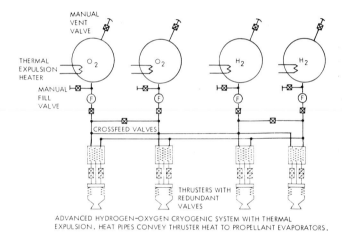

ADVANCED HYDROGEN-OXYGEN CRYOGENIC SYSTEM WITH THERMAL EXPULSION. HEAT PIPES CONVEY THRUSTER HEAT TO PROPELLANT EVAPORATORS.

Figure 5.59 Representative propulsion system schematics. *Courtesy of Boeing.*

interconnects between subsystems, communications, and OSIs, and the provision of space station or platform autonomy. These principal functions may be implemented in separate, partially integrated, or fully integrated systems. Figure 5.61 shows an early partition of space station operational data management functions. The figure does not imply a particular hardware or software architecture.

The term *architecture* is often applied to data management systems. The meaning is different than the traditional meaning applied to buildings, etc., and implies a description of how a system is organized and how it works. What the system looks like, i.e., how it is connected together, is often referred to as topology.

Distributed Systems

Distributed systems are networks of computing devices interconnected by data buses. Distributed systems may be as loosely connected as the Arpanet, a nationwide network that connects hundreds of computers for data communications, or as tightly coupled as an array of processors op-

erating in synchronized lockstep, processing data for which neighboring processors must exchange data for nearly every computational step.

Space systems have, until recently, relied mainly on centralized systems where all data processing is performed in one computer. Early steps toward distributed systems can be recognized in use of remote aquisition units for multiplexing instrumentation. Recent systems like the Space Shuttle and the IUS have employed a form of distributed system for redundancy, i.e., more than one computer doing the same job. Subsystems now are often designed with built-in microprocessors performing local control functions. The Space Shuttle main engine is an example of this. Present plans for space stations and platforms go much further, aiming for as throrough a distribution of computational effort as possible, even down to the individual subsystems. Sharing or reassigning computational assignments will also be done in order to level the workload. This is particularly critical when taking over essential functions from failed equipment.

Distributed systems are interconnected by data buses. The cable that connects a small computer to a printer or modem is a simple data bus. It operates on a particular protocol, e.g., RS-232; the protocol specifies the way devices connected to the bus are to communicate. Other aspects of the protocol, not bus-specific in the RS-232 case, are the ways in which the devices on the bus establish readiness to communicate. The computer, for example, queries the modem whether it is ready to transmit or receive, and queries the printer whether its buffer can accept more data.

More complex buses, i.e., those with many devices attached, use more complex protocols. Ethernet uses a collision-detection scheme. It is assumed that most of the time the bus is not busy. Whenever a device on the bus wants to send to another device, it puts the proper address on the message and launches it onto the bus. It then listens for the period of time needed for its message to reach the destination. If another message is received during this time, a collision (two messages on the bus at the same time) has occurred, and the original sender resends. Clearly, if the bus were heavily used, this protocol could lead to traffic jams.

Another protocol concept is the token passing ring. Bus access is controlled by a token (a digital sequence) which circulates about the ring. A station having a packet of data to transmit seizes the token and sends the packet. The token is then sent along to the next station on the bus.

Performance of these two protocols is compared in Figure 5.62. The collision scheme is slightly better for light traffic and is a little simpler. Token passing performs significantly better with heavy traffic.

Another protocol involves a multiply connected bus structure of somewhat arbitrary topology. Each station is pro-

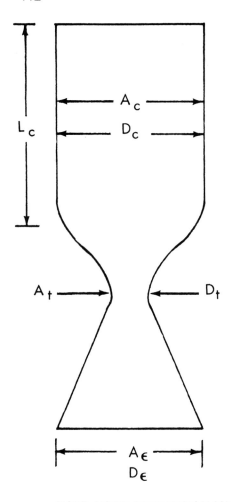

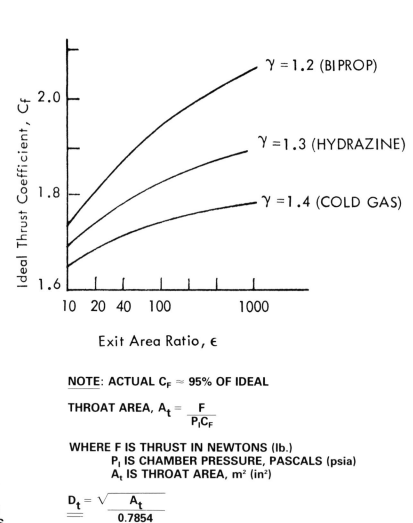

NOTE: NOZZLE EXPANSION ANGLE IS
USUALLY 15° IF CONICAL: MOST
NOZZLES USE A COMPOUND CURVE
COMPUTED BY NUMERICAL METHODS
FOR SUPERSONIC FLOW.

NOTE: ACTUAL $C_F \approx$ 95% OF IDEAL

THROAT AREA, $A_t = \dfrac{F}{P_1 C_F}$

WHERE F IS THRUST IN NEWTONS (lb.)
P$_1$ IS CHAMBER PRESSURE, PASCALS (psia)
A_t IS THROAT AREA, m^2 (in^2)

$D_t = \sqrt{\dfrac{A_t}{0.7854}}$

$A_\epsilon = \epsilon\, A_t$ WHERE ϵ IS AREA RATIO,
        TYPICALLY RANGES 40 TO 200.

$A_c = \dfrac{A_c/A_t}{A_t}$; $\dfrac{A_c}{A_t}$ TYPICALLY RANGES
        4 TO 20 FOR SMALL THRUSTERS.

$L_c = \dfrac{L^*}{A_c/A_t}$; L* IS AN EMPIRICAL PARAMETER,
        TYPICALLY 0.5 m (20 in.) FOR O$_2$ - H$_2$,
        1 TO 1.5 m FOR BIPROPS.

Figure 5.60 Thruster sizing relationships.

grammed to know the route structure (this implies that it can be reprogrammed if the route structure is changed or extended). Data packets are sent on the most direct route to distant stations. Each station along the way has store and forward capability.

If a station knows that a particular neighbor station is not working, it can select an alternate route. This is a much more complex protocol, but one very amenable to modifi-

cation and growth, which is why something like it is used for large telephone networks.

These protocols have a common feature in not being dependent on a centralized controller. Many protocols do operate with central controllers, but are subject to total shutdown if the controller fails.

Attempts to make protocols universal and not hardware-dependent except at the lowest levels have become quite

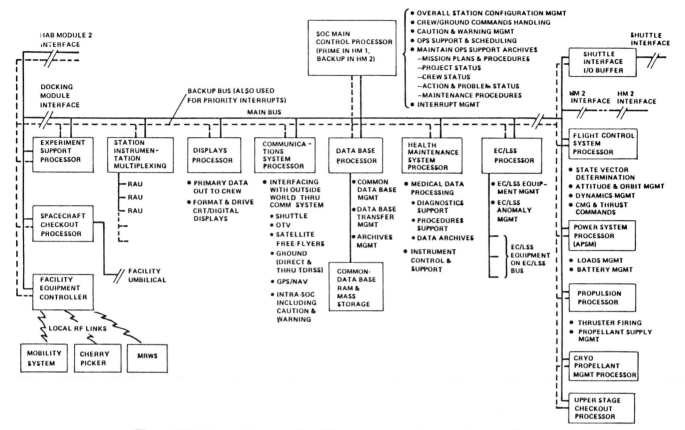

Figure 5.61 Space station operational data management functions. *Courtesy of Boeing.*

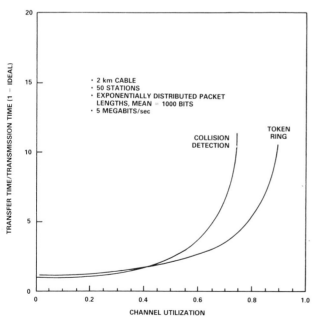

Figure 5.62 Data transmission protocol comparison. *Courtesy of Boeing.*

sophisticated. The International Standards Organization (ISO) has proposed an Open Systems Interconnect (OSI) standard for networks. The concept of this standard is illustrated in Figure 5.63. The intent of this standard is to

make the details of implementation transparent, so that users need only know the upper levels of the protocol to use it. NASA plans to adopt this standard for the space station end-to-end data system. If entirely successful, experimenters will be able to access their experiments onboard the space station, for certain aspects of experiment control and for data acquisition, through commercial computer networks. Security measures will prevent unauthorized access and intercept potentially hazardous commands.

Selection of bus structures goes along with selection of protocols. Again, there are many choices. Representative ones are shown in Figure 5.64; key advantages and disadvantages are summarized in the figure.

Buses themselves may use twisted wire pairs, coaxial cable, or fiber optics. Twisted pairs use very low impedances to reduce interference and are best suited for short runs and low data rates, up to a few megabits per second. Coaxial cables are Faraday shielded and are well suited up to 10 or more megabits. Fiber-optic strands carry data in the form of modulated light and are entirely immune to electromagnetic interference since they are glass and do not conduct electricity. The maximum possible data rate for fiber optics is not known (it is presently limited by the capabilities of the devices connected to the cables), but is certainly in the multi-gigabit range. Light signals are

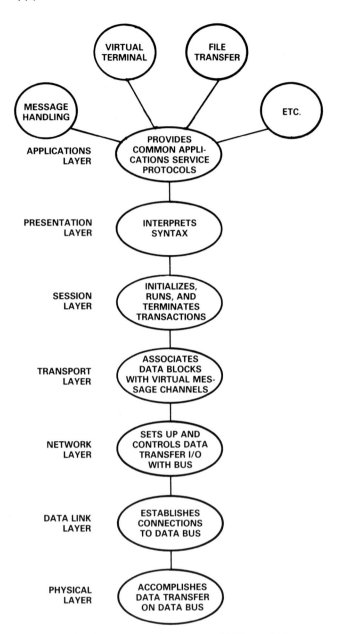

Figure 5.63 Open systems interconnect (OSI) standard.

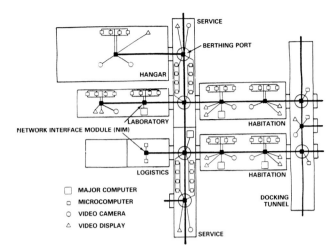

Figure 5.64 Representative bus structures. *Courtesy of Boeing.*

launched onto fiber optics by light emitting diodes or lasers and reconverted to electrical signals at the other end by photodiodes or similar devices. The present technology trend is to go to fiber optics for all but low data rate, short distance applications.

Software and Languages

As the cost of computing hardware has dropped dramatically over the past decade, the cost of software has come increasingly to dominate data management systems cost. Space systems have used assembler as well as high-level languages, but until recently, most space system computer programming has been assembler code. The Shuttle program pioneered the use of a high-level language and actually de-

veloped its own compiler, HAL-S. (The Shuttle needed a compiler that would support multitasking and a suitable one was not available.)

Assembler language has a one-to-one correspondence with machine instructions but uses mnemonics (words or character strings that convey an idea) rather than the numeric instructions of actual machine code. Words or character strings are also used as variables to refer to memory locations so that the programmer does not need to remember numerical addresses. Assembler language is still used for programming applications where complete access to all machine instructions is needed. This is true, for example, for some operating system and intermachine communications functions. (An operating system controls basic system operation like peripheral I/O and interrupt handling.) Intermediate-level languages like ''C'' provide the capabilities of an assembler with some of the convenience of a high-level language. ''C'' has been widely used to write operating systems.

Most high-level languages adopt a mathematics-like logic structure and syntax, as do Fortran, Basic, Pascal, etc. Some, like Lisp, have adopted structures amenable to symbolic logic. Cobol, designed for the business-oriented programmer, has an accounting-like structure.

High-level languages vastly improved programmer productivity for small programs and led to programs of great complexity. As complexity grew, productivity fell. The effort to successfully complete a program became nearly all devoted to design, test and verification, and debugging, and the advantages of high-level languages diminished. This problem has been attacked with some success by structured programming.

Before structured programming, programming styles were haphazard and often not directed at all toward readable, understandable code. Routines were many pages long, sparsely if at all commented, and made liberal use of intertwined "GO TOs". Some programmers seemed to impute the "encryption" attribute to the word "code" and wrote their programs accordingly.

Structured programming demands the use of short routines (thus many topical subroutines; the usual rule is that each subroutine serves only one basic purpose), liberal commenting, and declaration and explanation of all variables. It outlaws use of structures like "spaghetti code" that make logic difficult to follow.

The Department of Defense has recently issued a specification for a high-level language named Ada. Ada is designed for structured programming, and will include a comprehensive software development environment including analysis aids, editors, compilers, debuggers, libraries of standard routines, and test systems. Efforts are being made to develop automated code generation for commonly used procedures. Present NASA plans for space stations and platforms are not finalized, but it is virtually certain that the NASA space station will adopt Ada as the standard systems programming language.

Early high-level languages like Fortran and Basic have no provisions for multitasking; even recent languages do not have adequate facilities for communications among elements of a distributed processing system. Ada is designed specifically for distributed applications and will be all but a necessity for the space station if the planned distributed system is implemented.

Automation, Autonomy, and Robotics

Space platforms will be automated for normal operations and infrequently visited by human crews either via the Space Shuttle or from a space station. Crew visits will accomplish servicing functions not practical to automate, such as repair or installation of new equipment or instruments. Although space stations will be designed for continuous human presence, they may function in a man-tended mode part of the time, such as before enough habitation facilities are present for continuous occupancy. For this reason, and because crew time at a space station will be a valuable commodity, that which can be accomplished through automation and robotics probably will be.

Automation

Automation is often mentioned in the context of autonomy, artificial intelligence, and robotics. Automation was a subject of the prior section. When combined with the other terms it implies advanced techniques compared with usual space systems.

Autonomy

Autonomy is an important objective of the space station program. Autonomy means, in this case, freedom from dependence on ground-based mission control activities. Ide-

ally, the space station should be able to function independently of the ground except for resupply operations. This ideal will never be reached entirely, as it will always be cost-effective to provide some support functions from the ground. The practical objective is to alter ground-based operations from mission control to mission assistance and advice, and to reduce the numbers of people engaged in such activities from hundreds to a few.

Present-day spacecraft are far from autonomous, even if human crews are not present aboard. The most nearly autonomous spacecraft ever built are the outer planet Voyagers. They demanded a high degree of autonomy because the communications delays for instructions from Earth run into hours; moment-by-moment management of the spacecraft is not possible.

When the Space Shuttle flies, a large complement of mission controllers monitors the flight, plans crew activities, and provides consultation to the crews on subsystems management and handling of anomalies and emergencies. Aircraft of comparable complexity, however, are flown entirely by the crew onboard. Ground assistance is confined to navigation and traffic control.

The most important steps toward autonomy for the space station will be to provide sufficient automated intelligence onboard so that subsystems management need not rely on ground aids, and to provide onboard aids for day-to-day mission and activities planning. Fundamental techniques for these aids fall into the artificial intelligence field of expert systems, i.e., software systems that mimic the thinking behavior of human experts in solving problems in particular restricted fields of knowledge. Expert systems have been successfully developed for medical diagnosis and for certain battle management applications; these are as complex and difficult as the desired use on a space station. Concepts for comprehensive subsystems management are in an early state of development. One idea for a "housekeeping controller" is illustrated in Figure 5.65. This controller would coordinate the operation of the subsytems most concerned with the flow of energy through the space station, i.e., electrical power, EC/LS, and thermal control. It would operate in a supervisory role, interacting with the crew and directing operation of the subsystems. Each of the latter would include embedded automation for control of subsystem internal operation.

A second field of artificial intelligence with likely application is the use of natural communications, including advanced graphical techniques as well as natural language understanding and speech recognition, to make the operator/system interface extremely user-friendly. The state of the art in these areas is less well developed; a strategy for space station application will have to adopt a flexible stance as to how much capability is included initially and how much is added later. Graphical techniques are well advanced, with

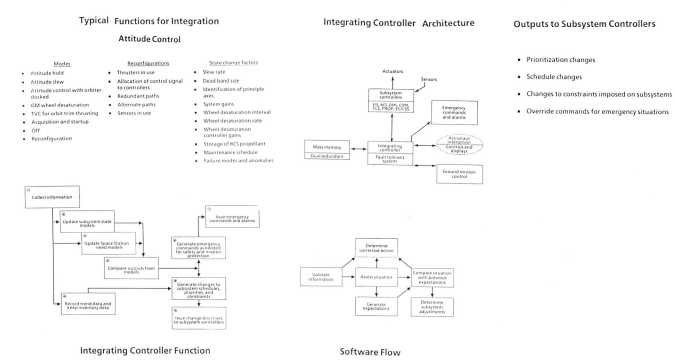

Figure 5.65 Space station subsystems integrating controller concept. *Courtesy of Boeing.*

icons (pictorial symbols with specific meaning), touch-screens, joysticks, etc. Speech recognition is rudimentary, without contextual understanding and with minimal ability to handle connected speech. A comparison of existing and future systems with contextual understanding is shown in Figure 5.66. Natural language understanding from text input is progressing (20 years after early attempts to write translation codes that were little more than dictionaries; an apocryphal story relates an early code that translated English ''The spirit is willing but the flesh is weak'' into Russian and back into English with the result, ''The vodka is strong but the meat is rotten.'') The long-range goal is to provide a computer system that is so user-friendly it needs no user's manual. This goal will probably not be fully reached in the initial space station but experts predict it is very possible by the year 2000.

Robotics

A robot is an automaton that manages its own task activity once programmed for the task. Industrial robots perform simple tasks, such as welding, according to a predetermined program with little human attention except for replenishing welding rods, repairs, reprogramming when the task is modified, etc. Despite the clear distinction between a robot and a human-directed machine, the term *robot* has often been applied to the latter where space systems are concerned. This misuse of the word *robot* is apparently mainly due to the popular media. The Shuttle RMS is called a robot arm; it is nothing of the sort—an astronaut directs its every move. Unmanned spacecraft are called robots even though a mission control center is in almost continuous command of the

machine. Planetary spacecraft, as mentioned above, have included true, if rudimentary, robotics because of communication delays.

Design and analysis studies for the space station are considering applications of true robotics. The manipulator arm on a space station, a derivative of the Shuttle arm, may be programmed to carry out routine, repetitive tasks, such as exchange of resupply modules, without human intervention. A free-flyer robot has been visualized to carry out simple maintenance tasks such as replacement of film in instruments. Such a free-flyer might also include a measure of artificial intelligence to be aware of and avoid interfering with EVA astronauts.

Teleoperators

A teleoperator is a device for conducting manipulative operations at a distance by remote control. Means for two-way communication of information must be provided so that the remote human operator can observe the operation and send controlling signals to the teleoperator. The term *robotics* is sometimes applied indiscriminately to the entire field of teleoperation and robotics.

This technology was pioneered by the nuclear industry for laboratory manipulations of materials or in areas where radiation environments prohibit direct human presence. The idea was popularized many years ago in science fiction; the term ''waldoes'' (referring to a control technique where the operator wears glove-like devices that pick up his arm and hand motions and convey instructions to the teleoperator to mimic these motions) comes from a science fiction story.

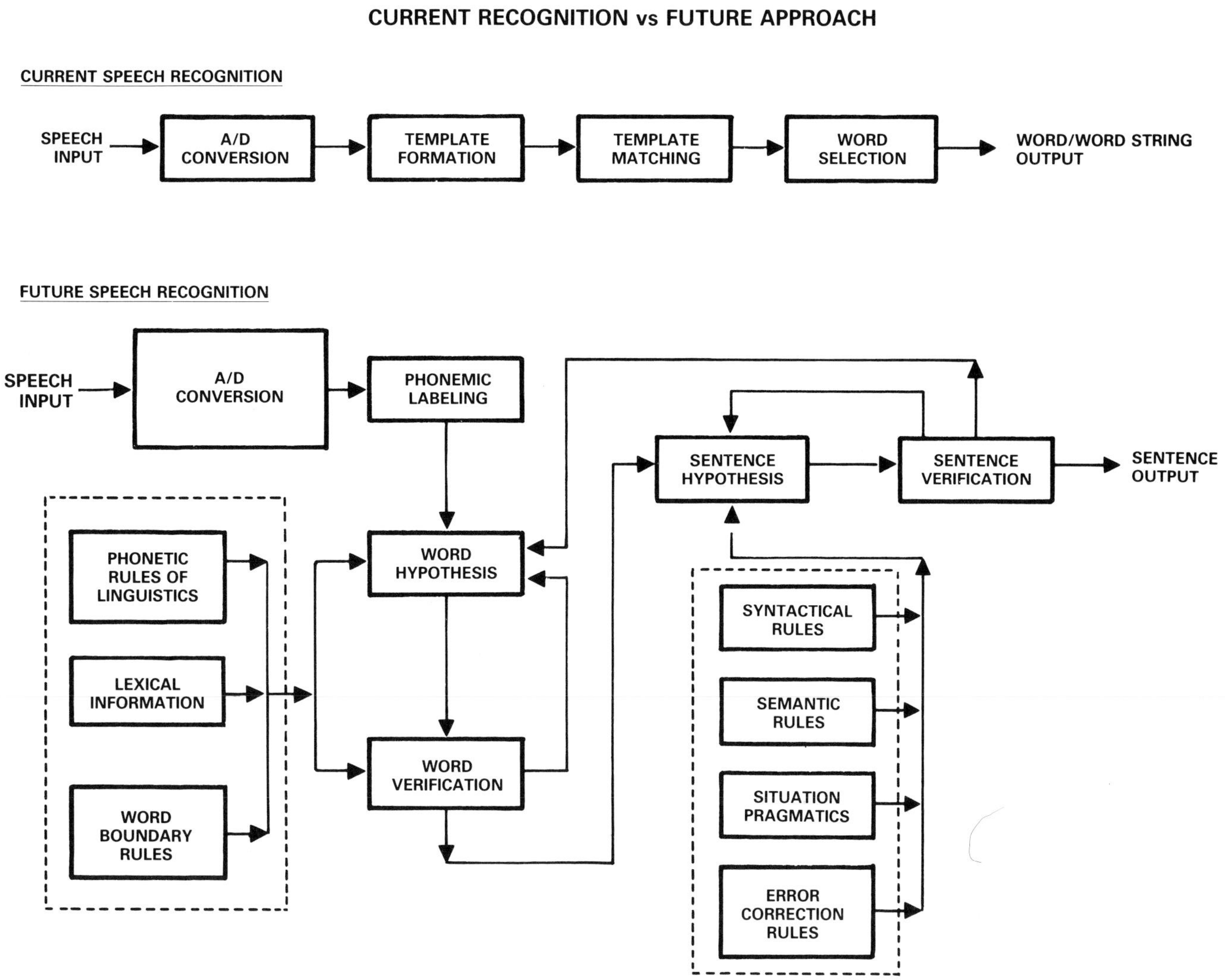

CURRENT RECOGNITION vs FUTURE APPROACH

CURRENT SPEECH RECOGNITION

SPEECH INPUT → A/D CONVERSION → TEMPLATE FORMATION → TEMPLATE MATCHING → WORD SELECTION → WORD/WORD STRING OUTPUT

FUTURE SPEECH RECOGNITION

SPEECH INPUT → A/D CONVERSION → PHONEMIC LABELING → WORD HYPOTHESIS → WORD VERIFICATION

PHONETIC RULES OF LINGUISTICS
LEXICAL INFORMATION
WORD BOUNDARY RULES

SENTENCE HYPOTHESIS → SENTENCE VERIFICATION → SENTENCE OUTPUT

SYNTACTICAL RULES
SEMANTIC RULES
SITUATION PRAGMATICS
ERROR CORRECTION RULES

Figure 5.66 Current speech recognition versus future approach. *Courtesy of Boeing.*

Early teleoperators relied on direct vision through heavy panes of leaded glass; some still do. Television cameras are now widely used as for the Shuttle RMS for which a combination of direct viewing and cameras is applied. Teleoperation technology is also coming into widespread use for undersea operations.

Teleoperation can effect a degree of human presence not presently possible through true robotics. Manipulative tasks, though limited by the dexterity of devices, can take advantage of human skill. Human visual perception, even as limited by a TV system, can far outperform robotics vision in many ways. Human judgment is brought into play.

Space station and platform operations appropriate to teleoperation include laboratory tasks where humans are not or should be present, e.g., for hazardous experiments, servicing of spacecraft where EVA may thus be avoided, and routine outside fly-around inspections.

In most experience with teleoperation, signal time delays

have been entirely negligible compared to human response times. The time delays anticipated for teleoperation uses on space stations and platforms are not so negligible. Even at the speed of light, the tortuous path that signals must take from a payload control center to a space station or platform and back (including as many as four round trips to geosynchronous orbit) can involve 1 to 4 seconds. Specialized operator training and a considerable slowing of tasks will be necessary to accommodate the time delays.

There are obvious similarities between robotics and teleoperation, especially in the manipulator hardware, and one less obvious but very important dissimilarity, i.e., in software. Teleoperators often use software to simplify the tasks for the human operator. The Shuttle RMS uses software to compute joint motions so that the operator need merely instruct the arm where to go and need not be concerned with details of how to get there. But software to emulate human intelligence and dexterity is not required. Therefore, teleoperation has a well-developed state of the art while robotics is far more primitive. A transition from teleoperation to robotics for many space uses must include extensive developments in artificial intelligence.

Communications

The distinction between data management and communications has become quite blurred. Communications are all going digital; communications equipment uses digital processing. This discussion considers those systems that employ radio-frequency electromagnetic signals and the processing thereof as communications.

Frequency Bands and Communications Links

Allocation of radio frequencies among various users to equitably share the limited resource is done by an international body, the International Telecommunications Union (ITU) through periodic meetings called World Administrative Radio Conference (WARC). WARC meetings are held every few years. A significant part of the deliberations covers the allocation of frequency assignments for space communications use. Many frequency bands are presently available for space use, but the most desirable ones are already crowded.

For many years, the S-band frequency band at slightly more than 2 gigahertz has been used for most spacecraft communications; S-band is still allocated and widely used. It is crowded and problems exist with interference. Frequency bands at C-band (4-6 gHz) and Ka-band are widely used by communications spacecraft at geosynchronous orbit, but the allocations do not allow these bands for communications with "research spacecraft," i.e., space stations or platforms (except communications platforms).

The principal means of communications with space stations and platforms in low Earth orbits will be through the Tracking and Data Relay Satellite System (TDRSS). The first satellite was launched in 1983. The nominal TDRSS configuration includes two satellites in geosynchronous orbit as shown in Figure 5.67. The system frequency plan includes S-band and Ku-band as illustrated in Figure 5.68.

TDRSS replaces a large number of ground stations and provides better coverage. Communications between the primary TDRSS ground station and the remainder of the network employs domestic communications satellites as illustrated in Figure 5.69.

Future growth of the tracking and data relay system is expected to employ advanced satellites and higher frequencies. One concept is called tracking and data acquisition system (TDAS) and proposes to use millimeter-wave frequencies, e.g., 65 GHz, for space-to-space communications and perhaps 20 to 30 GHz for up and down links through the atmosphere. (The atmosphere is essentially opaque at 65 GHz.)

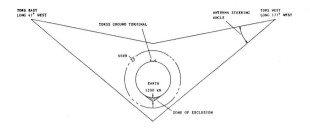

Figure 5.67   TDRSS configuration. *Courtesy of NASA.*

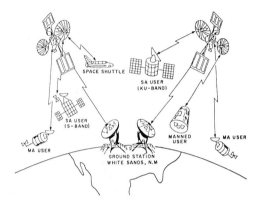

Figure 5.68   TDRSS frequency plan. *Courtesy of NASA.*

Space Station Communications Requirements

Space stations will be required to maintain communications with a variety of vehicles and systems, including TDRSS for relay to the ground, Space Shuttles, space-suited (EVA) astronauts working outside the space station, and other spacecraft. A summary of these communications requirements as presently understood is given in Figure 5.70.

Link Performance and Antenna Sizing

Link performance analysis deals with sizing communications system power and antennas so that the received signals are strong enough that the data to be sent can be extracted from the signal. The maximum possible capacity of an ideal

J.Harrelson

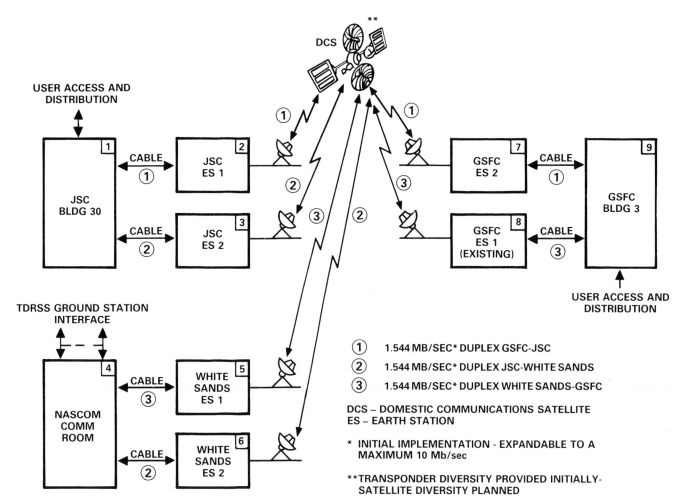

Figure 5.69 Use of domestic communications satellites for signal distribution. *Courtesy of NASA.*

Space Station External Data Rate Estimates

Communication Link	From Manned Space Station			To Manned Space Station		
	Data	Video	Voice	Data	Video	Voice
TDRS/TDAS	50 MBPS	60–120 MBPS	64 KBPS (4 16 KBPS CHAN)	<1 MBPS	1 CHAN (3–25 MBPS)	64 KBPS (4–16 KBPS CHAN)
ORBITER	<16 KBPS	—	32 KBPS (1 CHAN)	2 KBPS	—	32 KBPS
EMU/EVA	0–1 KBPS	1 CHAN	16 KBPS	1 KBPS	1 CHAN	16 KBPS
OMV	2 KBPS	—	—	4–64 KBPS	.3–25 MBPS	—
OTV	2 KBPS	—	—	16 KBPS	—	—
FREEFLYER	2 KBPS	—	—	4–16 KBPS	—	—
GPS	—	—	—	50 BPS	—	—
SPACE PLATFORM @ 28.5°	2–6 KBPS	—	—	4–64 KBPS (60 MBPS IF RELAY)	.3–25 MBPS	—
DIRECT-TO-GND.	16-128 KBPS		32 KBPS	2 KBPS		32 KBPS

Figure 5.70 Space station communications requirements. *Courtesy of NASA.*

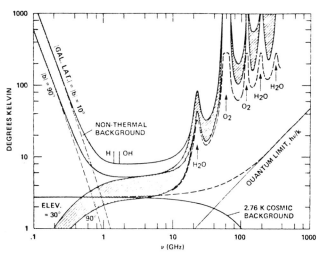

Figure 5.71 The terrestrial microwave window showing space noise sources. *Courtesy of NASA.*

channel is

$$C = W\log_2(1 + SNR) \qquad (5.15)$$

where C is capacity in bits/sec, W is bandwidth in hertz, and SNR is the signal-to-noise ratio. Actual systems approach this ideal within a few decibels. (The decibel, or db, is a measure of power ratio, db $= 10 \log_{10}$ power ratio; 10 db $= 10^1 =$ factor of 10; 20 db $= 10^2 =$ factor of 100, etc.) Actual systems do not go suddenly from perfect transmission to no transmission at a particular point, but their error rate increases as SNR decreases. For digital systems, the error rate is countable as the fraction of bits incorrectly received; performance requirements usually specify bit error rates from 10^{-6} to 10^{-3}.

Equation 5.15 is the basis for determining system power and antenna size because channel noise is always present and can be quantified. Thermal noise due to thermal motion of electrons is kT watts/hertz where k is the Boltzmann constant, 1.38×10^{-23} watts/kelvin. Thermal noise can arise from background sources, i.e., an antenna looking at the Earth sees the Earth's thermal RF radiation; thermal noise also arises in receiving devices. Cooling of devices improves their sensitivity and cooled devices are used in sensitive ground-based receivers for space communications. Space itself is noisy as is illustrated in Figure 5.71.

The power received by an RF receiver decreases with the inverse-square law, and is given by

$$P = (\text{power transmitted})(\text{transmitter antenna gain})$$
$$(\text{receiver antenna gain})\left(\frac{\lambda}{4\pi r}\right)^2 \qquad (5.16)$$

where r is the distance between transmitter and receiver, and λ is the wavelength of the radiation. Wavelength is related to frequency by $\lambda = c/\nu$ where ν is frequency in hertz

and c is the speed of light, 299,792 m/sec. Since typical communications wavelengths are much less than 1 meter and space communications distances are millions of meters, eq. 5.16 leads to very small numbers. The loss implied by eq. 5.16, called space loss, can easily exceed 200 db. Fortunately, data can be transferred with very tiny powers and antenna gain can recoup much of the loss.

A directional antenna reduces losses because its radiation does not spread isotropically through space but is radiated preferentially in one direction. If a directional antenna effectively illuminates only 1/1000 of the 4π sphere, its signal in its preferential direction is 1000 times as strong and it

Table 5.9 Link analysis example.

SSA Return Link, 2275 MHz, DG1, Mode 2, Data Rate 1.024 kb/sec, Rate 1/2 Coded			
Item Parameter	Worst Geometry	Adverse Tolerance	Remarks
1. Total transmitter power (dBW)	10.2	−1.0	note 1
2. Passive loss (dB)	−1.0	−0.3	note 1
3. Antenna gain (dBi)	4.9	−0.5	note 1
4. Pointing Loss (dB)	−0.2		note 1
5. Polarization loss (dB)	−0.6		note 1
6. Data/total power (dB)	−7.0		note 1
7. Free space loss (dB)	−192.3		note 1
8. Received power unity (dBW)	−186.0		sum of item 1 through item 7
9. Required acquisition power unity (dBW)	−198.2		STDN No. 101.2
10. Acquisition margin (dB)	12.2		item 8 minus item 9
11. Constraint loss (dB)	−0.5		note 2
12. RFI environmental loss (dB)	−1.5		note 3
13. Degraded effective power unity (dBW)	−188.0		sum of items 8, 11, and 12
14. Required effective power unity (dBW)	−196.8		STDN No. 101.2
15. Effective margin (dB)	+8.8	Sum −1.8 RSS −1.2	item 13 minus item 14

Note
1. From user communications terminal system design.
2. Based on user transponder partial compliance with user constraints. (Does not include data baseband system.)
3. SSA antenna 1.5° offpointing (preliminary degradation value).

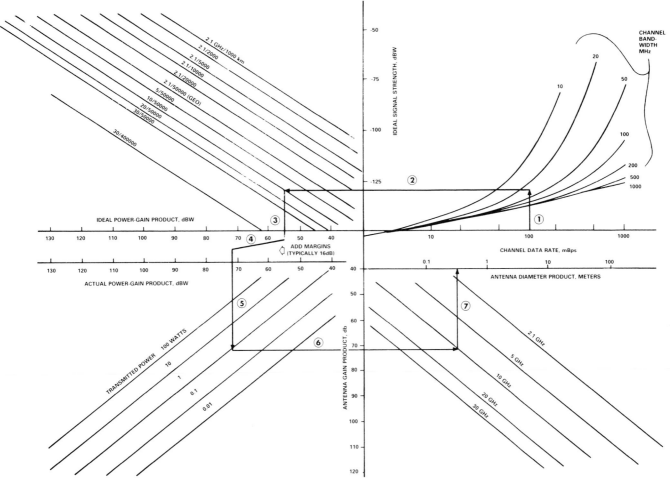

Figure 5.72 Communications link performance nomograph.

has a gain of 30 db. Such an antenna has a beam width of about 7°. A 1° antenna beam width provides a gain of about 46 db. The gain of an antenna is given by $\eta(\pi D/\lambda)^2$, where η is efficiency, D is aperture, and λ is wavelength. The gain of a 1-meter antenna at S-band ($\lambda = 0.13$) is about a factor of 470, or 27 db, at 80 percent efficiency. The gain of the 1000 foot (305 m) radio astronomy dish at Arecibo at S-band is about 4.4 million or 66 db.

Link analyses are normally performed in decibels, and gains and losses are additive (the db scale is logarithmic and decibels act like logarithms). Allowance must be made for the inability of actual systems to attain the Shannon ideal performance, and gain margins are inserted for imperfect antenna pointing and degraded equipment performance. Table 5.9 presents a typical link performance calculation applied to TDRSS.

Rough link performance estimates can be quickly done with a nomograph. The nomograph in Figure 5.72 solves for the product of antenna diameters. Any combination of receiver and transmitter antennas that equals or exceeds the diameter product will provide enough gain.

Antenna Types

There are an enormous number of antenna types, corresponding to a wide range of gains and bandwidths. High gains and narrow beams are of course not always desirable. Some applications demand wide-angle or even omnidirectional coverage. An antenna designed to achieve the latter is often called an "omni." Narrow-beam antennas are called high-gain and often abbreviated HGA. RF beams are normally polarized. The radiation is transverse, i.e., the mode of oscillation is transverse to the path. Polarization may be vertical or horizontal. Certain types of antennas create circularly polarized radiation; the direction of polarization rotates about the transmission path.

The simplest form of wide-angle antenna is the dipole, approximately one-half wavelength long. It is not omnidirectional as it has nulls in the direction of the "poles." A dipole has 3 db gain in the plane perpendicular to the "poles." Arrays of dipoles, either arranged on a reflector or in gangs called yagis, have gains of a few to about 10 db. Horns have somewhat higher gains. Gains above 20 db are usually implemented by dish reflectors, commonly ar-

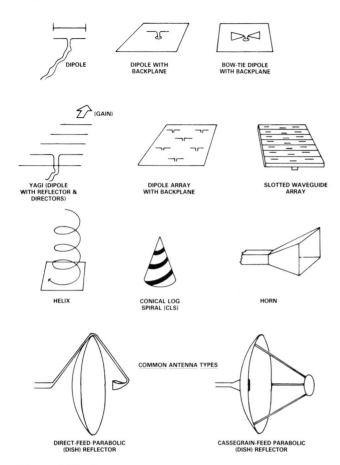

Figure 5.73 Antenna types.

plitude modulation (AM) in which the RF signal, the carrier, is modulated in amplitude by the information signal. Fourier analysis, or scanning the resulting signal with a narrow-band filter, shows that the amplitude-modulated signal contains the RF carrier plus modulation sidebands comprised of the carrier frequency ± the modulating frequencies. All of the information is actually contained in either of the sidebands (upper or lower). Certain modern communications systems take advantage of this by transmitting on only one of the sidebands, thus conserving both power and bandwidth.

In the case of frequency modulation (FM) the carrier amplitude does not change, but its frequency is modulated by the information signal. The resulting sidebands appear in coherent patterns and FM detectors respond to these patterns. Noise, which is random in nature, is suppressed. Commercial FM radio is wideband; the carrier frequency swing is much greater than the modulating frequency. Narrow-band FM is also used and conserves bandwidth. Narrow-band FM is similar to phase modulation in which the phase of the carrier is modulated. Phase modulation is most practical for digital information. Typically, the phase is advanced 90° for a "one" and is retarded 90° for a "zero." This is called biphase modulation. The data rate can be increased by permitting more phase states; quadraphase has four and is abbreviated QPSK (quadraphase shift keying).

Spread spectrum techniques are used for additional protection from natural and manmade interference. The RF carrier is first modulated by the information signal and then by a pseudo-noise signal at a very high data rate. The latter modulation spreads the spectrum because of its high data rate. At the receiver, the received signal is demodulated by a pseudo-noise signal with exactly the same digital sequence and exactly synchronized with the pseudo-noise modulator of the transmitter. The signal is thus despread. Only a signal exactly synchronized with the pseudo-noise demodulator will be despread, so noise is rejected. This technique is particularly effective against simple single-frequency jamming. Various schemes exist for synchronizing the transmitter and receiver.

Another technique for improving the performance of a channel is the use of error-correcting codes. If a single data bit is represented by several signal bits with one pattern for a "one," and another for a "zero," loss of a single signal bit will not cause loss of information; the error can be corrected. Spread-spectrum and error correcting techniques lead to channel performance closely approximating the Shannon ideal.

Multiple information channels may be impressed on a single RF carrier by using subcarriers; the subcarriers modulate the carrier and the information signals modulate the subcarriers. This technique is used commercially to transmit music programs over FM channels to commercial subscri-

ranged in a Cassegrainian configuration. High gains can also be achieved by phased arrays, often composed of dipole elements. These forms are illustrated in Figure 5.73.

Phased arrays are capable of high gain as are dish antennas. Phased arrays are more expensive, especially if each array element is active (some phased arrays have each active element feeding several array elements). Phased arrays can be electronically steered and thus can have extremely agile beams. If system noise is dominated by receiver device noise as is often true, the dish reflector possesses a major advantage because it concentrates signal energy on the receiver and thus improves signal-to-noise ratio. The dish has an apparent temperature equal to its actual temperature multiplied by $1 - r$ where r is reflectivity, which may be as high as 0.99. (An uncooled reflector-horn detected the cosmic background radiation, the radiation remnant of the "big bang" birth of the universe, at 3 K.)

Modulation and Signals

An electromagnetic signal must be modulated to transfer information. Morse code was an early simple form of on-off pulse modulation. Early broadcast radio pioneered ambers. The music signal is placed on a subcarrier that is above 20 kHz in frequency. Ordinary FM receivers do not detect the signal because the subcarrier and its sidebands are above the audio frequency cutoff of the receiver. At the high frequencies and great bandwidths available in the space communications bands, many subcarriers are often used.

Packetization is also used. Data streams are organized into packets with an identifying header and trailer. The packets are interleaved in the channel data stream and sorted at the receiver end. Because the channel data rate is higher than that of any subchannel, buffers must be used to match and synchronize data rates.

Chapter 6

Crew Systems and Crew Accommodations

Crew systems in early spacecraft were minimal and served mainly to keep the crew alive. Air was pure oxygen at 35 kPa (about 5 psia). Drinking water was provided from storage tanks or as a byproduct of fuel cells. Food was eaten from tubes or prepared sticks. Urine was dumped overboard, and solid wastes excreted into plastic bags taped in place and then sealed and placed in storage. There was no furniture, galley, shower, toilet, etc., nor was there any room for such amenities. This began to change with the Skylab which had a rudimentary galley, a toilet that worked, and a collapsible shower. Shuttle, except for its two-gas, 100 kPa (14.7 psi) atmosphere, is in many ways not as advanced as Skylab. (The two-gas atmosphere is a major improvement—low-pressure pure oxygen leads to respiratory irritation and a conscious effort to ingest plenty of fluids must be made to prevent dehydration.) Shuttle crews, of course, spend only about a week in orbit, and as more than one crewmember has observed, "camping out can actually be fun for a week."

Crew systems analysis applies, of course, mainly to space stations. Certain aspects apply also to space platforms if man-tended or crew serviced.

The Crew as a Subsystem

Since the people on board a space station fulfill useful functions, they may be viewed as a subsystem. Allocations of requirements and functions include the crew as recipients. Crewmembers provide a straightforward means of accomplishing functions that would be difficult or impossible without their presence.

Simple examples of the special capabilities of the crew include maintenance and repair, space structures assembly, and redundancy management. (The latter means that when redundancy is incorporated into a system to improve reliability, the system must be smart enough to detect failures and make whatever operating changes are necessary to utilize the redundancy.)

The Crew as People

Humans need a certain environment to survive. For short periods, this is similar to other subsystems; humans need thermal control, a source of energy, and a throughput of

certain fluids. For a human crew to remain productive, healthy, and effective over long periods, however, the proper physiological and psychological amenities must be carefully designed into a space system.

Interior Crew Equipment and Accommodations

Design criteria exist for the required volume of a confined space in which people are to reside and work over a period of time. These have been developed by observing the performance of people in such environments, in actual systems, and in simulations. The volume needed is observed to increase with habitation time. One of the best-known early results in this area is the Celentano criterion shown in Figure 6.1. Actual designs for historical and planned spacecraft are plotted on the figure. Contemporary thinking is that the Celentano curve dictates too small a volume, especially if any of the interior is to be used for work stations, laboratories, etc., as is true for space stations.

Health Maintenance

Humans adapt to zero g readily. Too readily, in fact. The design of crew physiological amenities deals mainly with this problem.

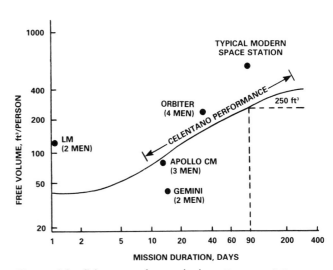

Figure 6.1 Celentano volume criterion. *Courtesy of Grumman Aerospace.*

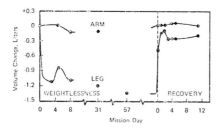

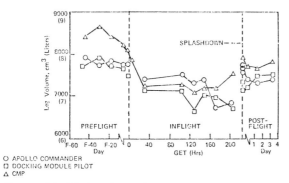

O APOLLO COMMANDER
□ DOCKING MODULE PILOT
△ CMP

Figure 6.2 Limb volume changes measured on Skylab 4 and Apollo-Soyuz. *Courtesy of NASA.*

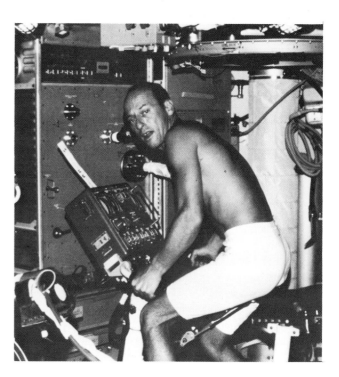

Redistribution of blood volume results from the lack of gravity force and causes one's face to appear puffy, causes some discomfort, but is not known to cause health problems. The cardiovascular system and the muscular system generally are stressed less than by bed rest in 1 g. This is not true of EVA; it is hard work but has not been frequent enough to serve as an exercise regimen. Early space flights in which the crews were confined for periods up to 2 weeks resulted in significant muscular debilitation - there were cases of people that literally could not stand up after landing. Russian crews have exhibited severe deconditioning after long flights despite regular exercise. Figure 6.2 shows muscle volume loss for the American Apollo-Soyuz crew.

Exercise became recognized as a necessity and was put into practice on the Skylab missions. Although not strictly necessary, it is practiced even on weeklong Shuttle flights.

Schemes to maintain muscular and cardiovascular condition have included bicycle ergometers and a treadmill (Figure 6.3). The Soviets have also used a "penguin suit" (Figure 6.4), trousers with elastic cords in them to maintain pressure on the leg muscles, and we and they have both used a device that produces a negative relative pressure surrounding the legs to stress the heart.

Experience has shown 1 to 2 hours of exercise a day to be necessary. A space station with six to eight people needs two exercise stations to avoid severe problems in scheduling

Figure 6.3 Bicycle ergometer and treadmill exercise devices. *Courtesy of NASA.*

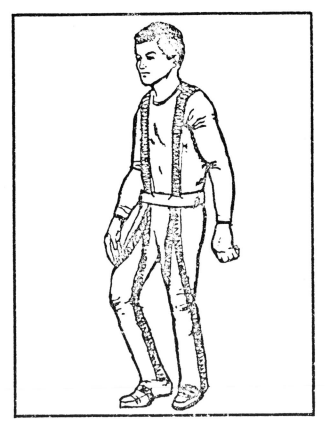

Figure 6.4 The "penguin" constant-loading suit worn by Soviet cosmonauts. *Courtesy of NASA.*

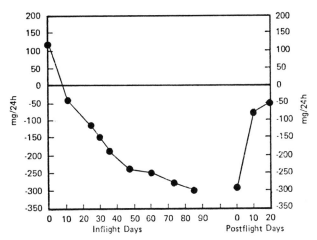

Figure 6.5 Calcium loss rates for Skylab 4. *Courtesy of NASA.*

exercise time for everyone. Exercise on a machine is boring. The two exercise stations should be co-located to permit conversation; a strong recommendation from astronauts is that some form of entertainment, e.g., TV, audio, or electronic text display for reading, be provided to relieve the boredom of exercise.

The exercise program was successful on the 84-day Skylab 4 mission; the crew returned in good physical condition. Insofar as we know, this has proven true on Soviet missions up to 237 days. We do not know how successful their penguin suits have been.

One of the adaptions the human body makes in zero g is decalcification of bones. Strong bones aren't needed in zero g. The loss rate is slow, on the order of 1 percent per month, and not well defined by U.S. flight data (we have had few long-duration flights). Calcium loss occurs through urine and feces. Typical U.S. flight data are shown in Figure 6.5. Means of preventing calcium loss are not known; human physiological research on a space station will certainly give calcium balance studies a high priority. Bone calcium recovers nearly to its preflight level a few months after a space flight. Effects of repetitive long-duration missions are not known. Unless preventive means are found, calcium loss may limit continuous zero g exposure to periods on the order of a year.

About half of the U.S. astronauts that have flown in space have experienced some degree of space motion sickness. It typically ensues soon after reaching orbit and subsides in 2 to 4 days, not recurring throughout the mission. Most experiences are mild, but in a few cases vomiting has occurred. There are various theories as to the cause, and active research is being carried out to find ways to minimize it. Space motion sickness is of more concern to Shuttle missions than to space station operations because of the difference in mission durations.

Provisions for medical care on past missions have been minimal. Skylab provided dental kits. First-aid capabilities have always been provided. Even though crews are selected for good health and receive excellent care, sooner or later a space station program will experience a serious medical emergency, either due to an accident or to an unexpected health problem.

Sudden decompression could occur to a crewperson due to damage to a space suit while EVA. Decompression is not immediately fatal and, unless a suit is completely torn asunder, will be partial. Quick action on the part of another crewperson, getting the endangered person into an airlock, would prevent a fatality provided that a hyperbaric chamber (a place where the atmosphere pressure can be raised to several times sea level pressure) were available for treatment of aeroembolism (the "bends"). To this end, the space station is being designed with at least one airlock capable of hyperbaric operation.

The space station data system will certainly include medical diagnostic data base aids and possibly an expert system software package for diagnostics; help from the ground would of course also be available. Two-way color TV appears important for medical consultation.

The early space station will have medical facilities similar to a well-equipped doctor's office - there isn't room for more. Normally, one crewmember will be a medical doctor

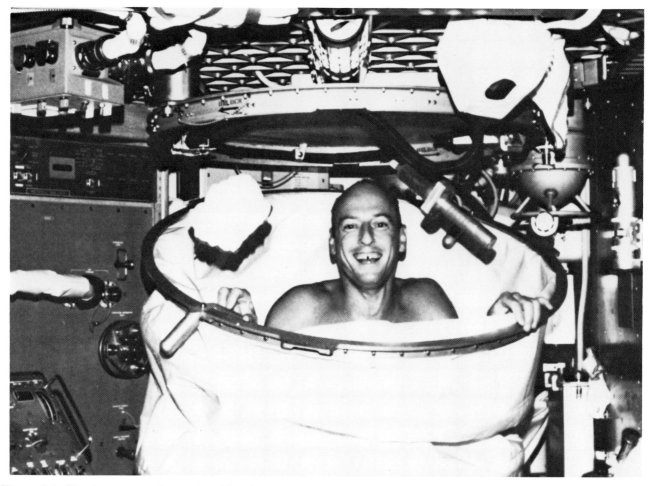

Figure 6.6   The shower system in use aboard Skylab. The ring in the crewman's left hand was raised and attached at the top to seal off the shower with its flexible liner. *Courtesy of NASA.*

and others will have paramedic training. As the station grows, more elaborate facilities will be added; the amount and nature will depend partly on earlier operational experience.

Shower and Handwash

The Skylab had a collapsible shower, shown in Figure 6.6. It was infrequently used, partly because its collapsible nature made it a nuisance to set up and take down, and partly because water for its use was rationed to about 4 liters per shower, and the crew had no way of knowing when the water for a shower would run out until it did. Skylab did not recycle water; all its water was aboard at launch.

Present thinking for the planned NASA space station is to have a permanent shower stall in one of the habitats. The shower door would seal tightly enough to keep water inside. With recycled water, strict rationing would not be necessary. Figure 6.7 illustrates a current handwasher concept mockup. The plastic ''bubble'' would have a hole in it big enough for two hands, and a foot pedal would start water spray flow. A gentle flow of air into the bubble through the hole

would keep water inside. The bubble could be removable to use the device as an eyewash, for example, in a lab where hazardous materials might be in use.

Galley and Food Service

Nourishing and appetizing food is important to crew morale, especially on long missions. Food service in space has gradually improved, and present plans are for this to continue in the space station system. Current reference designs include refrigerators, freezers, and ovens. The expense of electrical power and heat rejection in space makes the design of efficient food service equipment very important. This is especially true of ovens. The electrical heaters in conventional ovens consume several kilowatts. Forced-air convection or microwave ovens will probably be used.

A close approach to Earth-like food service is planned, with modifications as appropriate to minimize occupied space and to be compatible with the 90-day resupply interval and zero g. Day-to-day menu planning and snack service are contemplated. Growing fresh salad greens may be tried; the Soviets have done this. Because of the high value of

Figure 6.7 Mockup of space station handwasher concept. *Courtesy of Boeing.*

crew time, food preparation and cleanup effort will be minimized. Computers will aid planning for restocking provisions according to consumption. To get the fullest utilization of the station's facilities, the crew will operate on two shifts

as they did on Spacelab 1. Mealtime planning will aim for one meal with all the crew together to permit conferencing and enhance cooperation.

Average dry food consumption per crewperson is predicted as 0.62 kg per day. Most space station food will be supplied wet, i.e., frozen, refrigerated, or canned. The nominal allocation is:

Dry equivalent	0.62 kg/d
Water in food	0.50 kg/d
Food prep water	0.72 kg/d

The galley will also include a foldaway table large enough for the crew of six to eight to eat together, utensil storage and washing equipment, and a trash compactor for dry trash. Wet waste must be separately disposed of to prevent bacterial growth. Present thinking is to use the commode, but special hermetically sealed waste storage bags might be used.

A typical space station galley and wardroom concept is shown in Figures 6.8 and 6.9.

Emergency food and water provisioning will be distributed among the space station modules so that any module can serve as a safe haven in the event of an emergency. The safe haven design duration is presently specified as 28 days. If each safe haven has provisions for six people, about 100 kg of emergency food and 150 kg of emergency water must be stored in each pressurized module. Various safe haven schemes have been proposed. Some assume that more than one pressurized module will always be habitable (the present reference configuration has a total of five) and some do not designate all modules as safe havens. Selection of distribution of emergency supplies is a real-time operational decision; any module with air revitalization capability in its environmental control and life support system (EC/LS) can become a safe haven if stocked with supplies.

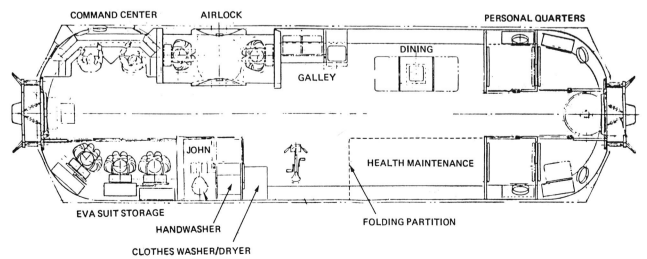

Figure 6.8 Space station galley and wardroom concept: layout. *Courtesy of Boeing.*

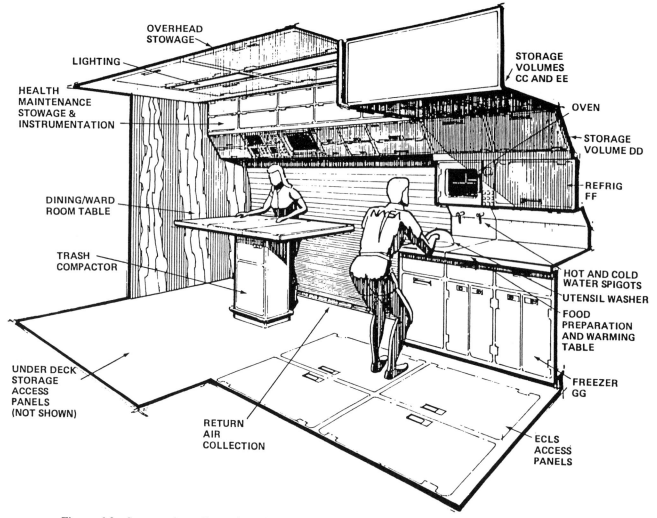

Figure 6.9 Space station galley and wardroom concept: illustration. *Courtesy of Walter Dorwin Teague and Boeing.*

Crew Quarters

The crew quarters of early spacecraft, including Apollo, were the pilots' couches. The Skylab was roomy and included the small crew private quarters as shown in Figure 6.10. The Shuttle does not have private quarters but provides a galley, wardroom, and work areas on both decks. The cabin arrangement of the Shuttle is shown in Figure 6.11.

Private personal space is a very important need for high human productivity on long-term space station missions. Although the crew habitation areas on a space station are generous compared to early spacecraft, astronauts have reported a strong confinement effect, especially on long missions. One cannot even go outside to be alone; EVA is always conducted using a buddy system and with continuous communications with other crewmembers. Private crew quarters are included in contemporary space station designs.

Mockups such as depicted in Figure 6.12 have indicated that about 2 square meters of floor area in private quarters will be adequate. Floor-to-ceiling heights of about 2 meters

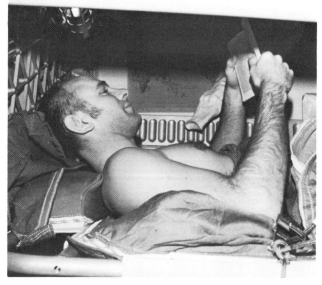

Figure 6.10 Skylab crew private quarters. *Courtesy of NASA.*

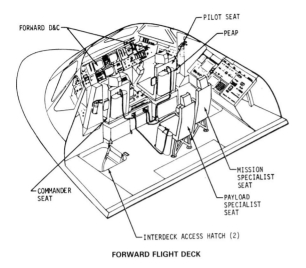

FORWARD FLIGHT DECK

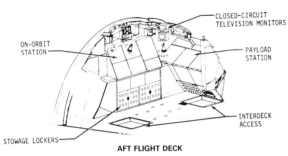

AFT FLIGHT DECK

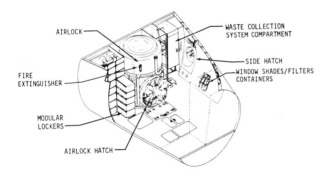

MID DECK (Accommodates four seats)

Figure 6.11 Shuttle cabin arrangement.

appear sufficient. Visual and noise screening should be provided so that the feeling of proximity of other humans is muted. Ventilation devices should be reachable from a sleeping position.

Entertainment items such as music and video with headsets, and reading materials, are effective privacy aids. Noise propagation will be a problem in the confinement of the space station and the structure will transmit noises readily. Adequate design data and methods for noise analysis and control do not presently exist.

Crews experienced in long-duration space flight have universally remarked on the desirability of windows. Skylab crews reported that watching the Earth ''go by'' out the

window was one of their favorite forms of entertainment. Placing windows in crew private quarters might be desirable, but most design solutions have concentrated on placing them in work and group off-duty areas.

An important factor in crew systems design is adjacency patterns. Hygiene facilities, especially toilets, should not be close to eating and food preparation areas. If there are two or more modules for habitation and crew work functions, the active functions, such as exercise, food preparation, and work involving talk or other noise and disturbance, should be in one module with sleeping and quiet areas in the other. Work areas should be designed for convenient consultation between crewmembers, e.g., two people should be able to share a window or work station. Suitable restraints should be provided, recognizing the zero-g operations.

Man-Machine Interfaces

A man-machine interface is a set of controls and displays through which a human interacts with a machine. The steering wheel, pedals, and dash instruments of a car are one, as are the keyboard and display of a computer or the flight deck of an airplane. A complex system like a space station needs several man-machine interfaces. Whether they look alike or different, they will certainly have different functions. Unmanned platforms will also use man-machine interfaces but those normally used will be on the ground, e.g.,

Figure 6.12 Mockup of space station crew private quarters. *Courtesy of Boeing.*

at a payload operations control center (POCC). Typical functions for man-machine interfaces at a space station are as follows.

1. Management of space station subsystems and operations will be automated so that their normal operation does not require crew attention. Automation can also be applied to failure and anomaly management, and may be. Decisions on how much to involve the crew in subsystems management will consider costs of crew time and of automation, need for human intellect and judgment, and the need to involve the crew often enough to maintain their skill and knowledge levels. We presently believe automation can be complete enough that crew involvement will be set by the last of these needs. Each crew shift coming on duty, for example, might interrogate subsystems status and obtain a history of any important events since they last checked.

2. Many of the space station missions will be controlled through a man-machine interface. Controls and display panels will be used for operation of scientific instruments such as telescopes. Instrument images may be displayed on board in addition to being sent to the ground, for crew interaction. Laboratory experiments and instruments will be operable from a control panel capable of automatic sequencing, data acquisition, and analysis. Teleoperators, manipulators, and robots will be controlled by the crew to accomplish servicing and construction operations.

3. Operations around the space station will be controlled by the crew as necessary to ensure safety. Vehicles flying nearby, platforms or maneuvering spacecraft, will be observed by crew members and remotely piloted or directed. Operations control stations will probably have direct viewing through windows as well as TV and navigational displays.

4. Man-machine interfaces will provide information retrieval, simulation, and training. The crew will be able to call up scientific and operational procedures, backup data, maintenance information, medical data, and anything else in the data base. Electronic displays will largely, but not entirely, take the place of paper. A versatile computer-driven display can operate as a simulator and training system to refresh crews on tasks they may have partly forgotten since their preflight training.

Man-machine interface equipment on space stations is expected to adopt much of current technology used in computer systems and aircraft such as the Boeing 767. Techniques of graphical display and interaction are advancing rapidly and some of the most advanced systems are found on personal and other small computers. Control devices include programmable legend switches (Figure 6.13), mice, touch-screens, and joysticks as well as conventional key-

Figure 6.13 Programmable legend switch (prototype). *Courtesy of Boeing.*

boards. Dedicated controllers will be used for functions such as remote control of nearby spacecraft and teleoperators.

Great emphasis is being placed on a ''user-friendly'' interface. Most space station crew members will not be highly trained computer specialists, but they will have to routinely operate one of the most powerful and sophisticated data management systems ever built when dealing with the space station system. In addition to being user-friendly, the interface must offer the capable user complete command over system resources, which many user-friendly interfaces do not. A number of approaches to this aspect of designing the man-machine interface are being discussed and at this writing none has been selected.

Voice recognition by computers has reached initial practicality. It is used in some industrial situations and development continues toward its use on aircraft flight decks for non-critical functions. Present voice recognition systems use template matching to ''recognize'' sequences of sounds that make up the words in their limited vocabularies. Most must be trained to the voice of an individual, and words must be spoken one at a time, carefully. The training, once accomplished, can be stored in memory and need not be repeated. Some of the more advanced systems recognize words spoken

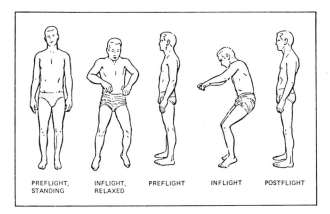

Figure 6.14 Human postural changes in zero g. *Courtesy of NASA.*

by anyone without a severe accent, or can recognize a limited amount of connected speech. Present expert forecasts are that a spoken command language of limited vocabulary will be available on the initial space station, for use by crew members whose hands are occupied. A much larger vocabulary will be accepted with keyboard input. By the year 2000, a natural language speech recognition and understanding system with a vocabulary of thousands of words should be available. It will not replace other means of man-machine interaction, but is expected to simplify much of it. As the space station data system becomes more "intelligent," less crew training will be needed for most operations.

Zero-g Design Considerations

Our daily lives are so all-pervaded by the force of gravity that it is difficult to "think zero g" in our design processes. This problem is particularly acute in detail work like the location of handles or the arrangement of instruments near a window.

The human body adopts a posture in zero g unlike normal Earth posture, as illustrated in Figure 6.14. Height increases by about 2 inches as gravity compression is removed from the skeletal system. Blood and fluids accumulate in the upper body as mentioned above. The body assumes a semi-crouched, relaxed position. A chair is an unnatural object in zero g and cannot be used unless one is strapped into it. Taking a sitting position is a strain and quickly becomes uncomfortable. Crew accommodations and equipment must be designed to be used with the zero g posture, or with a means of restraint to maintain other postures without muscle fatigue.

One cannot do any sort of physical work in zero g without restraint. Writing at a desk is a very difficult task because the pressure of a pencil on paper pushes one away from the work. Without proper restraints, one must hang on to the desk with one hand while trying to write with the other. Operating a keyboard is similarly difficult. Attempting to turn a bolt with a wrench causes one's body to rotate unless it is restrained. Application of any force or torque, however

small, brings about Newton's "equal and opposite reaction," often not noticed here on Earth with the natural restraint of gravity.

One hand can be used for restraint while the other is used for a task, but since people are accustomed to using two hands for most tasks, using one for restraint is unnatural. Foot restraints are better, and for a fixed work position, foot restraints plus some sort of mid-body brace or restraint are ideal.

The Skylab used metal grid floors with triangular holes into which would fit a foot restraint device on a crewperson's boot. Anywhere on the floor, a crewperson could insert and twist the locking device with one foot and be secured to the floor. Restraint arrangements near the Skylab window, however, were less satisfactory. It was difficult for two people to view something out the window and operate instruments such as cameras because adequate restraint arrangements had not been made.

Foot restraints need to be quite strong. A great mechanical advantage exists between the feet and forces applied by arms and hands. Leg muscles are strong and application of what seems a weak force by a crewperson will break away from a weak foot restraint. Suction cups and Velcro have been tried but are much too weak. Simple instep straps into which one can insert one's feet have also been tried but feet slip out too easily. Instep straps are OK for short-term casual use. Devices similar to ski bindings offer promise but a truly good solution has yet to be found. A good solution could be used both inside and outside for EVA. Any restraint device used for EVA, of course, must not have a failure mode that would trap a crewperson in the restraint.

Crews moving about inside a space station quickly adapt to a floating push-off and arrest means of locomotion. Designers should eliminate all sharp protuberances that might cause injury to a drifting crewperson. Switches and other control devices should be protected by guards to avoid inadvertent actuation by motion of people. It may assumed that anything that can be used for a handhold or place for feet to push off will be so used; these things should be designed sturdy enough to not be damaged by such use.

Many astronauts have expressed a consistent and strong preference for interior architecture designs with a familiar visual appearance, such as a "floor" and a "ceiling" and everything else arranged as it would be if a g force were present. This may seem inconsistent with the reports of astronauts enjoying zero g, but may be attributed to people's preference for familiar surroundings. Analysts and flight experience reports differ on whether "up" and "down" are important or whether it is merely important that unambiguous visual orientation cues be presented. The designer can take advantage of zero g by knowing that gravity does not restrict accessibility in space; everything need not be easily reached while standing on the floor. Each compartment or

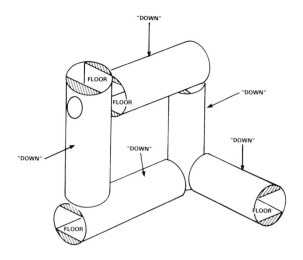

VISUAL ORIENTATION VARIATION IN SPACE STATION MODULE
PATTERN (MODULE ENDS REMOVED TO DEPICT FLOOR AND
CEILING LOCATIONS)

Figure 6.15 G-vector variation between modules.

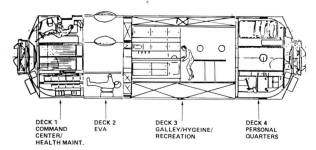

Figure 6.16 A "mixed-deck" arrangement having g-vector variation within one module. *Courtesy of Boeing.*

provide a self-contained environmental control and life support (EC/LS) system so that an oxygen-carrying umbilical is not needed. Body heat must be evenly removed from the entire body and rejected to space. "To provide these services for only a few hours will require more apparatus than a single man can handle. So the space doctors have almost given up," said Jonathan Norton Leonard, writing on future prospects for space flight in 1953. Predictions that a true space suit could not be built were widespread almost until the first suits were actually demonstrated.

room should, however, have a consistent "up" and "down" look.

In many contemporary space station designs, the g vector changes direction between compartments as illustrated in Figure 6.15. Some crew preference to avoid this has been expressed, but is not nearly so strong as the need to maintain a consistent up and down appearance within one compartment. "Mixed-deck" arrangements within one space station module have also been proposed as illustrated in Figure 6.16. This appears less desirable from the crew's point of view, but is probably acceptable if some important design or operational advantage accrues.

The design of space station interiors for long-term occupancy is a new form of architecture with relatively little experience to build on. Crews that have participated in long-duration missions consistently point out that attention to the details of interior design that make for comfort and convenience is very important to crew morale.

EVA Crew Equipment and Accommodations

EVA is the acronym for Extravehicular Activity, meaning space-suited operations. The suit is called an EMU for Extravehicular Mobility Unit. EVA activities will be an important part of space station operations and services.

History and Status of Suit Development

A human needs artificial pressurization above about 12 km (40,000 feet). The beginnings of space suit technology can be traced back to the 1930s and Wiley Post's high-altitude suit for aircraft. Emergency high-altitude suits were developed by the military after World War II. A true space suit, however, must do more than predecessor aircraft suits. It must offer some degree of full-body mobility and should

Figure 6.17 Crewman wearing Apollo space suit on the Moon. *Courtesy of NASA.*

SHUTTLE
EXTRAVEHICULAR MOBILITY UNIT

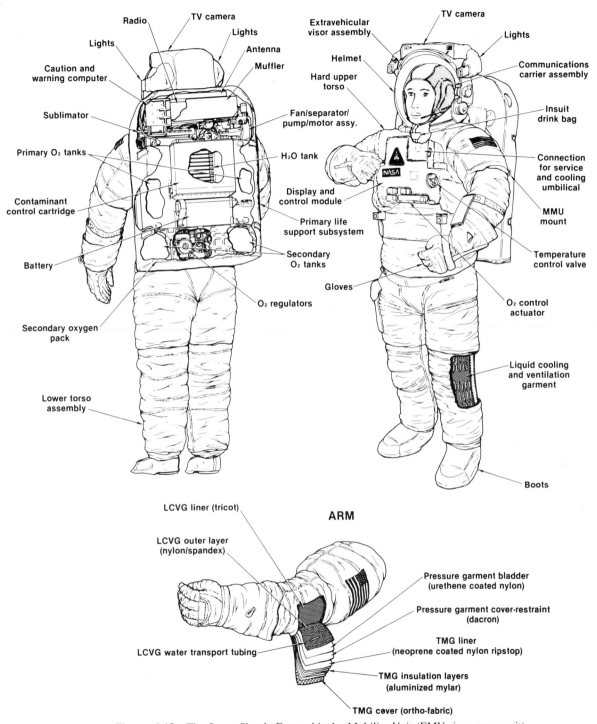

Figure 6.18   The Space Shuttle Extravehicular Mobility Unit (EMU, i.e., space suit).
Courtesy of United Technologies Hamilton Standard.

By the mid-1950s the Air Force had developed a partial-pressure suit that sufficed to keep an airman alive in a high-altitude emergency until the aircraft could be brought to lower altitude. By 1959, the Navy had developed a full pressure suit that was the technical precursor to the space suit used on the Mercury space flights. The Gemini suit was a full pressure suit with better arm and leg mobility and was the first American suit actually used for EVA, with Ed White's 20-minute "spacewalk" on Gemini 4. This suit did not have a portable EC/LS life support system and was

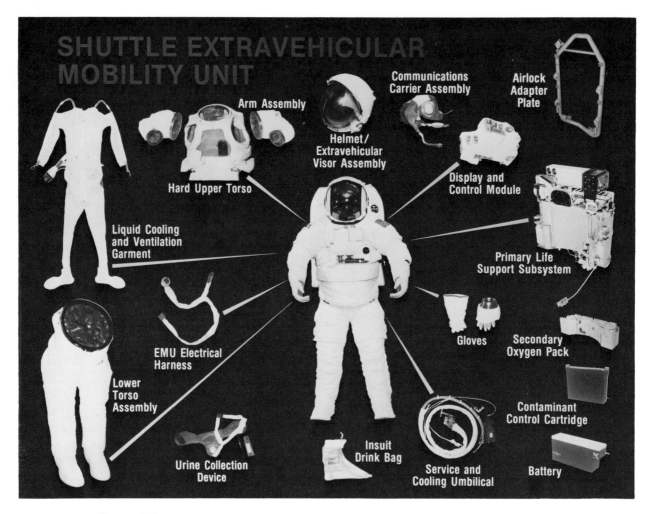

Figure 6.19 Components of the Shuttle EMU. *Courtesy of United Technologies Hamilton Standard.*

connected to the spacecraft by an umbilical which kept the suit purged with oxygen. The suit operated at about 24 kPa (3.5 psi); metabolic heat was removed by sweat evaporation from the skin. This suit proved poorly suited to EVA work. The visor, for example, fogged up when a crewperson was working hard. Sweat evaporation did not work well because the oxygen purge was uneven.

The Apollo suit had to be a fully functional space suit to permit locomotion by walking on the lunar surface. It had a portable EC/LS system capable of supporting EVA for about 8 hours with some margin. A liquid-cooling inner garment was first used on the Apollo suit and worked well. This garment covered the entire body except for head and extremities, was in contact with the skin for heat removal, and was made up of nearly contiguous networks of small tubing through which flowed a coolant liquid. The coolant temperature was adjustable. The Apollo suit also operated at 24 kPa on pure oxygen. CO_2 was removed by LiOH canisters. Heat was rejected by water evaporation, about 0.5 kg (1 lb) per hour at typical EVA metabolic rates, equivalent to moderate exercise. The Apollo suit is pictured in Figure 6.17.

The Skylab suit was a derivative of the Apollo suit, but did not include a portable EC/LS system as all Skylab EVA was planned and conducted adjacent to the vehicle so that umbilicals were practical. EVA was extensively used on Skylab for planned mission activities as well as for unplanned ones. The latter saved the mission, beginning with the solar wing repair and sunshade on the first crew visit. The Skylab missions had more unplanned than planned EVA hours.

The Shuttle suit is a new design with improved mobility and a new portable EC/LS. The Shuttle suit is similar in most respects to the Apollo suit. It is depicted in Figures 6.18 and 6.19. Subsystem functions are generally the same. Unlike the earlier suits which were individually tailored to each astronaut, the Shuttle suit is modular with a range of sizes for its parts such as arm and leg sections, and means of adjustment. Thus a Shuttle suit can be fitted to the crewperson by selection of appropriate part sizes and by adjustment.

All of these suits have employed similar design philosophy; they employ fabric design for the movable joints. The

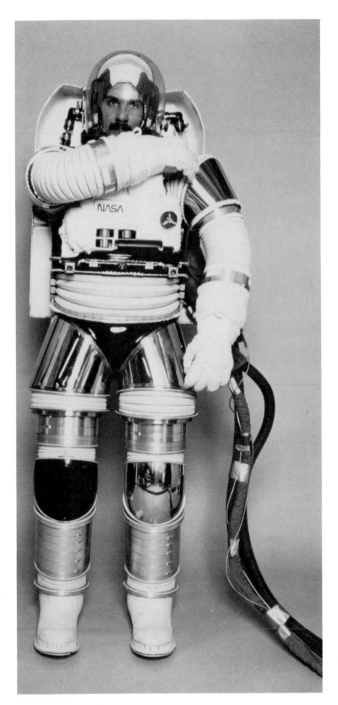

Figure 6.20 Hard suit designed for 8 psi operation. *Courtesy of United Technologies Hamilton Standard.*

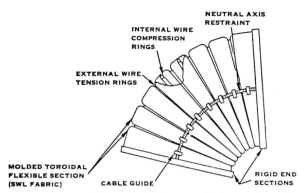

Figure 6.21 Typical hard suit joint—toroidal convolute elbow joint. *Courtesy of United Technologies Hamilton Standard.*

as if people had forgotten how routine it was on the surface of the Moon. The Solar Max repair and satellite retrieval missions with Shuttle have all but dissipated that attitude and EVA is now regarded as a routine operation for space station mission planning.

EMU (Suit) Design Considerations

Early suits tended to be immobile because internal pressure acted to straighten the joints as in the example of an inflatable figure of a man. This can be prevented if joints are carefully designed to maintain a constant volume as they move. Modern fabric suits meet this criterion rather well but exhibit friction resistance to motion because of the overlapping layers of fabric. As early as the 1960s it was recognized that mechanical joints of rigid parts with bearings or other hardware could be designed to have exactly constant volume and low friction. Several experimental "hard" suits of this nature have been built and tested; a recent example is shown in Figure 6.20. A representative joint is shown in Figure 6.21. Hard suits have tended to be somewhat larger and heavier than fabric "soft" suits, but future developments are expected to reduce this difference. A hard suit is more mobile than a fabric suit and can more easily be fitted with radiation shielding since the external surfaces are rigid except for the joints.

The Soviets were the first to accomplish an EVA. From the beginning, their suits have featured portable EC/LS systems. The Soviet suit used on their Salyuts is apparently a derivative of their earlier suits, and is depicted in Figure 6.22. The entire EC/LS unit hinges open, providing a large and convenient opening for the cosmonaut to enter the suit. It is easier to don and doff than the Shuttle suit, but both are relatively easy.

The Shuttle suit operates at slightly higher pressure, 28 kPa (4.1 psia) than its predecessors. The Shuttle cabin, however, operates at much higher pressure 100 kPa (14.7 psia). To avoid aeroembolism ("the bends") when going from Shuttle cabin pressure to suit pressure, a crewperson must breathe pure oxygen for about 3 hours, to purge nitrogen from the blood and body tissues. On recent missions, the

Shuttle suit uses a hard upper torso. Its shape is elliptic rather than cylindrical in cross-section, providing more useful work area for the crewperson's hands in front of the chest.

A number of years intervened between the last Skylab EVA and the first EVA on Shuttle. During this period an attitude developed on the part of some space engineers that EVA should only be used as an emergency measure. It was

 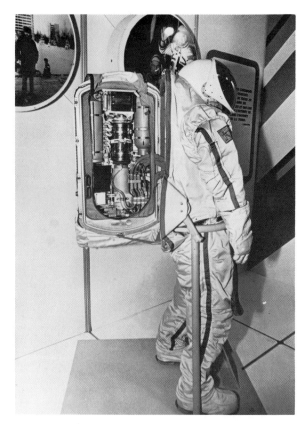

Figure 6.22   Soviet space suit used on Salyut.

Shuttle cabin pressure has been gradually reduced to about 65 kPa (9 psia) prior to EVAs to reduce prebreathe time and risk of bends. The large difference between cabin and suit pressures is a serious operational problem, and a suggested remedy is the use of a higher suit pressure. At present, 55 kPa (8 psia) is representative of the design pressure for future suits. Experimental hard suits have been operated at this pressure in tests.

The joint design principles for hard suits have not been applied to gloves, and may not be because of the small parts size that would be necessary. Volume compensation in gloves has been incomplete. The effort required to close one's hand in a glove under pressure is fatiguing on long EVA sessions involving a lot of hand work. The problem gets worse at higher pressures but can be compensated by better glove design. Final selection of a new suit pressure must consider adequate glove mobility as well as cabin pressure and how much lower suit pressure can be without risk of bends. Parametric relationships for cabin and suit pressures are shown in Figure 6.23.

Suit pressures significantly above 25 kPa permit two-gas suit atmospheres. Suit leakage for future suits is expected to be low enough so that only oxygen would be replenished by the portable EC/LS system; the initial nitrogen charge would be sufficient.

Another advantage of hard suit technology is increased life. A space station suit needs to be capable of at least dozens and preferably hundreds of uses without major refurbishment.

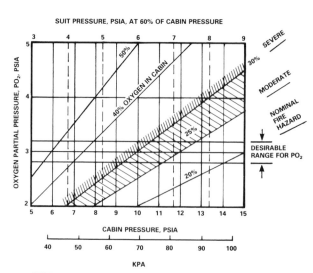

Figure 6.23   Parametric relationships for cabin and suit pressures.

Figure 6.24 Foot restraint platform on end of remote manipulator with astronaut holding satellite. *Courtesy of United Technologies Hamilton Standard.*

EVA Mobility

Locomotion is an essential part of EVA operations. On the Moon it was easy. In the zero g environment of a space station it is more difficult, but there are several solutions. Tethers are used to prevent accidental separation of an EVA crewperson from the vehicle. Even slow relative motions can result in large separations in periods less than an hour (see Chapter 3 on relative motions). The danger of a separated person being ''lost in space'' is real.

Handholds and cables along which one can move hand-over-hand have been used on Shuttle and work well provided that the crewperson's hands are not otherwise occupied. A foot restraint platform can be attached to the end of the remote manipulator system (RMS) (Figure 6.24) and a crewperson moved or positioned by the arm. Free motion, i.e., push off and arrest, has been used for short distances with a tether attached for safety. The man maneuvering unit (MMU) shown in Figure 6.25 has been highly successful on recent Shuttle flights. This device is a piloted spacecraft with full attitude control capability including an inertial measurement unit (gyro package). It is propelled by cold nitro-

gen gas stored in pressure tanks. Its attitude control features are what make it so useful for operations like satellite recovery.

EVA operations with the MMU are presently limited to about 1 km distance from the Shuttle (or a station). Future versions of the MMU may have greater delta v capability and operate at somewhat greater ranges.

Transporting crews over greater distances, e.g., for servicing missions, will probably use some sort of pressurized cabin carried by an OMV or OTV.

Tools and Equipment

Tools and equipment for EVA use are similar to those for inside use but must be designed for use with EVA gloves. Adequate restraints are more important because impromptu restraints such as makeshift handholds are less likely to be

Figure 6.25 Astronaut McCandless on first MMU test flight. *Courtesy of United Technologies Hamilton Standard.*

found. An EVA work station concept was depicted in Chapter 2, and a similar but simpler one has been used on Shuttle.

The Space Telescope is designed so that all nuts and bolts to be used for EVA servicing fit a single size of socket wrench (7/16″). Other designs for EVA servicing use similar simplified approaches to minimize the number and complexity of tools that must be used. Experimental power tools such as drills, saws, and nut drivers have been built.

Design of systems, tools, and equipment for EVA operations need only follow a few commonsense rules.

1. Make it accessible and keep tasks as simple as possible.

2. Be sure that tasks are compatible with mobility and vision limits of the EVA suit.

3. Ensure that tools can be readily used with pressurized EVA gloves.

4. Keep everything restrained so that tools, parts, etc., don't float away in zero g.

5. Provide adequate zero-g restraints for all work.

Chapter 7
Mass Properties Analysis

Mass properties analysis is simply the calculation of mass, center of gravity (or mass), and inertial properties of a design. It is indeed very simple in concept, but to paraphrase an old song, a good ''weights man'' is hard to find. The reason for this is that we always need mass properties data before a design is well defined, so the mass properties analyst must be able to fill gaps in data through good judgment and estimating techniques.

Methods of Mass Properties Estimating

The first key step in mass properties estimating is to develop a comprehensive list of the items to be included in the estimate. Such a list is usually called a work breakdown structure (WBS) - the term is typical of the contemporary trend to give simple things fancy names. The WBS actually originated in cost estimating and is discussed more thoroughly in Chapter 9. Cost estimating includes non-hardware items that have no mass, but it is clearly essential that mass and cost estimating be done for the same lists of hardware.

The WBS is an indentured list. It starts with entire systems such as ''space station,'' and progresses to lower levels such as ''pressurized module'' (level 2), ''structure'' (level 3), ''primary structure'' (level 4), ''ring frames'' (level 5), and sometimes all the way down to individual components.

Such lists are usually incomplete in early phases of preliminary design and often go only to level 2 or 3. An important element of the mass estimator's tool kit is a set of typical historical lists. The mass estimator will add items such as paints and sealers, allowances for extra thickness near welds (weld lands), and fasteners, often missing from a designer's list. A good example is a case where a mass estimator added the mass of a 747 aircraft cargo door to a space station pressure module design because he was convinced the designers would add the door as soon as they thought of ground access to the module interior for equipment installation and checkout. The door was kept in the mass statement although it never appeared in the design layouts for that particular space station.

With an adequate list in hand, there are several ways of mass estimating, depending on the amount of definition of the design. These are described here in approximate order of increasing accuracy.

Engineering judgment is sometimes the only alternative. Even with no design definition at all, a judgmental estimate may be made. The cargo door mentioned above is an example, and also an example of the use of analogy. Judgmental estimates can be adequately accurate, and in any case serve as placeholders for a more accurate estimate later.

Parametrics are widely used in conceptual design. This can be a simple factor such as 120 watts per square meter and 2 kg per square meter for a solar array, or as complex as the wing mass estimating equations used by Boeing for commercial jetliners. The latter employ an extensive suite of wing design parameters (span, airplane gross weight, aspect ratio, taper ratio, etc.) and are so accurate that they are used until late in the design process. Other parametrics are derived from plotting historical designs on a suitable curve, such as the mass of space station pressure vessels versus volume, as illustrated in Figure 7.1.

Analogy is very useful where a new design is similar to, or a modification of, an existing design. This is often the most practical approach to subsystems mass estimating. Given a list of ''black boxes'' for a subsystem, e.g., RF power amplifier, antenna coupler, cabling, high-gain antenna, it is usually convenient and reasonably accurate to assume that these items are of the same mass as existing

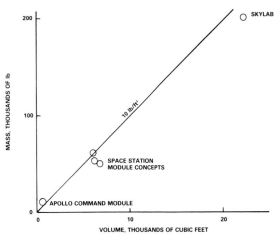

Figure 7.1 Mass and CG estimating trends for space station pressurized modules. *Courtesy of Boeing.*

equipment of similar function, characteristics, and application. The space business is now mature enough that an adequate data base exists for most subsystems.

Calculated mass is appropriate where design definition is sufficiently complete. The requisite completeness usually is reached first in structures and last in electronics. When a structural component has been designed and sized to accommodate its loads, its mass is determined by calculating the volume of metal and multiplying by the density of the particular alloy to be used. Similarly, when a "black box" is completely designed, its mass is determined by summing the masses of all its components and their mounting and installation provisions.

Measured mass is clearly the most accurate of all. When a design is built, it may be placed on a scale and weighed. Center of gravity and inertial properties can also be measured. One should not assume that even a measured mass is completely accurate unless one is confident that the design will not be changed in the future.

Growth allowance is the final step in mass estimating. Unless the entire vehicle is completed and resting on the weighing scale, it is appropriate to include an uncertainty allowance in the mass estimate. Historical results, described below, show that this is essentially always a positive number (the finished product will weigh more than the design estimate) and that the amount of a proper growth allowance is roughly inversely proportional to the completeness of design definition. Accurate growth estimating is a key element of the art and science of mass properties analysis.

Mass Estimating Methods

As implied above, mass estimating is a skill developed largely through experience. There are, however, a number of useful estimating aids that are readily prescribed.

Standard Work Breakdown Structure

A standard spacecraft mass estimating work breakdown structure, i.e., list of subsystems, is now in widespread use, listed in Table 7.1. This is not a formal standard, but is a common practice. Use of such a standard facilitates development of mass estimating data bases built up from past experience, since like system elements are grouped under the same headings for many programs and factors such as installation provisions are more nearly comparable.

Mass Estimating for Structural Elements and Shapes

Pressure vessels are usually made up of cylinders, spherical or elliptic end domes, or conical end sections, with flat or other special sections often closing out the ends. If the pressure vessel is a container, the internal volume and surface area are important. Geometric relations for these elements are given in Table 7.2.

Table 7.1 Standard work breakdown structure for spacecraft.

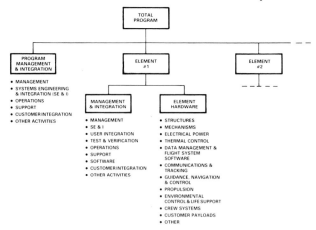

Table 7.2 Volume and surface area relationships for pressure vessel elements.

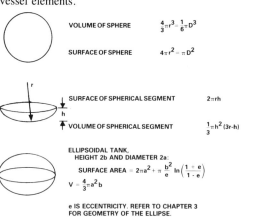

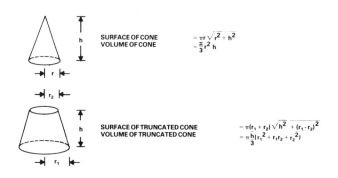

For propellant or consumables containers, one is frequently interested in the ratio of container mass to contents mass. This ratio is theoretically invariant with size. The volume of a sphere, for example, is given by $V = \pi D^3/6$. The wall thickness for a thin-walled spherical pressure vessel is $t = pD/(4\sigma)$ where p is pressure and σ is working stress. The volume of metal is $v = At$ where $A = \pi D^2$, and the mass of the vessel is $\rho_t v$. Taking the ratio of contents

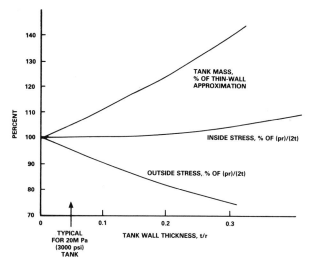

Figure 7.2 Thick-wall pressure vessels—comparison to thin-wall approximation.

mass to vessel mass, to vessel or tank mass

$$\rho_c V / \rho_t v = (2/3) \rho_c \sigma / (p\rho_t) \ . \tag{7.1}$$

The same expression holds for an endless cylinder except that the multiplier is 1/2 instead of 2/3.

Practical considerations often lead to variations from this ideal. Low-pressure vessels may be designed by "minimum-gauge" considerations. The minimum thickness of metal practical to work in tank fabrication is on the order of 0.6 mm (0.025 in). This, rather than pressure, may dictate wall thickness. Also, if the tank must be covered with an insulation blanket, e.g., for cryogenics, the blanket thickness will tend to be independent of tank size, and the blanket mass will be proportional to tank surface area rather than volume. Tank efficiency will increase with size as the volume/area ratio increases.

For a thick-walled pressure vessel, the variation in stress through the wall must be taken into account. Typical habitat modules and low-pressure propellant or consumables tanks up to 5 to 10 megaPascals (1000 psi or so) are adequately estimated by the thin-wall equations. High-pressure containers need thick-wall relationships for better accuracy. The maximum stress in a thick-walled pressure vessel may be expressed as

$$\sigma = \frac{\rho_r}{2t} \left[\frac{1 + \dfrac{t}{r} + \dfrac{t^2}{r^2} + \dfrac{1}{3}\dfrac{t^3}{r^3}}{1 + \dfrac{t}{r} + \dfrac{1}{3}\dfrac{t^2}{r^2}} \right] \tag{7.2}$$

where p is the internal pressure, r the inside radius, and t is the wall thickness. The maximum stress occurs at the inside wall. The relative stresses and mass of a thick-walled vessel are plotted in Figure 7.2 as a function of thickness-to-inside-radius ratio. A typical high-pressure vessel for a

space station or platform will operate at 20 megaPascals (about 3000 psi) and will have a t/r ratio of about 0.05 as indicated by the arrow on the figure. At this level, deviations from the thin-wall ideal are modest.

Idealized tank masses are adjusted to reflect fabrication and installation. Welded tanks are fabricated from segments. The tank wall is thickened near welds to allow for loss in strength resulting from weld heating. Tanks require fluid piping connections; internal fixtures such as fluid sumps, quantity gauging instrumentation, slosh baffles, and fluid delivery plumbing; safety provisions such as vent valves and burst diaphragms; and mounting fixtures. Weld lands and fabrication tolerances add 1 to 2 percent to tank weight and the other design provisions can add as much as 20 percent or so.

Mass of high-pressure or large tanks may be reduced by the use of filament winding, wherein a metal or plastic tank internal liner is wrapped with filaments of high-tensile material such as glass, graphite, or Kevlar. Analysis and design of filament-wound tanks is beyond the scope of this book, but the designer should be aware that significant mass reductions are possible, especially in the case of high-pressure tanks.

Structural Shells

Structural shells are often needed to connect system elements together. If a contiguous area covering for thermal, mechanical, and meteoroid protection is not needed, a truss structure often provides less massive interconnect. Minimum mass shells are designed with graphite-epoxy face sheets over lightweight aluminum or Nomex honeycomb core. Face sheets as thin as 0.25 mm (0.01 in) have been used in design studies. When shell loading dictates heavier structure, stiffened aluminum skin designs are often used.

Space Frame Trusses

A space frame truss can be the lowest mass structure for carrying compression or bending loads over significant distances. Taking compression loads as an example, a simple cylinder must have a certain minimum diameter-to-length ratio to avoid Euler buckling. It must also have a certain minimum wall-thickness-to-diameter ratio to avoid local crippling of the wall. These factors can result in structures that work their materials far below practical compressive strength limits. In such cases, a truss will usually be less massive. Since trusses can be readily deployed or erected in space, they also circumvent size limits imposed by launcher payload bay dimensions.

Only the longitudinal members of a truss carry the primary load imposed on the truss. The cross members only provide stability. A tetrahedral truss (triangular cross section) has 2.87 meters of total member length per meter of longitudinal member length. A hexahedral (box) truss has 3.12 meters per meter, not quite as efficient. In either case the efficiency of use of structural material, assuming that all members are made from the same sections, is about 30 percent. As noted, this may be much better than can be achieved by the alternatives.

For large trussworks, the mass of fittings needed to couple the members together will be about 20 percent. Thus the mass of a practical tetrahedral truss, compared to an ideal column working the structural material at maximum strength, will be about $(1.2)(2.87) = 3.44$ times greater. This assumes that the longitudinal members of the truss work the material effectively and that there are not significant mass penalties for environmental protection of the truss material.

Closed-section truss members can usually be worked effectively if the truss design is optimized for the application. Open sections such as hats or angles may buckle or cripple before the material approaches its working stress limits.

Subsystems Factors

Some mass estimating factors for subsystems were given in Chapter 5. Additional useful relations are summarized here.

Thermal control systems tend to be dominated by radiators. It is best to design radiator panels and determine their mass from fin thickness, tube size and spacing, etc., but rough estimates can be made using an estimating factor of 10 kg/m^2 of panel area. If the radiator radiates from both sides of the panel, the radiating area is twice the panel area. For very large thermal systems, say, in the megawatt range, the mass of plumbing to deliver coolant flow to the radiator panels becomes very significant, as it grows with roughly the square of radiator panel area. The mass of coolant flowing in the plumbing is usually significant and should not be overlooked.

Electronic equipment tends to package at about half the density of water. The mass of digital systems has decreased so rapidly that historical analogs may not be very useful. Power electronics is limited by power handling and heat dissipation. Power supplies typically weigh from 5 to 10 kg per kilowatt throughput. Very large or advanced systems could be significantly lighter; small (1 kW or less) systems are often dominated by control circuitry and hence heavier than the range given. The range does not include thermal control for the power electronics.

Propulsion and other systems that have consumables must include residuals and often reserves in the mass statement. Large liquid propulsion systems can have liquid residuals as little as 1 percent of propellant tank capacity. Values as great as 10 percent are often used for smaller systems. Residuals for gas or supercritical storage systems may exceed 10 percent. Pressurant gases or vapors must not be overlooked. Their mass can usually be estimated adequately from the perfect gas law, $pV = mRT/\mathfrak{M}$, where p is pres-

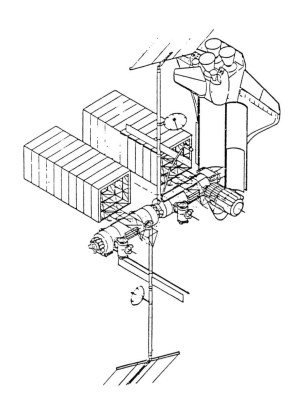

4 MAN SPACE OPERATIONS CENTER
EVOLUTIONARY BUILD-UP

NOTE: THIS IS PROBABLY THE FIRST CONCEPT THAT USED A "COMMON MODULE"

Figure 7.3 Space station modules with all subsystems functions, showing two such modules as a complete small space station. *Courtesy of Boeing.*

sure, V is tank volume, m is gas mass, $\mathfrak{M}$ is molecular weight, R is the universal gas constant 8314 joules/mol-°K (1545 Btu/mol-°R), and T is absolute temperature. Tank systems with positive expulsion systems can be much heavier than those without. The Shuttle water tanks, for example, use an internal metal bellows system to separate the water from the pressurant gas. One such water tank weighs 23 kg and holds 73 kg of water, for a tank fraction of 24 percent. At the other extreme, the liquid oxygen container for the Shuttle external tank weighs less than 1 percent of its contents weight.

Working Example

One of the most useful tools in mass estimating is a mass estimate for a similar system or one including similar equipment. As a part of Boeing studies of space station options conducted in 1982, a modular concept was created for which each module contained all elements of a small space station. Two such modules, as illustrated in Figure 7.3, comprised a complete, redundant station. Although no special claims for accuracy are made for the data relating to this design concept, its mass estimate (Table 7.3) does include entries for all space station subsystems and elements.

Table 7.3 Mass statement example for space station module. *Courtesy of Boeing.*

Index No.	Indent Level	WBS No.	Title	Mass kg (lb)	Rationale For Estimate
1	1	1.2.2.1	New Service Mod.	22214 (48973)	SUM
2	2	1.2.2.1.1	Structures	6798 (14987)	SUM
3	3	1.2.2.1.1.1	Press Membranes	4236 (9339)	SUM
4	4	1.2.2.1.1.1.1	Main Cylinder	3197 (7048)	- D = 3.556 m - L = 10.7 m - Thickness = 1 cm - 4 Cutouts @ 1.53 m dia. - A-Cyl - A-cut = 112.16 - 2219 Aluminum - 1% for welds, weld lands, and thickness tolerances.
5	4	1.2.2.1.1.1.2	Small Cylinder	242 (534)	- D = 1.93 m - L = 1.4 m - Thickness = 1 cm - Alloy & Tolerances per above.
6	4	1.2.2.1.1.1.3	Cone Sections	344 (758)	- Dmax = 3.556 - Dmin = 1.93 - H = 0.2 - Area = 6.04 Each - 2 Cones
7	4	1.2.2.1.1.1.4	Short Lateral Ext	114 (251)	- Docking/Berthing Port Support - D = 1.53 m - L = 0.3 m - Area = 1 m² Each - 4 Total
8	4	1.2.2.1.1.1.5	Port Partial Close	180 (397)	- Dmax = 1.53 m - Dmin = 1 m - Area = 1.05 m² - 6 Total
9	4	1.2.2.1.1.1.6	Cab Shell	159 (351)	- 7.15 m² of Shell @ 30 kg/m² - 7 Windows 3 cm thick and 0.2 m² - Less Cyl Sec Replaced (118) - Less Cone Sec Replaced (64)
10	3	1.2.2.1.1.2	Rings & Stiffen.	365 (805)	Sum
11	4	1.2.2.1.1.2.1	Ring Frames	64 (141)	- 8 in Main Cyl - Depth = 0.076 m - x-sec Area = 2.58 cm² - 2219 Alum
12	4	1.2.2.1.1.2.2	Main Sup. Rings	52 (115)	- Depth = 0.1 m - x-sec Area = 12.9 cm²
13	4	1.2.2.1.1.2.3	Main Sup. Trunn.	45 (99)	- 2 Side Fittings - 1 Keel Fitting - Fwd y-z Loads & Torsion - Titanium

Table 7.3 continued on next page

Table 7.3 Mass statement example for space station module (Continued). *Courtesy of Boeing.*

Index No.	Indent Level	WBS No.	Title	Mass kg (lb)	Rationale For Estimate
14	4	1.2.2.1.1.2.4	Main Sup. Trunn.	91 (201)	- 2 Side Fittings - X loads & Aft y-z Loads - Titanium
15	4	1.2.2.1.1.2.5	Sup Skin Dblrs	113 (249)	Insufficient Space To Locate Longerons; Must Heavily Reinforce Membrane in Region of Aft Support Trunnions
16	3	1.2.2.1.1.3	Hatches and Rails	935 (2061)	Sum
17	4	1.2.2.1.1.3.1	Entry Hatches	284 (626)	- 5 of 6 Ports Have Hatches - Based on Orbiter Airlock Hatch & Mechanism
18	4	1.2.2.1.1.3.2	Entry Hatch Frame	204 (450)	5 Frames; Estimate
19	4	1.2.2.1.1.3.3	Internal Rails	45 (99)	Estimate
20	4	1.2.2.1.1.3.4	External Rails	91 (201)	Estimate
21	4	1.2.2.1.1.3.5	Battery Compartmt	220 (485)	- Surface Area Estimated 11.3 m² - Unit Mass 9.76 kg/m² (2 lb/ft2)
22	4	1.2.2.1.1.3.6	Tankage Support	91 (201)	Estimate
23	3	1.2.2.1.1.4	Deployed Struct.	554 (1221)	Sum
24	4	1.2.2.1.1.4.1	Array Mast	224 (494)	- Length 26 m - Diam. 0.66 m - T-bar 0.125 cm - Graphite Epoxy @ 1660 kg/m³ - Basic Mass 4.3 kg/m - 100% Factor for Hinge Joints and Mechanisms
25	4	1.2.2.1.1.4.2	Array Strongback	43 (95)	- Length 10.8 m - Basic Mass 2 kg/m - 100% Factor for Cannister Attach Points
26	4	1.2.2.1.1.4.3	Array Support	136 (300)	Estimate for Launch Support Structure and Release Mechanisms
27	4	1.2.2.1.1.4.4	RCS Booms	65 (143)	- Length 9 m & Dia. 0.46 m - T-bar 0.125 m - Graphite Epoxy - Basic Mass 3 kg/m - 20% Factor for Base Hinge Joint & Mechanism
28	4	1.2.2.1.1.4.5	RCS Boom Support	18 (40)	Launch Support Structures and Release Mechanism
29	4	1.2.2.1.1.4.6	Misc. Sec. Struct.	68 (150)	Estimate
30	3	1.2.2.1.1.5	Interior Struct.	706 (1561)	Sum

Table 7.3 continued on next page

Table 7.3 Mass statement example for space station module (Continued). *Courtesy of Boeing.*

Index No.	Indent Level	WBS No.	Title	Mass kg (lb)	Rationale For Estimate
31	4	1.2.2.1.1.5.1	Floor Supp Frames	77 (170)	- 7 Frames, 8 cm² Equivalent, 3 m Long - Titanium
32	4	1.2.2.1.1.5.2	Floor Longerons	27 (60)	- 2 Beams 2.4 cm² Cross Sec., 12.5 m Long - Titanium
33	4	1.2.2.1.1.5.3	Floor	162 (357)	36 m² @ 4.5 kg/m²
34	4	1.2.2.1.1.5.4	Ceiling Frames	68 (150)	Scaled From Floor Frames (Ceiling Is Smaller)
35	4	1.2.2.1.1.5.5	Ceil. Longerons	22 (49)	Scaled From Floor; Ceiling is 10 m Long.
36	4	1.2.2.1.1.5.6	Ceiling	120 (265)	- Same Unit Mass As Floor - 2.66 m Wide × 10 m Long
37	4	1.2.2.1.1.5.7	Interior Partit.	232 (511)	- 12 Wall Sections 2 m Wide by 2.15 m High - 4.5 kg/m²
38	2	1.2.2.1.2	Mechanisms	408 (899)	Sum
39	3	1.2.2.1.2.1	Berthing Ports	340 (750)	5 Ports
40	3	1.2.2.1.2.2	Docking Port	68 (150)	One Port
41	2	1.2.2.1.3	Thermal Control	1364 (3007)	Sum
42	3	1.2.2.1.3.1	Integral Radiator	793 (1748)	- Scaled From SOC HM - 50 m² vs. 170 m² - Includes Skin, Tubes, Pedestals, Coolant, Stand-offs, and MLI
43	3	1.2.2.1.3.2	Fin Radiator	240 (529)	- 14 kWth - 30 Deg C Mean Temp - 3.43 m²/kW (2 Sides) - 48 m² @ 5 kg/m²
44	3	1.2.2.1.3.3	Plumbing & FLuid	54 (119)	- Equivalent of 52m of 2 cm Dia × 1 mm Wall CRES Tube - 20% Margin for Fittings - Includes Freon Fill
45	3	1.2.2.1.3.4	Water-Freon HTX	25 55	Ham Standard Estimate
46	3	1.2.2.1.3.5	Heat Pipe HTX	35 (77)	Rough Estimate Based On Vendor Dimensions
47	3	1.2.2.1.3.6	Pump Packs	35 (77)	Ham Standard Estimate
48	3	1.2.2.1.3.7	Cold Plates	136 (300)	12 Plates; Based On Ham Standard Estimate
49	3	1.2.2.1.3.8	Tanks & Pressurant	23 (51)	Estimate
50	3	1.2.2.1.3.9	Thermal Coatings	23 (51)	Estimate
51	2	1.2.2.1.4	Primary Propulsion	0 (0)	(No Primary Propulsion)

Table 7.3 continued on next page

Table 7.3 Mass statement example for space station module (Continued). *Courtesy of Boeing.*

Index No.	Indent Level	WBS No.	Title	Mass kg (lb)	Rationale For Estimate
52	2	1.2.2.1.5	Auxil. Propulsion	587 (1291)	Sum
53	3	1.2.2.1.5.1	Tankage	404 (891)	- 4 Shuttle Water Tanks - Filled Mass Interconnected With Emergency Water
54	3	1.2.2.1.5.2	Valves	45 (99)	30 Valves @ 1.5 kg Each
55	3	1.2.2.1.5.3	Fill & Drain	9 (20)	6 Ports @ 1.5 kg Each
56	3	1.2.2.1.5.4	Umbilical Plates	10 (22)	2 Plates @ 5 kg Each
57	3	1.2.2.1.5.5	Port Interconnect	20 (44)	2 Ports @ 10 kg Each
58	3	1.2.2.1.5.6	Lines	20 (44)	0.17 kg/m × 40 m + 30%
59	3	1.2.2.1.5.7	Thrusters	36 (79)	18 Thrusters @ 2 kg Each
60	3	1.2.2.1.5.8	Instrumentation	43 (95)	Estimate
61	2	1.2.2.1.6	Ordnance	10 (22)	Deployment Releases
62	2	1.2.2.1.7	Electrical Power	3478 (7667)	Sum
63	3	1.2.2.1.7.1	Solar Array	768 (1693)	- 170 W/m^2 - 79 kW Raw Power BOL - 20% Degradation At EOL - SEPS/PEP Technology
64	3	1.2.2.1.7.2	Power Conditioning	234 (516)	Technology Staff Estimate
65	3	1.2.2.1.7.3	Energy Storage	1298 (2862)	Sum (Regen Fuel Cell)
66	4	1.2.2.1.7.3.1	O$_2$ Gas & Tanks	197 (434)	- 68 kg Gas - Tank Mass 1.9 × Gas
67	4	1.2.2.1.7.3.2	H$_2$ Gas & Tanks	255 (562)	- 8.5 kg Gas - Tank Mass 29 × Gas
68	4	1.2.2.1.7.3.3	Fuel Cells	364 (802)	4 Shuttle Fuel Cells
69	4	1.2.2.1.7.3.4	Electrolysis Units	364 (802)	Set Equal To Fuel Cells For Lack Of Definiton
70	4	1.2.2.1.7.3.5	Misc. Equipment	118 (260)	10% Of Above For Plumbing, Elec, Thermal, Etc.
71	3	1.2.2.1.7.4	Array Main Cable	168 (370)	Tech. Staff Estimate
72	3	1.2.2.1.7.5	Bussing	200 (441)	Same
73	3	1.2.2.1.7.6	Harnesses & Control	500 (1102)	Same
74	3	1.2.2.1.7.7	Misc. Equip & Boxes	200 (441)	Same
75	3	1.2.2.1.7.8	Interior Lights	60 (132)	Same

Table 7.3 continued on next page

Table 7.3 Mass statement example for space station module (Continued). *Courtesy of Boeing.*

Index No.	Indent Level	WBS No.	Title	Mass kg (lb)	Rationale For Estimate
76	3	1.2.2.1.7.9	Emerg. Battery	50 (110)	To Run Emergency Lights, Com, & Data Mgmt.
77	2	1.2.2.1.8	Guid., Nav., & C	420 (926)	Sum
78	3	1.2.2.1.8.1	CMGs	300 (661)	Allowance Pending Final Sizing of CMGs
79	3	1.2.2.1.8.2	Computer & IMU	120 (265)	Derived From SOC Estimate
80	2	1.2.2.1.9	Tracking & Comm	653 (1440)	Sum
81	3	1.2.2.1.9.1	RF Equipment	524 (1155)	Sum
82	4	1.2.2.1.9.1.1	Signal Proces.	22 (49)	Technology Staff Estimate
83	4	1.2.2.1.9.1.2	Digital Proces.	22 (49)	Same
84	4	1.2.2.1.9.1.3	Switching Netw'k	20 (44)	Same
85	4	1.2.2.1.9.1.4	Modul & Preamps	40 (88)	8 Units @ 5 kg.
86	4	1.2.2.1.9.1.5	GPS Rcvr & Proc.	23 (51)	Technology Staff Estimate
87	4	1.2.2.1.9.1.6	EVA Rcvr/Xmtr	20 (44)	Same
88	4	1.2.2.1.9.1.7	Radar Processor	20 (44)	Same
89	4	1.2.2.1.9.1.8	Ku-Band Amps	47 (104)	Same
90	4	1.2.2.1.9.1.9	S-Band Amps	110 (243)	Same
91	4	1.2.2.1.9.1.10	Tracking Radar	65 (143)	Same
92	4	1.2.2.1.9.1.11	Hi-Gain Antenna	34 (75)	Same
93	4	1.2.2.1.9.1.12	Mast & Drive	20 (44)	Same
94	4	1.2.2.1.9.1.13	CLS Antennas	8 (18)	Same
95	4	1.2.2.1.9.1.14	L-Band Antenna	4 (9)	Same
96	4	1.2.2.1.9.1.15	UHF Antenna	9 (20)	Same
97	4	1.2.2.1.9.1.16	Horns & Drive	10 (22)	Same
98	4	1.2.2.1.9.1.17	RF Cabling	50 (110)	Estimate
99	3	1.2.2.1.9.2	Intra-S/S Voice	36 (79)	Sum
100	4	1.2.2.1.9.2.1	Voice Terminals	16 (35)	8 @ 2 kg

Table 7.3 continued on next page

Table 7.3 Mass statement example for space station module (Continued). *Courtesy of Boeing.*

Index No.	Indent Level	WBS No.	Title	Mass kg (lb)	Rationale For Estimate
101	4	1.2.2.1.9.2.2	C & W Equip.	20 (44)	Estimate
102	3	1.2.2.1.9.3	C & T Support	93 (205)	Sum
103	4	1.2.2.1.9.3.1	TV Cameras	20 (44)	Four @ 5 kg
104	4	1.2.2.1.9.3.2	Digital Proces.	23 (51)	Estimate
105	4	1.2.2.1.9.3.3	Cable Harnesses	35 (77)	Estimate
106	4	1.2.2.1.9.3.4	Audio/Data Cable	15 (33)	Estimate
107	2	1.2.2.1.10	Data Management	481 (1060)	Sum
108	3	1.2.2.1.10.1	Cont & Disp Panel	81 (179)	15 m² Aluminum Sheet Equiv
109	3	1.2.2.1.10.2	CRT Displays	120 (265)	6 @ 20 kg
110	3	1.2.2.1.10.3	Keyboards & Disp	50 (110)	Estimate
111	3	1.2.2.1.10.4	Remote Terminals	60 (132)	3 @ 20 kg Each: 1-Galley, 2-Crew Quarters
112	3	1.2.2.1.10.5	Computers	120 (265)	6 @ 20 kg
113	3	1.2.2.1.10.6	Wiring & Bussing	50 (110)	Estimate
114	2	1.2.2.1.11	Instrumentation	100 (220)	Allowance for Non-Dedicated Instrumentation
115	2	1.2.2.1.12	Crew Accommodat.	306 (675)	Sum
116	3	1.2.2.1.12.1	Dining Table	21 (46)	Small Table
117	3	1.2.2.1.12.2	Recreation Equip.	100 (220)	Estimate
118	3	1.2.2.1.12.3	Health Maint.	100 (220)	Allowance For Undefined Equipment
119	3	1.2.2.1.12.4	Sleep Restraints	21 (46)	Two Restraints
120	3	1.2.2.1.12.5	Writing Desks	21 (46)	Estimate
121	3	1.2.2.1.12.6	Personal Stowage	20 (44)	Estimate
122	3	1.2.2.1.12.7	Misc. Items	23 (51)	Estimate
123	2	1.2.2.1.13	EC/LS & Crew Sys.	1911 (4213)	Sum
124	3	1.2.2.1.13.1	EC/LS	1324 (2919)	Sum
125	4	1.2.2.1.13.1.1	Controls & Disp	34 (75)	-Dedicated Equipment -Ham Standard Estimate
126	4	1.2.2.1.13.1.2	Thermal/Vent Pack	45 (99)	Ham Standard Estimate

Table 7.3 continued on next page

Table 7.3 Mass statement example for space station module (Continued). *Courtesy of Boeing.*

Index No.	Indent Level	WBS No.	Title	Mass kg (lb)	Rationale For Estimate
127	4	1.2.2.1.13.1.3	Dehumidifier	39 (86)	Same
128	4	1.2.2.1.13.1.4	CO_2 Removal	54 (118)	Same
129	4	1.2.2.1.13.1.5	Catalytic Oxidizer	25 (54)	Same
130	4	1.2.2.1.13.1.6	Odor Control	9 (20)	Same
131	4	1.2.2.1.13.1.7	Atmos. Monitor	23 (51)	Same
132	4	1.2.2.1.13.1.8	Emerg O_2 Stor & Gas	111 (245)	Based on Shuttle Atmos. Storage Tanks
133	4	1.2.2.1.13.1.9	Emerg N_2 Stor & Gas	256 (564)	Same
134	4	1.2.2.1.13.1.10	Water Qual Monitor	54 (119)	Ham Standard Estimate
135	4	1.2.2.1.13.1.11	Waste Water Tks	69 (152)	3 Shuttle Tanks, Empty
136	4	1.2.2.1.13.1.12	Potable Water	606 (1336)	6 Shuttle Water Tanks, Full
137	3	1.2.2.1.13.2	Crew Systems	587 (1294)	Sum
138	4	1.2.2.1.13.2.1	Waste Collection	41 (90)	Same as Shuttle Toilet
139	4	1.2.2.1.13.2.2	Hot/Cold Water Sup	23 (50)	Ham Standard Estimate
140	4	1.2.2.1.13.2.3	Shower	54 (120)	Same
141	4	1.2.2.1.13.2.4	Hand Wash	25 (55)	Same
142	4	1.2.2.1.13.2.5	Clothes Wash/Dry	41 (90)	Same
143	4	1.2.2.1.13.2.6	Food Refriger.	23 (51)	Same
144	4	1.2.2.1.13.2.7	Oven	34 (75)	Same
145	4	1.2.2.1.13.2.8	Dishwasher	14 (31)	Same
146	4	1.2.2.1.13.2.9	Backpack Recond.	27 (60)	Same
147	4	1.2.2.1.13.2.10	Emerg CO_2 Remov.	23 (51)	Same
148	4	1.2.2.1.13.2.11	Storage Cabinets	100 (220)	Same
149	4	1.2.2.1.13 2 12	EVA Suit	182 (401)	One Suit
150	2	1.2.2.1.17	Mission Equipment	1844 (4065)	Sum
151	3	1.2.2.1.17.1	ACS Propellant	0 (0)	Covered Under 1.2.2.1.5.1
152	3	1.2.2.1.17.2	Atmosphere	100 (220)	Density × Volume

Table 7.3 continued on next page

Table 7.3 Mass statement example for space station module (Continued). *Courtesy of Boeing.*

Index No.	Indent Level	WBS No.	Title	Mass kg (lb)	Rationale For Estimate
153	3	1.2.2.1.17.3	Spares	644 (1420)	Roughly 15% of Subsys. and Equip. Mass
154	3	1.2.2.1.17.4	Food	200 (441)	Emergency Supply
155	3	1.2.2.1.17.5	LiOH Cartridges	665 (1466)	Emergency Supply for CO_2 Removal
156	3	1.2.2.1.17.6	Utensils & Tools	235 (518)	Estimate
157	2	1.2.2.1.18	Mass Growth Allow.	3854 (8497)	33% Of Identified Mass Except For: - Pressure Membrane - Fluids - Mission Equipment

Center of Gravity and Inertial Properties

While the acquisition of reliable weights data is the most challenging data gathering aspect of mass properties analysis, the calculation of inertial properties is the most challenging from the analytical standpoint. Inertial properties calculation is sufficiently tedious that, as a practical matter, it is usually not done unless a convenient computer routine is available. Finding the center of gravity of a system is prerequisite to calculation of inertial properties. This, too, is greatly aided by a suitable computer routine.

Center of Gravity

The center of gravity of an assemblage of elements is found by a simple weighted averaging procedure. (In physics, the center of gravity is usually called the center of mass.) Beginning with any arbitrary reference point, the center of gravity is found by summing the products of the masses and x,y,z offsets of each element (the *moments*) and dividing by the total mass of all elements. The offset for each element must of course be measured to the center of gravity of the element itself. In equation form:

$$x_{cg} = \sum_i x_i m_i / \sum_i m_i \qquad (7.3)$$

and similarly for y and z.

The center of gravity of an assembly is important both from the standpoint of launching it in the Space Shuttle and from considerations of propulsion and flight control.

Inertial Properties

The inertial properties of an object define its rotational motion response to torques and are used to compute gravity gradient torques. The moments and products of inertia define inertia with respect to angular acceleration resulting from torques, and symmetries with respect to coordinate axes. An object that is symmetric with respect to a set of axes has zero products of inertia. The associated axes are called the principal axes.

The moment of inertia about any particular axis is often treated as a scalar value in simple rotating motion analysis. This is adequate, for example, to calculate the angular momentum of an object rotating about a principal axis. In Chapter 3, we used the inertia tensor to find gravity gradient torques. Angular momentum and the direction of rotation of an object are vector quantities; they have a direction, usually given as the direction of the axis of rotation. Analogous to the expression for momentum in linear motion, the expression

$$\mathbf{L} = \mathbf{I}\omega \qquad (7.4)$$

defines angular momentum. The term $\mathbf{I}$ can be viewed as the ratio of angular momentum to angular velocity. Because it is obtained by dividing one vector by another, it has the properties of a tensor of the second rank, and its quantities are those of a 3×3 matrix,

$$\mathbf{I} = \begin{pmatrix} I_{xx} & I_{xy} & I_{xz} \\ I_{yx} & I_{yy} & I_{yz} \\ I_{zx} & I_{zy} & I_{zz} \end{pmatrix}.$$

Since the inertia tensor is symmetric about its diagonal, diagonally symmetric products of inertia are equal, i.e., $I_{yx} = I_{xy}$. Typical of the diagonal elements, of the inertia tensor is I_{xx} which can be calculated as

$$I_{xx} = \sum_i m_i r_i^2 \qquad (7.5)$$

where r_i is the distance of the i-th element from the x-axis. Also, the off-diagonal elements are typified by I_{xy} which is given as

$$I_{xy} = -\sum_i m_i x_i y_i \qquad (7.6)$$

where x_i and y_i are coordinates with respect to the center of

Table 7.4 Inertia primitives.

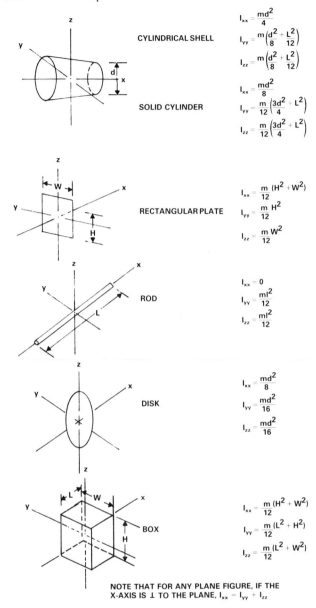

$I_{xx} = \frac{md^2}{4}$

CYLINDRICAL SHELL $I_{yy} = m\left(\frac{d^2}{8} + \frac{L^2}{12}\right)$

$I_{zz} = m\left(\frac{d^2}{8} + \frac{L^2}{12}\right)$

$I_{xx} = \frac{md^2}{8}$

SOLID CYLINDER $I_{yy} = \frac{m}{12}\left(\frac{3d^2}{4} + L^2\right)$

$I_{zz} = \frac{m}{12}\left(\frac{3d^2}{4} + L^2\right)$

$I_{xx} = \frac{m}{12}(H^2 + W^2)$

RECTANGULAR PLATE $I_{yy} = \frac{m\,H^2}{12}$

$I_{zz} = \frac{m\,W^2}{12}$

$I_{xx} = 0$

ROD $I_{yy} = \frac{ml^2}{12}$

$I_{zz} = \frac{ml^2}{12}$

$I_{xx} = \frac{md^2}{8}$

DISK $I_{yy} = \frac{md^2}{16}$

$I_{zz} = \frac{md^2}{16}$

$I_{xx} = \frac{m}{12}(H^2 + W^2)$

BOX $I_{yy} = \frac{m}{12}(L^2 + H^2)$

$I_{zz} = \frac{m}{12}(L^2 + W^2)$

NOTE THAT FOR ANY PLANE FIGURE, IF THE
X-AXIS IS ⊥ TO THE PLANE, $I_{xx} = I_{yy} + I_{zz}$

mass. Analogous expressions are used for the other inertia tensor terms.

It is often more practical to calculate the inertial properties of a complex object by subdividing it into elements with primitive geometric shapes, computing the moments of inertia of these shapes about the local center of gravity of each, and then summing up the inertia of the entire object. Inertias of primitive shapes can be found in the literature; those for a few common shapes are given in Table 7.4.

The primitive shapes that comprise a complex object like a space vehicle are most often oriented, with respect to the body axes of the vehicle, in an attitude different than that for which the principal inertias of the shapes are given in Table 7.4. The inertia tensors of the primitive shapes must

be transformed to the proper coordinate system in order to obtain their correct contribution to the inertia of the entire vehicle.

Transforming an inertia tensor is slightly more complicated than transforming a vector as defined in Chapter 3. The transformation matrix is defined from the sines and cosines of the rotation angles exactly as for a vector transformation, but the matrix multiplication, instead of $\mathbf{x}^1 = A\mathbf{x}$ as for a vector, is

$$\mathbf{I}^1 = A\mathbf{I}A^T \qquad (7.7)$$

where A^T is the transpose of A. Matrix multiplication is not commutative, hence the order of products given must be preserved.

This will be clearer with an example. Figure 7.4 illustrates a cantilevered space station solar array with a 50° beta tilt applied to track the sun which is assumed to be 50° out of the orbital plane. We wish to obtain the inertia tensor of the assembly so as to ascertain its gravity gradient torque.

The assembly is analyzed as five components: a 48-meter mast centered on the coordinate axes, two 200-kg drive and slip-ring assemblies, and two 500-kg rectangular solar panels. The mast may be modeled as a rod, the drives as mass points (their inertias about their centers of gravity are very small compared to their mr^2 terms), and the arrays as rectangular plates. Inertia tensors for the rod and plate were given in Table 7.4. All orientations in the table are selected so that the geometric primitives will have off diagonal products of inertia equal to zero. For the rod, $I_{yy} = I_{zz} = ml^2/12$, and $I_{xx} = 0$. We could easily observe that because the rod is oriented on the x-axis in the table and on the y-axis in our example, $I_{xx} = ml^2/12$ and $I_{yy} = 0$. However, we will illustrate the use of a transformation. The needed rotation is 90° about the z-axis (either direction). The matrix multiplication according to eq. 7.7 is

$$A\mathbf{I}A^T = \begin{pmatrix} 0 & 1 & 0 \\ -1 & 0 & 0 \\ 0 & 0 & 1 \end{pmatrix} \begin{pmatrix} 0 & 0 & 0 \\ 0 & ml^2/_{12} & 0 \\ 0 & 0 & ml^2/_{12} \end{pmatrix} \begin{pmatrix} 0 & -1 & 0 \\ 1 & 0 & 0 \\ 0 & 0 & 1 \end{pmatrix}.$$

Taking the second multiplication first, the intermediate and

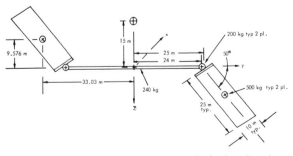

Figure 7.4 Space station solar array example for inertia calculations.

final results are

$$
\begin{pmatrix} 0 & 1 & 0 \\ -1 & 0 & 0 \\ 0 & 0 & 1 \end{pmatrix} \begin{pmatrix} 0 & 0 & 0 \\ ml^2/_{12} & 0 & 0 \\ 0 & 0 & ml^2/_{12} \end{pmatrix}
$$

$$
= \begin{pmatrix} ml^2/_{12} & 0 & 0 \\ 0 & 0 & 0 \\ 0 & 0 & ml^2/_{12} \end{pmatrix}.
$$

The matrix multiplications have moved the I_{yy} term to I_{xx} as desired. Since the mast is centered on the coordinate axes, its mr^2 terms are zero. The mast contributions to tensor are $I_{xx} = I_{zz} = 240 \text{kg} \times (48 \text{ m})^2/12 = 46,080$ kg-m².

The rotations for the array panels are illustrated in Figure 7.5. Each panel is first rotated about its y-axis so that it is facing upward, and then about its new z-axis to obtain the 50° beta tilt. On the left we have depicted rotating the object and on the right the equivalent coordinate rotations (remember that transformations rotate coordinates, not objects). The transformation matrix is given by (x rotation) (y rotation). The numerical value of the matrix is

$$
\begin{pmatrix} 0 & 0 & -1 \\ -.76604 & .64279 & 0 \\ .64279 & .76604 & 0 \end{pmatrix}.
$$

Taking the formulas for the inertia tensor of the rectangular plates from Table 7.4, and setting up the problem, we obtain

$$
I' = \begin{pmatrix} 0 & 0 & -1 \\ -.76604 & .64279 & 0 \\ .64279 & .76604 & 0 \end{pmatrix} \begin{pmatrix} 30208 & 0 & 0 \\ 0 & 4167 & 0 \\ 0 & 0 & 26042 \end{pmatrix}
$$

$$
\begin{pmatrix} 0 & -.76604 & .64279 \\ 0 & .64279 & .76604 \\ -1 & 0 & 0 \end{pmatrix}.
$$

Results of the calculation are, for each solar panel

$$
I' = \begin{pmatrix} 26042 & 0 & 0 \\ 0 & 19448.3 & -12822.7 \\ 0 & -12822.7 & 14926.6 \end{pmatrix}
$$

Note that the value for I_{zz} in the original orientation has become I_{xx}. This is expected, as the solar panel is edgewise to the space station x-axis direction, the same as the reference rectangular plate in Table 7.4 is edgewise to the z-axis. Also note that I_{yy} is greater than I_{zz}. This is also expected since the tilt of the panel presents a greater projection onto the z-axis than onto the y-axis. The cross products are I_{yz} and I_{zy}; this is expected because the panel is symmetric about the y-z plane. The cross products are equal as required. They are negative because the panel extends into the (+,+) and (−,−) quadrants of the y-z plane (refer to eq. 7.5).

The mr^2 terms must be added to complete the inertia tensor

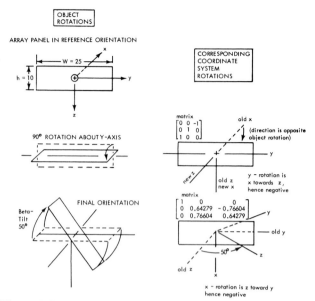

Figure 7.5 Solar array panel rotations for inertia calculations.

calculation. Because the centers of mass for the solar panels have y and z offsets from the center of mass of the entire assembly, they generate I_{yz} products of inertia, computed by

$$
I_{yz} = -33.08 \times 9.576 \times 500 = -158,148.
$$

A summary of the entire inertia tensor calculation is presented in Table 7.5. Note that the I_{yz} contribution of the solar panels due to their center of mass offsets is greater than that due to orientation of the panels themselves. This serves to underline the importance of the mr^2 terms to the inertial properties of large space vehicles.

Finally, if the entire solar array-mast assembly were offset from the center of mass of the entire space station as illustrated in Figure 7.4, an additional mr^2 term equal to the mass of the assembly multiplied by its offset squared would

Table 7.5 Example inertia properties calculation for the configuration described in Figure 7.4 (values are kg-m²).

Item	I_{xx}	I_{yy}	I_{zz}	I_{xy}	I_{xz}	I_{yz}
Solar Panel #1 About Its c.g.	26,042	19,448	14,297	0	0	−12,823
Solar Panel #2 About Its c.g.	26,042	19,448	14,297	0	0	−12,823
Solar Panel #1 mr^2 term	591,340	45,849	545,490	0	0	−158,148
Solar Panel #2 mr^2 term	591,340	45,849	545,490	0	0	−158,148
Hinge Unit #1	115,200	0	115,200	0	0	0
Hinge Unit #2	115,200	0	115,200	0	0	0
Mast	46,080	0	46,080	0	0	0
Sums	1,511,244	130,594	1,396,054	0	0	−341,942

be required to give the complete contribution of the solar array-mast assembly to the space station inertia tensor. As noted in Chapter 3, however, if the remainder of the space station flies with a different orientation strategy than the solar array, it may be important to calculate their inertia tensors separately.

Mass Growth Trends and Prediction

After the Apollo mission mode of lunar orbit rendezvous was selected in 1962, it was necessary for the spacecraft project in Houston, Texas, and the Saturn rocket project in Huntsville, Alabama, to agree on the mass of the Apollo spacecraft assembly that the Saturn would launch on a trajectory to the Moon. This value would then serve as the design requirement for the rocket.

The agreed-upon figure was 75,000 lb. At that time it seemed to have more than enough margin for error. The Saturn designers, on their own, decided to set their performance target at 85,000 lb, and later raised it somewhat more. This was fortunate, because the spacecraft mass "throw weight" for Apollo 11 was over 90,000 lb. Later Apollo missions, with the addition of such things as the lunar rover "golf cart," reached about 115,000 lb.

Mass growth, of course, was the reason for the dramatic increases in spacecraft mass between 1962 and Apollo 11 in 1969. The original estimate for a fully fueled Lunar Module was 22,000 lb. This grew to about 32,000 lb. The original estimate for an Apollo Command Module was 8000 lb; it grew to nearly 13,000 lb. Interestingly, the Apollo Service Module grew very little.

Clearly, mass growth presents a problem to space systems designers. Mass growth prediction is an essential part of the mass estimator's job. If mass growth exceeds the lift capability of a selected launch system, a major program disruption is likely to occur, even to the point of cancellation. While mass growth is of somewhat less concern in the case of space stations and platforms than in the case of high-performance aircraft or propulsion systems, the lift capability and center of gravity limits of the Space Shuttle are firm constraints. The number of Shuttle flights needed to place a space station or platform in orbit is of both cost and schedule concern.

Causes of Mass Growth

There are four principal causes of mass growth: ignorance, the "Christmas tree" effect, intentional underestimating, and amplification of mass growth by positive feedback. Mass increase due to discretionary changes in design requirements is not, strictly speaking, "growth." It is, however, included with true growth effects in program mass histories.

Ignorance, i.e., of requirements and of the technical subtleties of design, is the main root cause of mass growth.

Overall objectives are usually well understood even in the beginning of a design effort. Immature concepts and incomplete definition are the main forms of ignorance. It is likely, for example, in an initial concept of a power subsystem, to make fairly accurate estimates of the solar array and power processor masses but overlook the power cables and harnesses that must interconnect them. Design details such as secondary structure, brackets, clamps, fasteners, hookup wire, plumbing and ducting, instrumentation, access panels and doors, inspection and test provisions, and paint and sealers do not ordinarily show up until late in design development. But they surely will be in the finished product, and they will have mass and cost.

Ignorance of operating environments and other requirements can lead to management decisions to apply extraordinary design margins. The Apollo Command Module heat shield was designed to withstand at least twice the predicted heating environment. Large uncertainties existed in the predictions because of lack of test data at high velocities. The predictions turned out to be about right, and the heat shield could have been much lighter. But who, given the ignorance of the time and the national importance of the project, would have recommended a riskier course?

In a conceptual or preliminary design phase, ignorance and lack of detail must be provided for by mass growth allowance.

The *Christmas tree effect* is the tendency to adorn a program or a design with nice-to-have, or perhaps essential, additions. One may speculate that available space within a space station module will, sooner or later, be used to accommodate someone's experiment or gadget. The initial Shuttle design included an "OMS kit," an extra set of tanks that were to be placed in the payload bay to carry extra orbit maneuvering propellant for some missions. Budgetary pressures eliminated the OMS kit, and the Shuttle program has done well without it.

The early phases of most space programs are competitive, with more than one contractor vying for each important assignment. The customer, usually a government agency, wants high performance and low cost. The customer probably uses a cost model that is driven by mass (see Chapter 9). Intentional underestimates most often are simply putting the best possible interpretation on one's estimates rather than outright falsification. (Falsification accusations are often heard from losing bidders.) If your statistical history of design mass growth indicates that you should use a 30 percent mass growth allowance, will you if you believe your competitor will use 10 percent?

Intentional underestimating is not the exclusive province of contractors. During the final phases of Shuttle preliminary design, reasonable and prudent mass growth allowances were eliminated from the system design by the NASA administrator because they were causing the size of the propulsion system to exceed limits imposed by the original program cost-per-flight estimates of $10.7 million in 1971 dollars. Eliminating mass growth allowances did not eliminate mass growth, and the Shuttle's initial performance capability fell short of the target 65,000 lb by about 25,000 lb. Incremental improvements and uprating are recovering the lost performance and the target will be attained by about 1986. (The present cost per flight far exceeds the original target for reasons having little to do with propulsion system size.)

Mass growth inadequately covered by growth allowances is compounded by a feedback effect that exists in almost all systems. Mass growth in an aircraft structure requires added fuel to carry the weight, added wing to carry the fuel, and still more structure to carry the extra fuel and wing, etc. Mass growth of an Apollo spacecraft required more heat shield which required more parachutes which required more structure, etc.

This effect is less severe in space stations and platforms because they do not carry much propellant; most of their systems are relatively insensitive to mass. There is feedback in structure to carry launch loads and in attitude control systems. The main concern for these systems, however, is the mass and center of gravity limits of the Shuttle. Many space station modules will be sized near one of these limits and the limits cannot be violated.

Representative Histories

These histories are taken from a Boeing-funded study of mass growth aimed at creating a statistical basis for mass growth allowances during conceptual and preliminary design activities.

The design of the Saturn S-1C (Booster) stage was initiated by NASA in 1961 and later turned over to Boeing in 1962. The S-lC, although far larger than any rocket stage ever built, was founded on well-known technology, and the NASA design team was conservative in their mass estimating. Consequently, little mass growth occurred, as shown in Figure 7.6. Design changes, mainly in the fuel and oxidizer tanks, reduced mass in the S-1C-4 and subsequent vehicles.

The Saturn S-II (second) stage history is shown in Figure 7.7. The first unit, S-II-1, experienced a typical growth of about 20 percent. A vigorous mass reduction effort, coincident with that conducted on the S-1C, in response to mass increases in the Apollo spacecraft, reduced mass of S-II-4 and subsequent vehicles.

North American (now Rockwell) was awarded a contract for the Apollo Command and Service Modules in late 1961. The first NASA reported mass was 8150 lb. Because of the many new aspects of the Apollo mission, design changes necessitated a "block change," incorporating many major design revisions, early in the program. The first unmanned

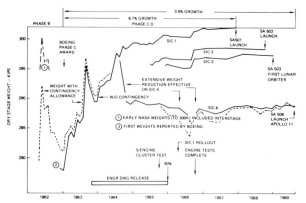

Figure 7.6 Mass growth history for Saturn S-1C. *Courtesy of Boeing.*

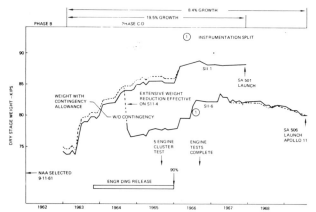

Figure 7.7 Mass growth history for Saturn S-II stage. *Courtesy of Boeing.*

test flight of a Block I module was at a mass of 11,000 lb. Subsequent Block II changes, many in response to the fire on the launch pad in 1967, resulted in a maximum reported mass of nearly 13,000 lb as shown in Figure 7.8. At this point the design was relatively mature and continuing improvements led to mass reductions after 1967. CM-106 was the unit used on Apollo 11, the first lunar landing.

The most consistent mass growth data for the Apollo Lunar Module are the reported values for total separated mass (i.e., separated from the Apollo Command and Service Modules at initiation of the landing itself), about 2/3 of which was propellant. Early NASA studies of the LM estimated a mass of 22,000 lb, and this was the value estimated in the winning Grumman proposal for the LM. As shown in Figure 7.9, post-proposal analyses soon raised the estimate to about 27,000 lb; at the completion of preliminary design, the value was about 28,500 lb and this was used as a control weight. By mid-1965 it was realized that LM mass growth was endangering the entire mission and a Super Weight Improvement Program (SWIP) was begun. As much as $20,000 per pound was spent to remove mass from the design. After 1966, mass growth abated, but further stringent measures including shortening of the lunar staytime for

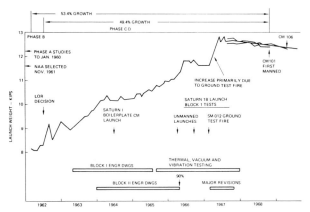

Figure 7.8 Apollo command module mass growth history. *Courtesy of Boeing.*

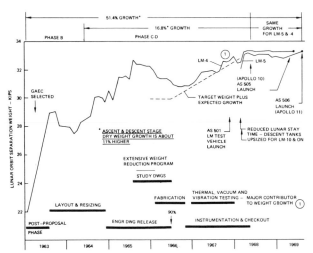

Figure 7.9 Mass growth history for Apollo Lunar Module. *Courtesy of Boeing.*

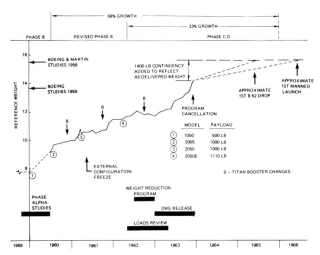

Figure 7.10 Mass growth history for X-20 (Dyna-Soar) space vehicle. *Courtesy of Boeing.*

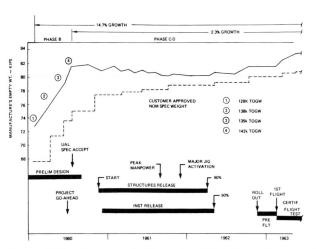

Figure 7.11 Mass growth history for 727 jetliner. *Courtesy of Boeing.*

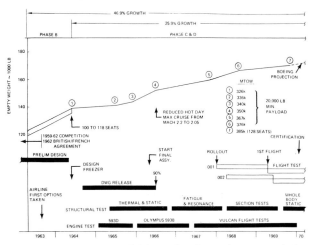

Figure 7.12 Mass growth history for Concorde supersonic jetliner. *Courtesy of Boeing.*

Apollo 11 were necessary to achieve the first successful landing.

Air Force studies of a winged, manned orbital spacecraft were begun with Boeing and Martin in 1958. The program was called X-20 Dyna-Soar (short for dynamic soaring) and entered preliminary design in 1960. Boeing was selected as the development contractor and the program continued through 1963. Serious problems with mass growth were experienced, as shown in Fig. 7.10. Program mass growth to completion is a projected value in the figure. Growth necessitated several changes to the Titan booster, including development of the solid rocket first stage; this launcher configuration later became the Titan III.

The mass history of the 727 jetliner is shown in Figure 7.11. Rapid growth occurred during preliminary design, partly as a result of requirements changes—the airplane got bigger—but almost none occurred after design freeze. This is representative of a well-understood design executed by an experienced design team using proven technology. The

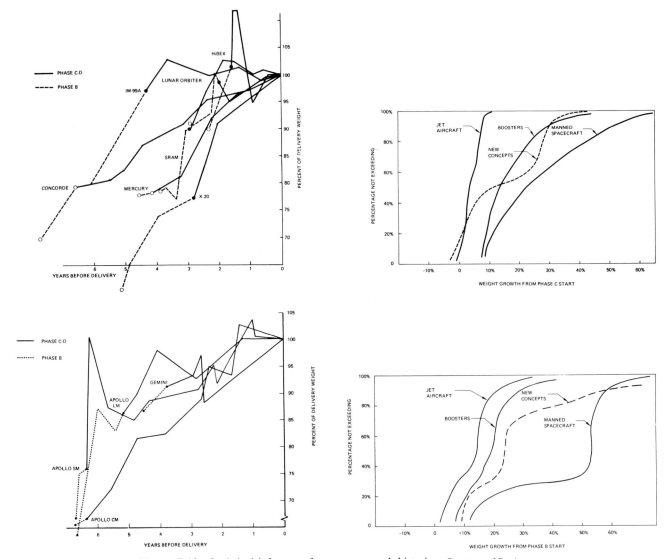

Figure 7.13 Statistical inferences from mass growth histories. *Courtesy of Boeing.*

727 made significant advances in the application of high-lift devices to a commercial aircraft, but was, in the main, a low-risk program.

The mass history of the Concorde supersonic transport is an interesting contrast, as shown in Figure 7.12. This airplane, the first commercial supersonic jetliner, represented much higher technical risk than the 727 and the mass growth history reflects it. Its growth, however, was less than that for the manned spacecraft presented earlier.

Mass Growth Allowances and Design Margins

It is common practice in the aerospace industry to apply a 10 percent mass growth allowance to systems in conceptual and preliminary design. As the above examples show, 10 percent is usually not enough; growth allowances should consider the maturity as well as the novelty of a design concept. Preliminary design activities at the Johnson Space Center at Houston have often applied growth allowances as

much as 50 percent based on Apollo Command Module and Lunar Module experience.

Growth allowances derived from historical statistics will include a portion for the Christmas tree effect as well as intentional underestimating (unwarranted optimism?) inasmuch as these have occurred on past programs. These factors are in large part a management problem. Management usually knows (usually directs) how much optimism is inherent in an estimate. If optimism is necessary for a win or to keep a program out of funding trouble, a "get-well" plan should be held in reserve. Management is responsible for preventing the Christmas tree effect from eating into reasonable and prudent growth allowances, or for having a get-well plan here also.

The get-well plan can be simply to accept substandard performance initially, knowing that incremental design improvements will make up the shortfall over time. This has served well on the Shuttle program. Missions demanding specification performance from the Shuttle have not materialized early in the program; the needed performance is anticipated to be available by the time needed.

At the conclusion of a preliminary design and definition effort, if the design concept is worked out in detail, a 10 percent growth allowance is sufficient to provide for design details added in the design drawing release cycle. Significant changes in the design can easily cause a 10 percent growth allowance to be exceeded.

There are no reliable rules to apply to conceptual designs. History indicates that anywhere from 10 percent to 50 percent margins are appropriate as indicated in Figure 7.13. If a concept is well understood or based on similar systems already developed, the low end of the range usually applies. New or first-of-a-kind concepts usually merit larger margins.

Another factor to consider is the importance of the feedback effect. How much will an increase in mass of a subsystem be magnified when the design is iterated to reflect the impact of the increase on all other subsystems? This effect is modest for space stations and platforms.

Growth allowances are normally applied only to new design hardware. Existing components for which the mass is known, and consumables such as food and propellants, are excluded from the mass subtotal multiplied by the growth allowance factor to obtain the growth allowance.

Design margins are factors applied to actual operating conditions to set design conditions. They are not the same as and not a substitute for mass growth allowances. Design margins minimize risk or failure and provide for future growth. Examples are the application of factors of 1.4 to 2 or greater to maximum design loads to establish ultimate structural capability of a part, and use of components with maximum power, voltage, or temperature ratings significantly above the maximum expected operating conditions. An example future growth margin would be the design of Shuttle payload bay trunnion fittings on a space station module for greater mass than that of the module plus its growth allowance, anticipating future growth of the module to greater mass. (This is *not* a mass growth allowance.) A thorough discussion of design margins is beyond the scope of this book; the reader should consult appropriate texts in each technical discipline concerned.

Chapter 8

Configuration and Design Integration

The creation of a design configuration—a set of sketches, drawings, or illustrations that shows what a design looks like and how it is arranged—is a human creative process. No formula or recipe for it exists. One can only describe how it is done by successful configurators and propose at least one orderly sequence of thought processes that has produced useful results. The first part of this chapter deals with this phenomenon. The second part discusses the more analytical subject of design integration, "getting it all together," which usually proceeds in concert with configuration development. Both processes build on all that has gone before in this book. The complete configuration development job is the product of both activities; a configuration must of course be technically sound as well as arranged rationally.

Configuration Development

A configuration for a space station or a platform, much as for any complex system, must respond to many constraints, requirements, and figures or merit. Configurators have a comprehensive knowledge of these design shaping factors and apply them in a more or less structured fashion to the evolution of a configuration from rough sketches to finished drawings. Typically, configurators begin with constraints such as the dimensional and center of gravity (CG) limits of the Shuttle payload bay, and progress to design requirements derived from missions and other factors such as crew considerations. Finally they evaluate those configuration options that meet constraints and requirements according to figures of merit such as cost, mass, and growth potential.

Configuration development is a visual and graphical process that seems to flow from the extraordinary ability of the human mind to visualize, recognize, and interpret geometric patterns. Development of a configuration idea can begin as simply as a constraints diagram such as sketched in Figure 8.1, progressing to freehand sketches (Figure 8.2), to more detailed pictorial drawings (Figure 8.3), and finally to interior arrangement and subsystems installation details, illustrations, and models (Figures 8.4 and 8.5).

Creation of space station configuration concepts is greatly aided by an insight developed during the NASA Space Sta-

tion Concept Development Group activity of 1983–84. Space station configuration problems were separated into three issues that are only weakly coupled:

1. Overall configuration arrangement including flight attitude strategy, pointing, viewing and physical accommodations for missions, sun tracking by the solar array, and operational factors such as Shuttle approach and berthing
2. Pressurized module interconnect patterns
3. Pressurized module internal arrangements

The following discussion of constraints, requirements, and figures of merit keys on these three aspects of configuration design. The designer of unmanned space platforms need consider only the first of these aspects.

Design Constraints

The primary constraints on space station and platform configurations to be launched by the Space Shuttle are payload bay dimensions, payload structural attachment requirements, the Shuttle lift capability, and the center of gravity limits of the payload bay. These were described in Chapter 2.

Payload bay diameter sets the maximum module diameter. Clearances for relative movement between the payload and the Shuttle payload bay (the dynamic envelope) are provided by the payload. Maximum payload diameter for well-supported payloads is typically 4.42 m (174 in) rather than the ideal 4.57 m (180 in). Cantilevered payloads may need significantly more clearance.

A 4.42 m module severely constrains options for internal arrangement; a larger diameter would be preferred. Concepts for accommodating larger diameters include heavy-lift versions of the Shuttle, typically permitting about 7.5 m diameter, and the Shuttle aft cargo compartment concept, also permitting 7.5 m diameter but restricted to rather short length. The aft cargo compartment, attached to the aft end of the external tank, is in a severe acoustic environment. No plans presently exist for development of heavy lift systems. Further, modules larger than the Shuttle payload bay cannot be returned to Earth. These factors have prevented diameters larger than 4.42 m from being seriously consid-

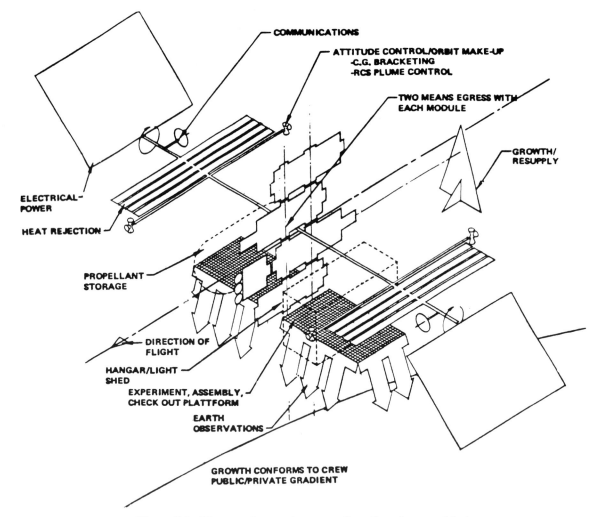

Figure 8.1 Diagram of constraints on configuration. *Courtesy of Boeing.*

ered for the initial NASA space station, despite their advantages for interior arrangements.

Diameter limits are not as severe a constraint on unmanned platforms. Larger diameters might simplify design

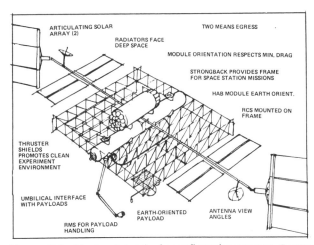

Figure 8.2 Freehand sketch of a configuration concept. *Courtesy of Boeing.*

by reducing the amount of deployment needed to attain final configuration. For complex structural arrangements, Shuttle loads can be a significant design driver because maximum loads are in the fore-and-aft direction at launch and in the transverse (downward) direction for landing. Studies of large platform configurations have also shown problems with payload bay center of gravity (CG) limits. Most platform systems, packaged for launch, are low enough in density that they will exceed the Shuttle forward CG limit before the limit mass or 29,500 kg (65,000 lb) is reached. Shuttle CG limits were described in Chapter 2. Platforms to be placed in high-inclination orbits are constrained by significantly lesser Shuttle lift capability, 10,000 to 15,000 kg depending on inclination and altitude. Design strategies for these platforms often rely on integral propulsion to raise the platform to the mission orbit altitude, permitting the Shuttle delivery altitude to be quite low, and thus maximizing lift capability. Polar mission altitudes are often higher than the maximum altitude the Shuttle can reach at high inclination.

Nearly all space station concepts and some platforms require more than one Shuttle launch for delivery and assembly on orbit. (A small space station like the Soviet Salyut could be delivered on a single Shuttle flight.) Assembly implies that the Shuttle must be berthed to the part of the system already in orbit. Then the element delivered in the payload bay must be removed and installed, either by the RMS on the Shuttle or by one on the station or platform, as depicted in Figure 8.6. A free-flying assembly such as illustrated in Figure 8.7 might someday be possible, but with the present level of Shuttle operations experience it is viewed as too risky.

Shuttle and other transportation operations should have approach and departure corridors as depicted in Figure 8.8. Further, space station and platform configurations must provide suitable locations for Shuttle berthing including tail clearance, payload unloading and loading, and payload storage and handling provisions suitable for their missions and operations.

Programs and configurations are sometimes constrained by other factors, including use of certain items of existing hardware or software, program decisions arising from non-technical factors, and cost or funding rate limitations. It is not practical to deal with these in this book except to note that cost constraints and ways of dealing with them are discussed at some length in the next chapter.

The constraints described affect overall configuration by placing limits on the hardware element building-blocks, and

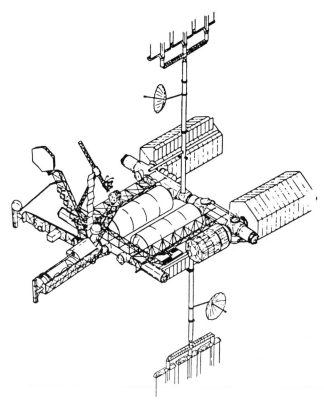

Figure 8.3 Pictorial drawing of a space station configuration. *Courtesy of Boeing.*

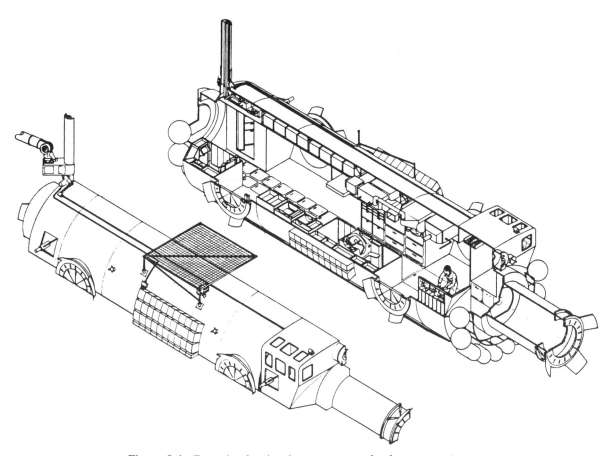

Figure 8.4 Example of an interior arrangement sketch. *Courtesy of Boeing.*

Figure 8.5 Model of a "raft" space station concept with Shuttle and large antenna structure. *Courtesy of Boeing.*

through the assembly and Shuttle operations factors. Module interconnect patterns may be influenced by assembly considerations. Clearly, the internal arrangements of pressurized modules must consider the overall geometric envelopes imposed by constraints, but they are little affected otherwise.

Requirements

The requirements that most strongly affect overall configuration arrangement are those issuing from mission viewing, pointing, and physical accommodation, and from flight strategy and controllability considerations. Table 8.1 lists missions from a NASA space station mission model that impose viewing or pointing requirements on the station. Physical accommodations—for missions such as space construction technology, orbit transfer vehicle operations, and spacecraft servicing—occupy space on the station structure, but do not have pointing or viewing needs.

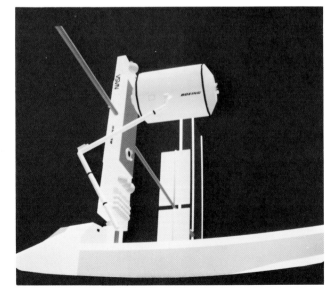

Figure 8.6 Assembly of space station modules using the Shuttle RMS (from a computer-generated simulation). *Courtesy of Boeing.*

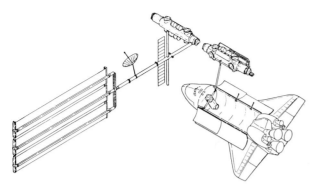

Figure 8.7 Free-flying assembly concept (discarded as too risky). *Courtesy of Boeing.*

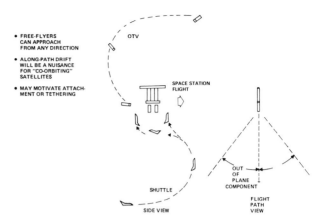

- FREE-FLYERS CAN APPROACH FROM ANY DIRECTION
- ALONG-PATH DRIFT WILL BE A NUISANCE FOR "CO-ORBITING" SATELLITES
- MAY MOTIVATE ATTACHMENT OR TETHERING

OTV

SPACE STATION FLIGHT

OUT OF PLANE COMPONENT

SHUTTLE

SIDE VIEW

FLIGHT PATH VIEW

Figure 8.8 Transportation approach and departure corridors. *Courtesy of Boeing.*

Stellar and solar pointing and viewing are both nearly inertial (as seen from Earth orbit, the Sun moves slowly relative to the stars), but stellar instruments must point away from the Sun. Many would be damaged if the Sun were to enter their field of view. Note that both Earth and anti-Earth (away from Earth) pointing are needed. Both imply an Earth orientation. Some instruments need to point along Earth's magnetic field lines. This is not a fixed Earth orientation.

If a space station or platform is Earth-oriented, Earth and anti-Earth pointing will remain fixed much of the time.

Some instruments might not need gimbals at all, but many will, as their pointing relative to the local vertical will not be fixed. Stellar and solar instruments must slew to compensate for spacecraft rotation in inertial space. Magnetically oriented instruments require modest slewing, depending on the orbit inclination and orientation.

Inertially oriented space stations and platforms have most often been defined as fully or partially solar-oriented. Solar-

Table 8.1 Typical mission accommodations requirements. *Courtesy of Boeing.*

Reference number	Name	Int/ext	Size (m)	Mass (kg)	Pointing Direction	Pointing Acceleration-stabilization	Pointing FOV	Contamination sensitivity	Remarks
SAA 0001	Spectra (cosmic ray nuclei)	E	3.3, 4.8, 3.8	3 000	AE/E	1 deg	140 deg	Low	
SAA 0002	Space plasma laboratory	E	Spacelab pallet	3 200	E/V	1 deg	40 x 90 deg	Low	Multiple instruments, E-gun, arcjet, high peak power
SAA 0003	Solar optical telescope	E	4D x 7L	6 600	S	10″	0.5 deg	Medium to high	Subplatform
SAA 0004	SIRTF	E	4D x 8L	7 000	Stellar	10″	0.5 deg	E (light and condensate)	Possible platform candidate
SAA 0005	Transition radiation and ion calibration	E							Timeshare with SAA 0001
SAA 0006	Star Lab	E	2D x 7L	3 300	Stellar	2″	0.5 deg	Medium to high light	Subplatform
SAA 0201	LIDAR facility	E	Spacelab pallet	2 000	E	1′	0.5 deg	Low	Nadir pointer, attached to pressure module, optical path, infrequent use
SAA 0307 and SAA 0401	LS and MPS laboratories	I	Modules	15 000	None			Low	Removable for return to Earth; external equipment
TDM 2010	Materials performance	E	3 x 2 x 0.2	700	Solar			Low	Locate with array
TDM 2060	Construction	E	Various, large	Various	Gravity gradient			Low	Extensive EVA
TDM 2260	Earth observation instruments	E	Optical devices	Up to 5000	E	1″		Medium to high	Timeshare with LIDAR

Legend:
E   Earth   AE   Anti-Earth   D   Diameter
S   Sun   V   Various   L   Length

viewing instruments thus need not gimbal unless their field of view is small relative to the Sun; then they must slew slightly to scan the entire solar disk. Stellar instruments still must gimbal albeit slowly except when moving from one object to another. Slewing an entire spacecraft to track sky targets has usually been deemed impractical except for single-mission vehicles such as a space telescope.

Whichever flight orientation strategy is selected for a multimission space station or platform, slewing payloads on gimbals will be necessary. Polar platforms are designed to be Earth-oriented because most payloads (but not all) are Earth viewers. Astrophysics platforms are designed to be inertially oriented and may possibly use target slewing of the entire platform if all instruments are to be boresighted on the same target at any given time. Space stations have been designed for both inertial and Earth-oriented operation. One capable of maintaining inertial attitude can be operated Earth-oriented as an option but the converse is generally not true. Keeping a configuration well enough balanced for practical inertial orientation becomes difficult for larger stations with diverse missions; refer to Chapter 5 for a discussion of controllability.

The issue of dynamic controllability is the motivator for a class of structurally stiff configurations. Cantilevered solar arrays, usually mounted on quite flexible masts or booms, cause space stations and platform configurations to exhibit structural resonant frequencies on the order of 0.05 hertz (one cycle of oscillation per 20 seconds). It is possible to raise the frequency to above 1 hertz by adopting rigid designs with no large cantilevered elements.

Gravity gradients, in addition to introducing control requirements on a configuration, introduce a gravity bias on any part of a space station not at the center of gravity. The net acceleration is the difference between gravitational and centrifugal accelerations. For an Earth-oriented station this may be expressed as

$$a = \left| \frac{\mu}{r^2} - \omega^2 r \right| \qquad (8.1)$$

where μ is Earth's geopotential, r is the local radius from the center of the Earth, and ω is the angular rate of motion of the orbit. ω^2 can be expressed as μ/r_o^3 where r_o is the radius from the center of the Earth to the center of gravity of the space station. Combining these relations, we obtain

$$a = \frac{\mu(r_o^3 - r^3)}{r_o^3 r^2}. \qquad (8.2)$$

If $r_o \approx r$, the expression is approximated as $3\mu\delta r/r_o^3$, equal to about 4×10^{-6} m/sec^2 for a typical orbit, or $4 \times 10^{-7}g$, per meter of δr.

Acceleration disturbances, from 10^{-5} to $10^{-3}g$ in random directions, are anticipated on a space station due to normal crew motion. It has been widely believed that because of these disturbances, little benefit would be obtained by reducing steady-state (bias) gravity gradients below 10^{-5} g. The disturbance of microgravity processes, however, is sensitive to the duration of the acceleration disturbance. Crew motion disturbances have a representative frequency on the order of 1 hertz. Recent theoretical studies of microgravity processes have shown that such crew-induced accelerations will disturb microgravity processes no more than steady-state accelerations of about 10^{-6} g. This leads to the desirability of locating microgravity laboratories within about 3 meters of the station CG vertically and about 10 meters horizontally. The CG of larger space stations may shift more than this due to mission operations, leading to a potential need or desirability for some form of active CG control.

Environmental considerations exert some influence on configurations. Concepts have been advocated that achieve low drag by orienting the solar arrays in a "streamlined" attitude; as the arrays do not track the sun, they must be much larger than a sun tracking array of the same average electrical output. (High stiffness rather than low drag was the main motivation for these concepts.)

Meteoroid and debris environments lead to pressurized module designs with meteoroid shields that often double as thermal radiators. These work best if a separation of several centimeters or more between the shield and the pressure shell is provided. This serves to reduce the maximum practical interior diameter for pressurized modules. Deployable shields having very little separation until deployed have been considered. The radiator panel/shields are large, massive panels that must be adequately supported for launch; designing a structurally sound deployment system could well be challenging.

It is very desirable to separate sensitive instruments from contamination sources such as propulsion thrusters, crew airlocks, vacuum vents from laboratories, and Shuttle berthing facilities. These are sources of contaminating gases and vapors that can condense on optics and other sensitive surfaces, especially if the surfaces are cold. Contaminants can also intrude into the line of sight of instruments, degrading data quality.

A space station is large enough that contamination sources may be located remote from sensitive items. The NASA baseline "power tower" configuration discussed below is so arranged, and other arrangements that serve the same need are practical.

Crew factors and safety may have a significant influence on module interconnect patterns. Debate continues as to the need to provide more than one access or egress path from each inhabited module. Multiple egress reduces the risk that a crewperson will be trapped between a hazard such as a fire and a safe exit from an unsafe module. Multiple access prevents the loss of any module from making others inaccessible. These factors are diagrammed in Figure 8.9.

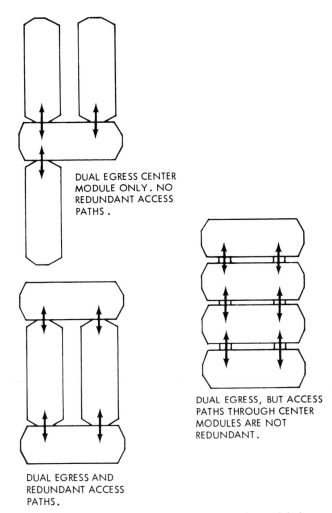

DUAL EGRESS CENTER
MODULE ONLY. NO
REDUNDANT ACCESS
PATHS.

DUAL EGRESS, BUT ACCESS
PATHS THROUGH CENTER
MODULES ARE NOT
REDUNDANT.

DUAL EGRESS AND
REDUNDANT ACCESS
PATHS.

Figure 8.9 Multiple egress and access factors for module interconnect.

Having a consistent visual up-and-down in the way module interiors are arranged has been advanced as a desirable feature. Most module interconnect patterns and interior arrangements do not adapt to this easily if at all.

Module interior designs have considered transverse, longitudinal, and mixed deck arrangements as illustrated in Figure 8.10. There is not a clear-cut preference, as the comparison in Table 8.2 shows. The present trend is toward the longitudinal deck. The Spacelab is arranged this way. It appears to be clearly preferable for a laboratory, where all available interior volume is best devoted to one large workspace. The transverse deck approach suffers from having no spacious interior volumes and has been criticized as likely to induce claustrophobia in crew members. There have been no tests or simulations to demonstrate this concern. The mixed-deck arrangement appears to offer the most efficient use of interior space for a habitat or operations module.

The common module concept, where all pressurized modules are variants of the same basic design, offers convincing

cost savings (see Chapter 9) and has presently been adopted as the baseline design approach for the NASA space station. The degree of flexibility of interior arrangement possible with a common module approach has not been determined. Although it seems that a common deck arrangement would be necessary, design innovation may find ways to preserve the cost savings of commonality while offering alternatives in interior configuration.

Configuration Concepts and the Creative Process

Ideally, we should at this point present a proven method and rationale for deriving a configuration from the constraints and requirements that may be laid upon us. Unfortunately, no such logic exists. The best we can do is present a few parts of such a logic that seem to work, and insights from past experience, blended with an anecdotal history of how presently favored design concepts came into being and evolved.

General Arrangements

Space station general arrangements are dominated by how the solar arrays are designed and how missions are accommodated. A cantilevered solar array approach has long been popular, represented by dozens of configuration concepts. The Space Operation Center (SOC) and space platform concepts depicted in Chapter 1 used cantilevered arrays. This idea probably originated with the modular space station concepts developed during the early 1970s. During these early in-depth studies, much attention was given to internal arrangements and subsystems design, and relatively less to overall external arrangement. Figure 8.11 is representative of these. The figure is remarkable in that no mission accommodations are evident in it. One can only suppose that the missions contemplated for this particular concept were all of the internal laboratory variety, and hence would not show up in an external general arrangement illustration.

About midway through the 1970s, considerable interest began to develop in large space structures. Studies were funded by NASA to define means of designing and constructing large structures in space. Various projects from radio telescopes and radar to solar power satellites were studied and design concepts generated. Operational studies of how the Space Shuttle, a space station, or a construction base might be used to construct such projects were also carried out. Space station concepts began to be influenced by construction needs.

One of the first concepts that reflected this construction emphasis is illustrated in Figure 8.12. The concept is more an artist's rendering than a well-thought-out engineering scheme, but the theme of spreading out the configuration to accommodate construction operations and projects is clear. This configuration has a serious flaw in that it is depicted in a flight attitude that would experience gravity

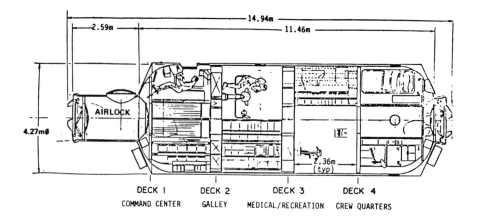

TRANSVERSE ARRANGEMENT
(HABITAT)

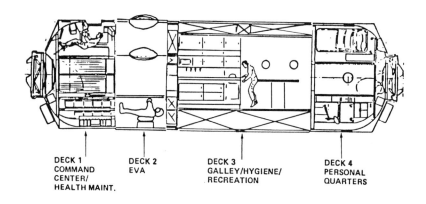

MIXED ARRANGEMENT
(HABITAT)

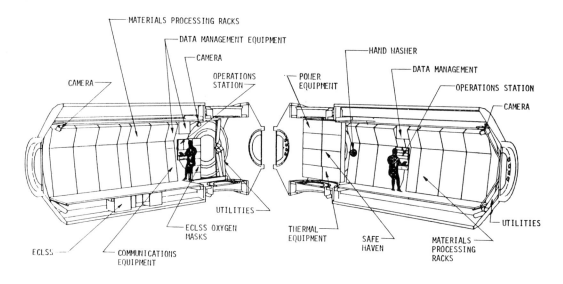

LONGITUDINAL ARRANGEMENT
(MICROGRAVITY AND MATERIALS PROCESSING LAB)

Figure 8.10 Alternative module interior arrangements. *Courtesy of Boeing/JSC.*

Table 8.2 Evaluation factors for alternative interior arrangements. *Courtesy of Boeing.*

FEATURE	BOLOGNA SLICE	LONGITUDINAL	MIXED
FLOOR SPACE	52.5 M²	44.5 M²	53.6 M² ✓
• GROSS			
• DELTA DUE TO STORAGE IN CEILING		+3.7	+1.9
ECLS	• LEAST PROBLEMS ✓	• SOME PROBLEMS	• MOST PROBLEMS
MAINTENANCE IMPACTS			
• PRESSURE SHELL ACCESS	• EASIEST ✓	• LEAST EASY	• NEXT EASIEST
• SUBSYSTEMS ACCESS	• EASIEST ✓	• LEAST EASY	• NEXT EASIEST
HUMAN FACTORS			
• VERTICAL REF.	• CONSISTENT ✓	• CONSISTENT ✓	• INCONSISTENT BUT NOT UNREASONABLE
• VISUAL VARIETY	• NO VARIETY	• NO VARIETY	• GOOD VARIETY ✓
GROUND OPERATIONS			
• MFG OPS	• HIGH BAY BLDG REQ'D	• NO PROBLEM ✓	• WOULD REQUIRE HIGH BAY BLDG AND ROTATING CONST FIXTURE
• TRAINING OPS	• NO PROBLEM ✓	• NO PROBLEM ✓	• PROBLEMS
• LAUNCH SITE OPS	• SOME PROBLEM DURING MAKE-READY DUE TO VERTICAL ORIENTATION	• NO PROBLEM ✓	• PROBLEMS
OTHER FACTORS	• SKYLAB WAS THIS CONFIG	• SPACELAB WILL BE THIS CONFIGURATION	

gradient torques beyond the ability of any reasonable control system to handle.

By 1980, space station concepts were characterized by the Space Operations Center (SOC) and Manned Space Platform (MSP) concepts described briefly in Chapter 1. The SOC was designed for modest space construction projects, spacecraft servicing, and to serve as an operations base for orbit-to-orbit rocket stages. The MSP was designed mainly to serve science and applications missions, i.e., as a laboratory. The SOC was to fly Earth-oriented. It was recognized that the presence of construction projects, propellant tank farms, and spacecraft servicing operations would cause configuration variations leading to gravity gradient control problems if an inertial attitude were selected. The MSP, however, was designed to fly in an inertial attitude. This simplified Sun tracking of the solar arrays and was satisfactory for this relatively fixed configuration.

The mission requirements for these concepts were somewhat assumptional in nature. The differences in configuration approach reflected differences in the mission assumptions as well as differences in design philosophy.

The mission studies that NASA undertook in 1982 and 1983 were intended to clarify the mission needs for a space station and provide a more rational basis for design requirements. Subsequent to these studies, a mission model and set of mission requirements were published by NASA; a summary of the mission model was presented in Chapter 1.

Figure 8.11 Modular space station concept from early 1970s. *Courtesy of NASA/JSC.*

Figure 8.12 Early ancestor of the power tower concept with large space structures missions. *Courtesy of Boeing.*

Based on the mission model, further concept identification was undertaken by NASA in 1983 and 1984. A spectrum of concepts was identified as shown in Figure 1.12. The ''CDG planar'' and ''tube-module'' arrangements were direct derivatives of the MSP and SOC approaches; the others represented new thinking.

The ''dual-spin'' design was originated by Hughes Aircraft. The idea was to spin-stabilize the entire space station by supporting a large ring-shaped solar array from four Shuttle external tanks delivered to orbit and attached to the space station in a cruciform. The spinning array and tank assembly would have enormous angular momentum, providing inertially stabilized operation. Originally, the space station habitats were to be built into or attached to the tanks, creating artificial gravity, but the zero-g laboratory requirements for the space station made that impractical. The concept then evolved into one with a despun (nonrotating) center section including the habitats and laboratories. The spinning array and tank system became, in effect, a large power supply and stabilization

system, an exact analog to the spin-stabilized spacecraft Hughes builds for communications markets. The concept was later discarded because its apparent problems in assembly and mission integration were judged to outweigh its advantages in control stability. This concept certainly deserves credit for being one of the most innovative approaches devised during this period.

The ''delta'' and ''tee'' configurations were devised by JSC to embody great structural stiffness, avoiding dynamical controllability concerns associated with very flexible configurations. Figures 8.13 and 8.14 illustrate these concepts.

The delta was originally designed with the pressurized modules located at the apexes of the delta triangular shape and connected by tunnels. This created a nearly balanced inertial configuration. The solar array is on one of the three rectangular surfaces, supported by the delta truss structure. The solar array is pointed at the Sun by aiming the entire vehicle, thus the need for inertial balance.

Figure 8.13 The "delta" space station configuration. *Courtesy NASA/JSC.*

The mission studies conducted while these configurations were evolving led to large increases in the power budgets of the space station designs. This, for the delta, meant that the structural truss and solar array must increase in size to match the growing power requirements, and the tunnels interconnecting the modules became unreasonably long. Consequently, the configuration changed to have all the modules at one apex as in the illustration. Initial gravity gradient controllability studies indicated a tractable control problem, but later studies considering Shuttle berthing and various mission accommodations exposed serious control problems. At the same time, analyses of the controllability of flexible configurations were showing that the issue of their controllability was much less difficult than had been earlier supposed. As a result of these findings, the delta concept was abandoned.

The tee concept was similarly motivated; it was also a stiff configuration although not nearly as stiff as the delta. The tee flew in a gravity gradient stable attitude and did not pose the static control problems of the delta. Its solar array and support platform were originally designed to fly in a local horizontal attitude. The module cluster was attached

to a truss structure extending vertically downward from the array platform. This arrangement was highly stable for gravity gradients. The tee offered another advantage. Because the array was always near local horizontal, it presented very low drag compared to Sun-tracking arrays.

The tee solar array did not, of course, track the Sun. Illumination geometry studies indicated that the array efficiency was very poor for large beta angles, when the Sun is far out of the orbit plane. A modest tilt about the roll axis of 17° resolved that problem; the array efficiency at the maximum beta of 52° with 17° tilt is the same as for zero beta and zero tilt.

The tee solar array, however, was not very efficient. Its output characteristics presented a problem to electrical power system design, especially if batteries were selected for energy storage. Batteries need a nearly constant charging rate with some decrease (taper) in the rate near full charge. The tee was ill-suited to this need. Further, the tee array output was roughly sinusoidal with time whereas a tracking array has essentially constant output except when shadowed. The tee array, however, needed to be about three times as

Figure 8.14   The ''big tee'' space station configuration. *Courtesy of NASA/JSC.*

large as a Sun-tracking array of the same average output. The consequent cost implications led to the demise of the tee concept.

The delta and tee concepts represented a departure from traditional thinking in that a large truss structure rather than the module assembly was the structural backbone for the space station. This idea was a part of the concept of Figure 8.12, but was not at that time mainstream thinking. The use of a truss structure as a backbone permitted designers to create ''spreadout'' configurations with more room to accommodate missions. When the delta and tee were discarded from the list of favored configurations, their structural backbone principle was retained.

The truss structure backbone idea appeared in a Boeing concept created by designer Jack Olson in 1983; the concept is depicted in Figure 8.15. The need for spreading out was not yet recognized and this concept received little notice at the time. It is now viewed as the ancestor of the modern ''power tower'' NASA configuration which is depicted in Figure 8.16.

The power tower is designed to fly Earth-oriented in a gravity gradient stable attitude. It accommodates stellar and

solar viewing missions at the top of the configuration; although gimbaling is necessary in view of the Earth orientation of the vehicle, a clear view is available. The power

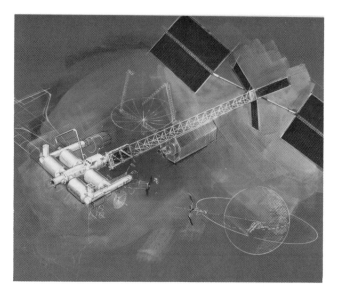

Figure 8.15   Early power tower configuration concept. *Courtesy of Boeing.*

Figure 8.16 NASA power tower baseline, September 1984. *Courtesy of NASA/JSC.*

section offers room for growth to the high power levels that may be needed to support commercial endeavors in materials processing. The tower truss offers adequate space for work and storage areas and hangars. A wide variety of module interconnect patterns can be accepted with little impact because the module pattern is not part of the backbone structure. Earth viewing has a clear field at the bottom. Transportation approach and departure corridors are clear. Laboratory modules are probably close enough to the center of gravity; this needs further verification.

All types of general arrangements appear to have been investigated. Innovation cannot, of course, be fully predicted but the flight mode matrix presented in Figure 1.13 appears to cover all possible options. Spinning configurations, which date back to the old Von Braun concept of the 1950s, have for now been eliminated. Spinners may very well come back at some future date when space stations serve mainly as habitats, even hotels in orbit, but the multimission nature of present space station plans does not favor spinners.

Configurations designed to feature stiffness as their uppermost attribute seem to have been eliminated by the problems introduced in attaining high stiffness, combined with analyses that have mitigated concern as to the dynamic controllability of the more traditional mast-and-boom flexible concepts.

Remaining are the inertial options like the MSP and the Concept Development Group (CDG) planar, and the Earth-oriented power tower type. Unmanned space platforms devoted to astrophysics will almost certainly adopt the inertial approach. The manned station presently has been designed as a gravity gradient oriented (power tower) system. The concept is well suited to the present mission mix. A radical change in the mission mix, or other circumstances unforeseen at this writing, could lead to a change from the power tower approach. For now, the power tower seems to be a good compromise for a multimission, highly adaptable manned space station configuration and the prediction is that something like it will be retained.

Module Interconnect Patterns

The space station general arrangement is nearly independent of the module interconnect pattern. This is particularly true for designs that employ a truss structure backbone. If the module interconnect pattern is the structural backbone, it is partially constrained by its structural requirements. Systematic studies of module interconnect alternatives in 1983 identified cluster, planar, and branched concepts as illustrated in Figure 8.17. The cluster concept was motivated by the perceived need to maintain a neutral gravity gradient potential, that is, a roughly spherically symmetric arrangement. Later it was recognized that the module interconnect

CLUSTER

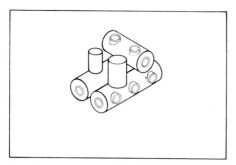 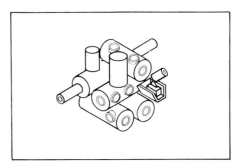

PRO
- TWO OR MORE EGRESS PATHS
- INERTIAL SYMMETRY PERMITS ALL ORIENTATIONS

CON
- OPS WORKSPACE RESTRICTED; MOBILITY DIFFICULT TO IMPOSSIBLE
- DIFFICULT TO ASSEMBLE, BUT RMS REACH OK
- POOR MODULE SURFACE THERMAL VIEW FACTORS
- GROWTH IS LIMITED

BRANCHED

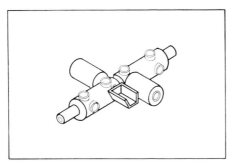 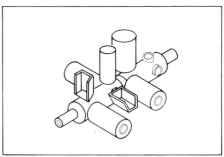

PRO
- CAN GROW INDEFINITELY
- MORE FLEXIBLE FOR INSTRUMENT POINTING AND ATTACHMENT
- FAIR TO GOOD THERMAL

CON
- OPERATIONS WORK SPACE CUT UP – MOBILITY DIFFICULT
- LACK OF DUAL EGRESS PATHS VIOLATES JSC SAFETY RULE
- TENDS TOWARD LARGE INERTIA DIFFERENCES

PLANAR

CREW 4-6   CREW 8-12

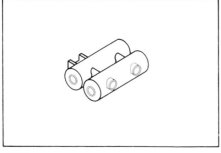 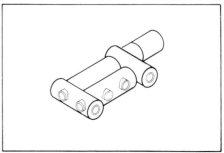

PRO
- AMPLE WORK SPACE FOR OPERATIONS
- TWO OR MORE EGRESS PATHS
- CAN BE ASSEMBLED BY SHUTTLE/RMS
- FAIR TO GOOD THERMAL VIEW FACTOR

CON
- INERTIAL DIFFERENCE OUTGROW CMG CAPABILITY FOR INERTIAL ORIENTATION
- EARTH ORIENTATION RESTRICTED TO STATION PLANE IN ORBIT PLANE
- LIMITED GROWTH

Figure 8.17 Cluster, planar, and branched interconnect options. *Courtesy of Boeing.*

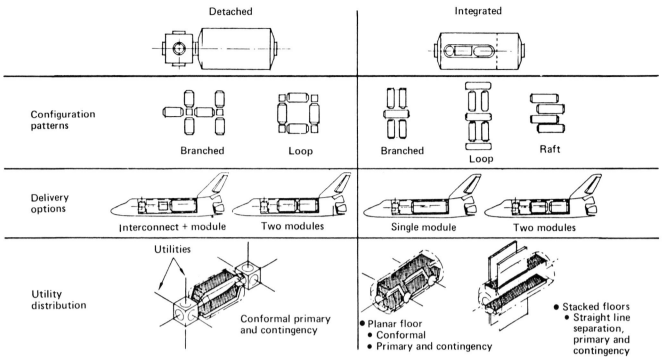

Figure 8.18 Module interconnect pattern options. *Courtesy of Boeing.*

pattern has relatively little influence on overall configuration gravity gradients except when an exceptionally bad pattern is chosen, but at the time of the interconnect study described in Figure 8.17, spherically symmetric options were considered as potentially attractive.

Despite the other potential advantages of the spherical pattern, it was discontinued because the thermal view factors from the individual modules are poor, the module cluster presents assembly problems, and freedom to move an RMS-type manipulator about the space station structure is limited.

The tradeoff between branched and planar patterns centers on the safety issue of dual egress. Planar patterns lend themselves to a "racetrack" circular arrangement with dual egress from every module for certain numbers of modules such as four. The branched arrangements reduce the amount of traffic traversing modules to get to other modules. There are many variants on the basic branched and planar patterns as shown in Figure 8.18. One of particular interest is the "raft" configuration. It uses side-to-side berthing of modules to achieve dual egress paths from any number of modules. The interconnect of utilities (power, data, water, etc.) between modules is also especially simple. Raft configurations can be arranged almost like a multistory building as depicted in Figure 8.19. The intermodule passageways are like elevator shafts without elevators; a shaft alone is adequate in zero g. The raft gives up the idea of dual access paths. Loss of a center module in a raft arrangement would isolate the modules on either side, since both access paths pass through each module. A mid-module pressure-tight bulkhead and door would eliminate this shortcoming, but

there are others. The side berthing fixtures on the modules must fit within the Shuttle payload bay dimensional limits; the module diameter must be reduced to make room. The passageways in the middle of the modules occupy much internal space that could otherwise be productively used.

A number of novel arrangements have been proposed. One of these uses spherical interconnect units between modules to create a tetrahedral module pattern as shown in Figure 8.20. This is very rigid but that seems not to be an important attribute. Traffic patterns among the modules are claimed to be efficient, but the non-orthogonal pattern might be confusing to humans who tend to think in terms of up and down, right and left. The pattern is not complete until six modules are in place. This seems to be the greatest disadvantage since incremental growth is awkward.

Usable space within the modules is maximized if interconnect units are used to effect branching or corners. Interconnects as an integral part of the module design reduce the number of individual hardware items that must be procured and simplify the interconnection of utilities. Separate interconnect units may be a bottleneck; they double the number of interconnection interfaces.

Use of the Shuttle external tank as a space station module is a recurring theme. The tank is a sturdy pressure vessel quite adequate for a space station atmospheric pressure of 10 pascals (14.7 psia). The hydrogen tank is about 8 meters in diameter and 30 meters long; its interior volume is equivalent to seven or eight typical payload-bay compatible modules. It costs nothing (in terms of Shuttle performance) to

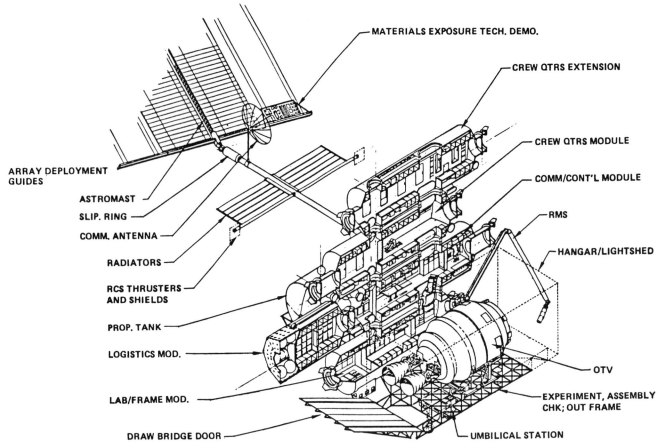

Figure 8.19 Raft configuration concepts showing interior cutaways. *Courtesy of Boeing.*

deliver a tank to orbit. The empty tank could be vented of residual propellants and pressurized with air. It seems so logical!

This idea is frequently ''discovered.'' The reasons why it is impractical are not popular with its discoverers, but they are conclusive. First, the large size means that only one pressurized module would be used except for rather large stations; the safety of redundant modules is sacrificed. Second, assembly and checkout of the module must be done in space. A space station module is much more than a tank pressurized with air; it is a highly complex spacecraft unit comprised of many subsystems. The external tank is filled with cryogenic propellants at launch; designing and qualifying space station subsystems to survive immersion in these fluids is totally impractical. Thus they would have to be installed in orbit. This, in turn, is a labor-intensive process and one far beyond any foreseeable state of the art for robotics. To avail ourselves of a large ''free'' space station pressure vessel, we must accept assembly and checkout labor cost (i.e., the cost of astronaut labor in orbit) several hundred times what we would pay in an aerospace factory. It is a hopelessly bad cost tradeoff.

Similar critiques can be leveled against schemes for inflatable space station pressure modules. Further, the long-

life properties of elastomeric materials suitable for inflatables in the space vacuum, ultraviolet, and radiation environments are not well known, and what is known is far from encouraging. Inflatables are usually invoked to get around the diameter limits imposed by the Shuttle payload bay. If one demands relief from these limits, however, a heavy-lift launch vehicle is the most direct and probably the least expensive solution.

One suggested use for the external tank in orbit has promise: to use it simply as a tank full of air, as a pressurized hangar or workshop for spacecraft servicing, so that servicing may be done in a shirt-sleeve environment. Even this use requires some installations, e.g., lights and communications, but these may be simple enough to consider doing on orbit.

Internal Arrangements

Internal arrangement needs and options have been discussed above as well as in Chapter 6. The development of interior arrangements should follow a few simple guidelines.

- Develop a comprehensive list of requirements so that everything that must be accommodated in the interior is known.

Figure 8.20 Tetrahedral interconnect arrangement.

- Make commonsense allocations of requirements to modules, e.g., group quiet and noisy habitat functions together and separate laboratory from habitat functions.
- Consider crew convenience and operations, e.g., the toilet doesn't belong in the galley, and evaluate people traffic patterns.
- Take the steps necessary to visualize actual size relative to people—mockups are very useful and even a full-size layout with chalk on a floor can go a long way toward visualizing actual size.

The Creative Process

Creativity is a spontaneous process. There is not a formula for it. There are, however, ways to facilitate it.

Know all the constraints. Know them thoroughly enough so that a violation of one will be immediately recognized and dealt with. Constraints are usually not to be violated, but if an idea is good enough, any constraint in its way should be challenged.

Know and understand requirements and their implications. Challenge those that lead to unreasonable solutions. The purpose of requirements is to guide the design process. The only requirements that come from on high are fundamental physical laws. The rest come from people and can be changed by people.

Develop and understand a set of evaluation and selection parameters to have a definitive way of measuring one concept against another. Know what drives these parameters. If cost is important (it usually is), understand what drives cost and why.

Devise a scheme to categorize and compartmentalize concepts and separate different aspects of the design problem.

Anything that structures and organizes thinking is helpful. The separation of general arrangement and module interconnect issues, and the flight modes matrix of Figure 1.13, are excellent examples. Table 8.3 provides additional guidance and hints.

Then let the imagination go to work. Try things on paper. Freehand sketches and diagrams are great for trying out many ideas quickly. Group discussions as in a class project or by a design team can be very productive. Use a blackboard. Having different people concentrate on different aspects of a problem is highly productive. When considering

Table 8.3 Space station design philosophy guidelines. *Courtesy of Boeing.*

SUBJECT	REQUIREMENT	RATIONALE
ORBIT ALTITUDE	• 500 KM (270 N. MI.)	• ESSENTIAL TO PROVIDE FORMATION-FLYING ACCESS TO ASTROPHYSICS OBSERVATORIES • ACCESSIBLE BY DIRECT INSERTION • LOWER DRAG FOR LARGE SOLAR ARRAY
CONTAMINATION CONTROL	• DESIGN FOR LOW CONTAMINATION	• PROTECT SCIENCE PAYLOADS
PORTS AND POINTING	• PROVIDE AT LEAST FOUR SCIENCE PORTS IN ADDITION TO OPERATIONS PORTS • USE CMG'S TO ENABLE EITHER EARTH OR INERTIAL ORIENTATION	• ACCOMMODATE SCIENCE MISSIONS • BOTH MODES NEEDED
CG, MASS, INERTIA	• MAINTAIN SHUTTLE COMPATIBILITY • MAINTAIN INERTIAL POINTING CAPABILITY	• THESE REQUIREMENTS ARE "OBVIOUS". ENSURING THEY ARE MET REQUIRES DETAILED ANALYSIS
OMV	• PROVIDE SPACE-BASED OMV CAPABILITY; CREW CAB AS GROWTH ITEM	• NEEDED FOR SATELLITE SERVICING

SUBJECT	REQUIREMENT	RATIONALE
EVA	• PLAN FOR ROUTINE USE OF EVA	• MAXIMIZES BENEFITS OF MANNED PRESENCE
UTILITIES	• PROVIDE UMBILICALS TO BRING UTILITIES TO EXTERNAL PAYLOADS	• PAYLOADS IN HANGARS OR BEING HANDLED EXTERNALLY WILL NEED SERVICES
HANGAR AND STORAGE	• PROVIDE A COMBINATION HANGAR AND PAYLOAD BAY SURROGATE • PROVIDE AMPLE EXTERNAL TIE-DOWN AND STORAGE SPACE FOR TOOLS AND EQUIPMENT	• PAYLOADS AND UPPER STAGES NEED PROTECTED WORK SPACE • DETAILED OPS ANALYSES REVEAL NUMEROUS SMALL TOOL AND EQUIPMENT ITEMS
WORK SPACE	• PROVIDE AMPLE, NON-INTERFERING WORK SPACES FOR SERVICING, SCIENCE AND CONSTRUCTION	• SATELLITES, PLATFORMS AND CONSTRUCTION ARTICLES ARE LARGE • INTERFERENCE IS A PROBLEM
RMS	• PROVIDE A MOBILE (TRACKED) RMS	• NECESSARY TO PROVIDE PAYLOAD HANDLING WITH SPREAD-OUT WORK AREAS

SUBJECT	REQUIREMENT	RATIONALE
PROPELLANT STORAGE	• PROVIDE AN EFFICIENT PROPELLANT TRANSFER AND STORAGE FACILITY FOR SPACE-BASED OTV (GROWTH ITEM)	• WITHOUT A PROPELLANT T&S SYSTEM AS AN OPERATIONAL BUFFER, THERE IS NO BENEFIT TO SPACE BASING
FLEXIBILITY OF OPERATIONS	• PROVIDE SOFTWARE FOR ON-BOARD RESOURCES ALLOCATION AND MISSION PLANNING IN REAL TIME	• BE USER-FRIENDLY; ELIMINATE THE INSTITUTIONAL HASSLE AND LEAD TIME FOR DETAILED PREPLANNING
AIRLOCKS	• PROVIDE AT LEAST TWO EXTERNAL AIRLOCKS LOCATED CONVENIENTLY TO WORK AREAS, BUT NOT EXHAUSTING AIR DIRECTLY ON SENSITIVE PAYLOADS	• MINIMIZE TIME LOST TRANSLATING FROM AIRLOCKS TO WORK AREAS • MINIMIZE CONTAMINATION • INTERNAL AIRLOCKS LOUSE UP CONFIGURATIONS
QUIET/ACTIVE MODULES	• SEPARATE CREW SLEEP AND REST AREAS FROM ACTIVE WORK AREAS. PROVIDE PRIVATE QUARTERS. PROVIDE WINDOWS.	• THESE ARE THE HIGHEST PRIORITIES IN ACCOMMODATIONS ACCORDING TO EXPERIENCED FLIGHT CREWS

SUBJECT	REQUIREMENT	RATIONALE
REDUNDANT PATHS	• PROVIDE REDUNDANT PATHS FOR CREW PASSAGE AND CRITICAL UTILITIES	• PREVENT A SINGLE ACCIDENT OR FAILURE FROM DISABLING MORE THAN ONE MODULE
DISTRIBUTED SYSTEMS GROWTH	• DEVELOP A SUBSYSTEMS ARCHITECTURE SO THAT EACH MODULE IS AS SELF-SUFFICIENT AS POSSIBLE	• ENHANCES COMMON MODULE APPROACH • ENHANCES GROWTH POTENTIAL • ENHANCES SAFETY AND GRACEFUL DEGRADATION
MAINTAINABILITY	• DESIGN FOR EFFICIENT MAINTENANCE: BIT, DIAGNOSTICS SOFTWARE, EASE OF ACCESS AND REMOVE AND REPLACE; OPERATE WHILE BEING MAINTAINED	• MAINTENANCE LABOR MUST BE MINIMIZED TO MAXIMIZE CREW USEFUL WORK
AUTONOMY	• PROVIDE A HIGH DEGREE OF ONBOARD AUTONOMY THROUGH AUTOMATION AND USE OF EXPERT SYSTEMS	• MINIMIZE MISSION CONTROL AND SUPPORT COSTS
COMMONALITY	• PURSUE COMMON MODULE APPROACH • USE INDUSTRY STANDARD RATHER THAN UNIQUE DESIGN WHERE POSSIBLE	• REDUCE DDT&E COST • REDUCE SPARES PROGRAM COST

ideas, evaluate thoroughly and wring out every good aspect before discarding. Most bright ideas are eventually discarded for sound reasons, but almost every one will have at least one good, salvageable feature. Save those! Good designs have been made from the good aspects of impractical ideas.

Drawings are essential to this process; they should be used early, continually, and liberally. Freehand sketches are good for roughing out ideas, but scale drawings are important to establish successful design and packaging approaches. Three-dimensional computer-aided design (CAD) systems are highly recommended for configuration development. The use of a good 3-D (e.g., solids modeling) CAD system to present various isometric and perspective views of a complex three-dimensional configuration closely approaches the effectiveness of mockups and models for visualization and assessment of arrangement feasibility and practicality.

Design Integration: The Systems Engineering Process

This book is concerned mainly with the technical aspects of space station and platform design. Systems engineering includes aspects that are mainly nontechnical but essential to the orderly development and production of a design. An overview of the entire process is important to contextual understanding of the technical aspects of design integration. Alternative recipes for the practice of systems engineering exist. Here we will briefly describe one that consists of six parts: requirements and specifications development, trade studies and analyses, interface documentation and control, operations and logistics analysis, configuration management, and technical assessment and integration.

A *specification* is a formal document that sets forth all the requirements a system design must meet, and how meeting those requirements is to be demonstrated. Specifications for large systems such as space stations and platforms normally include a top-level system or program specification and subordinate specifications for the systems, subsystems, and components that contribute to the entire program. A specification normally exists for every hardware or software item to be delivered in fulfillment of a contract.

A typical list of top-level program requirements fills a page or two. A complete system specification comprised of all the derivative requirements applicable to the system as a whole is a substantial document. When all the subordinate specifications are included, the total is likely to be thousands of pages.

Trade studies and analyses are conducted to establish requirements subordinate to program requirements. A program requirement might specify that a space station is to accommodate six people; subordinate requirements would deal with the accommodations within each module, the air

and water quality, crew safety standards, food service, and so on.

Analyses and trade studies are conducted to find the best ways of creating subordinate requirements. Program requirements, for example, might call for servicing a space station with the Space Shuttle and for delivery of a certain level of power to users. Analyses of the mission model would estimate payload delivery needs. The power level would set solar array size, hence drag and propulsion requirements and thus propulsion resupply. A trade study would select the space station altitude. Higher altitudes beget less drag but also less Shuttle performance. Subordinate trades address the type and efficiency of solar arrays, the selection and performance of propellants, and so on, using evaluation criteria such as minimum cost to guide design decisions. Each decision is rendered as one or more design requirements.

There are usually multiple criteria, e.g., weight, safety, cost, and three general approaches for their use.

1. Evaluate each option against each criterion in a tabular format. Use a checkmark to indicate the preferred option for each criterion; then count the checkmarks.
2. Segregate criteria into "must pass" and relative categories. Screen options to eliminate those that fail a "must pass" criterion. Evaluate the remainder.
3. Define a single unifying criterion. This may be "points" via weighting factors. Sometimes cost is used (everything is converted to a cost). Cost is undoubtedly better than "points" but arguments ensue as to the validity of the cost conversions.

An effective approach is to flunk those options that cannot be fixed to get by the "must pass" criteria and use cost to evaluate the rest. There will often be more than one competitive option as regards cost estimates. Common sense is the discriminator of last resort (as well as the design tool of first resort that should be used to obtain the options in the first place).

Interfaces are the formal descriptions of the means by which one item is installed and operates with respect to others. For example, a thermal control and ventilation unit (thermal/vent pack) will be installed in a pressurized module. The applicable *interface control document (ICD)* will specify the installation provisions such as: bolt spacing, type, material, and torque; power and data plug details including pin functions by number as well as voltages, currents, impedances, and data logic characteristics; airflow quantity, temperature and humidity, any cooling provisions; and maintenance provisions. ICDs are another aspect of requirements documentation.

Operations and logistics analyses are often included in the systems engineering process. These concentrate on how a system is to be operated and provided with supplies, consumables, and spare parts. This is an extensive subject, the source of many design requirements, that can only be hinted at here. Many issues are addressed: How is the item to be processed for launch? What is to be tested and where? How is it packaged and integrated into the Shuttle ground operations flow? What happens on orbit? How is the unit to be installed and activated, e.g., what is turned on first, power or data or cooling? What do all these considerations impose as design requirements?

Another very important specification issue is verification. How is the adherence to requirements to be verified? There are three basic methods.

1. Similarity, used when the design is very much like another that has already been qualified for the subject service. This is usually applied when an existing qualified design is to be used in a similar service, or the modification of a design is judged not to alter its qualification for use.
2. Analysis, when the design or its service environment is so well understood that engineering analysis suffices to achieve confidence.
3. Test.

Testing includes developmental, qualification, and acceptance testing. Development testing supports the design process, proving design validity. Qualification is concerned with design and operating environments. Will the design function and survive for its intended life in the operating environment—pressure, temperature, radiation, vibration, load, etc.? Qualification testing normally exceeds expected operating conditions to provide a margin of confidence. Acceptance testing verifies that the item as produced functions and will survive. Acceptance testing normally does not exceed expected limits and is conducted so as not to consume a significant portion of the operating life of an item.

Configuration management is intended to ensure precise knowledge of actual configuration. Was the item built exactly as designed? (Usually not!) Were there any differences between the item qualification tested and the production units; if so, are the differences significant? After maintenance or field modification, what is the configuration?

If there is anything more frustrating than not knowing why something failed, it is not knowing why it succeeded, for instance, after a series of failures. Exact knowledge of how a complex system comprised of hundreds of thousands of parts was built is a monumental problem. Were there any deviations from procedure and processes? Were there, for example, any instances of jury-rig procedures on the shop floor because of mistakes or things that simply didn't install the way the drawings indicated? Are there any anomalistic parts? The only way to find out is by having a complete record of part numbers, lot numbers, and manufacturing histories. Who built the units, and when?

Configuration management deals with three baselines.

1. The requirements baseline—these are the requirements that dictate the design and everyone concerned agrees and has signed off.
2. The design baseline—this is what the design is and the official set of documentation that defines the design; everyone agrees and has signed off; deviations between the requirements and the design are accounted, understood, and accepted.
3. The as-built baseline—this is what was actually built; any differences between the design and as-built are accounted for, understood, and accepted.

Technical assessment includes design integration, discussed in the following paragraphs, and technical performance measurement. Technical performance measurement (TPM) is a formalized procedure, often made an official part of a contract and a basis for payment of incentive award fees. TPM provides a documented measure of the quality of a design. TPM could be as simple as comparing as-designed weight or cost to specification or target weight or cost. TPM targets often represent better than specification performance. Most TPM systems involve several to a few dozen parameters, all included in a point system that serves to measure the overall quality of a design compared to what is desired. TPM systems are usually set as a part of contractual negotiations. Contractors are often asked to propose a TPM system including the parameters, the targets, and the overall points system as a part of proposals for systems developments.

Reviews are conducted as a buy-off procedure to ensure technical adequacy. Reviews cover the gamut from minor events such as informal weekly reviews within a contractor's organization to major events. The principal major events in a program are:

1. Program Requirements Review (PRR) - the top-level program requirements are reviewed and approved.
2. System Requirements Review (SRR) - the top-level system requirements are reviewed and approved. This occurs as a part of the preliminary design process.
3. Preliminary Design Review (PDR) - the system preliminary design and the system specifications are reviewed and approved. The preliminary design includes layouts and graphical descriptions of all elements as well as performance, design and operating points, operational concepts, etc. Approval of the PDR means that detailed design may proceed.
4. Critical Design Review (CDR)—Review and approval of the fabrication design, i.e., drawings. Approval of the CDR means that fabrication of the developmental design may proceed.
5. Acceptance of deliverable hardware. Qualification and acceptance test records and configuration management

records are reviewed to ensure that the contracted hardware is acceptable for delivery.

6. Flight Readiness Review (FRR)—this is the final review of all hardware, operations, procedures, etc., before flight or launch. Approval of the FRR initiates final launch processing. There are later checkpoints, e.g., various pad tests. Preparations for a launch can of course be interrupted whenever a problem is detected, but the FRR is the last *formal* review before a flight.

Design Integration: Technical Interrelationships

Technical specialists prefer to practice in isolation. This is merely human nature; people are most comfortable working with what they know best. Thermal design and analysis engineers would prefer not to be bothered about electronics equipment installation issues, and so forth. Design integration deals with the interrelationships among subsystems and technical disciplines in order to ensure that a design will function smoothly and efficiently as an integrated whole. Interrelationships are analyzed through systems trades, interdisciplinary analyses of how subsystems interact with each other and with the operating environment.

These studies are best initiated by creating a table of technical interrelationships. The table is a matrix, prepared at the level of major subsystem elements. The influence of a power system solar array on other subsystem elements, for example, will be different than that of energy storage or distribution. Across the top of the table is written "influencing element," and down the left-hand side, "influenced element." Solar array area, established by total space station or platform power needs, affects drag and hence propellant requirements. At the intersection of "solar array area" (influencing) and "propellant storage" (influenced) is the appropriate notation; an analysis is to be conducted to quantitatively define the relationship.

Two examples of interrelationships trade studies are given below to illustrate the nature of the genre. A typical preliminary design effort would encompass hundreds of such studies.

Heat rejection from a space station or platform, being subject to the fourth-power Stefan-Boltzmann law, is very sensitive to the temperature at which heat must be rejected. Different heat sources on a space station or platform reject heat at different temperatures. The thermal loop may be either variable-temperature, single-phase, or constant-temperature, two-phase. Selection depends not only on idealized performance of the thermal loop but also interaction with the thermal sources.

Heat sources will need heat removal over a range of temperatures. A typical list for a pressurized module includes the following:

Source	Thermal Power, kW	Temperature, Deg. C	Data Source
Refrigerator	0.1	5	EC/LS—equipment descriptions
Water cooler	0.05	5	Same
Humidity control	1.0	5	EC/LS—Appendix C See note below
Cabin thermal control	4.0	10	EC/LS plus aircooled equipment
Cabin electronics	4.0	30	Cold-plated equipment
Lab experiment air cooling	10.0	40	Lab experiment power loads

Note: Cabin water vapor input is 4.2252 kg per person per day per the EC/LS algorithm table. The heat load for an 8-person crew is 4.2252×8 kg/day $\times 580$ kcal/kg $\times 4186$ J/kcal, divided by 24 hours per day and 3.6 million J/kWh, resulting in slightly less than 1 kilowatt-thermal.

If a single-phase cooling loop is used, the loads may be ordered so that the fluid passes through the heat exchangers for the lowest-temperature loads first, then through those for the higher-temperature loads. A diagram like Figure 8.21 shows temperature-energy profiles for the cooling fluid. The fluid warms with an assumed constant specific heat as it absorbs heat. The fluid must always be colder than the thermal loads from which heat is removed for heat transfer to occur. In Figure 8.21 it is clear that thermal control of the cabin at 10 °C sets thermal loop conditions with a radiator inlet temperature of about 20 °C if 10 kW are removed or about 40 °C if 20 kW are removed. The radiator outlet temperature will be about 0 °C in either case.

Reference to Figure 5.42 shows results for a cylindrical module radiator 4.4 meters in diameter and about 7 meters

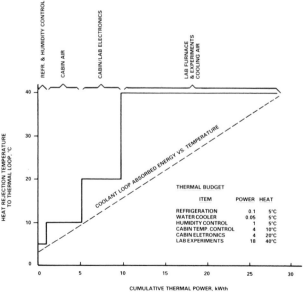

Figure 8.21 Thermal profile for single-phase heat transport loop.

long, with a design delta T of 20 °C. The curves indicate that this radiator, if it has a selective coating, can reject over 20 kW with an inlet temperature of 40 °C. If the selective coating is severely degraded, less than 20 kW can be rejected. (For an accurate analysis, additional curves for different design delta Ts should be used.)

Ordering loads on a thermal bus restricts flexibility. A two-phase bus can absorb heat without temperature change, but the entire bus must be at the lowest temperature the bus serves. Since there is a significant penalty for rejecting heat at lower temperatures, a single two-phase bus may be an unattractive solution. A set of three two-phase buses could be set with one for humidity control and refrigerator loads, one for cabin air cooling, and one at typical electronics/lab experiment temperatures.

Propulsion may be integrated with another subsystem. One approach is to integrate it with electrical energy storage, assuming use of hydrogen-oxygen regenerable fuel cells. An equipment commonality benefit may be obtained, but all propellant must be delivered by the logistics system (presumably in the form of water to be electrolyzed) as the regenerable fuel cell system does not produce net propellant. Another approach is to look to the EC/LS system for consumables surpluses. Many years ago it was suggested that biowaste, e.g., wet feces, be heated in a resistojet for orbit makeup propulsion. Present concerns about contamination of space station instruments indicate this not to be practical. However, the EC/LS system also produces CO_2, and methane as surpluses from human metabolism and CO_2 reduction. Analyses of EC/LS fluids balances using the algorithms summarized in Appendix C as illustrated in Figure 8.22, show that EC/LS resupply is minimized when enough water is supplied (as wet food or with food) so that oxygen needed for metabolism and cabin leakage is generated by water and CO_2 reduction. Since there is oxygen in the food, not all CO_2 need be reduced. Both CO_2 and methane will be available for propulsion if desired. Figure 5.55 shows that roughly 10,000 newton-seconds of daily impulse is about the maximum needed for a space station like the present NASA baseline. A resistojet operating on a CO_2-methane mixture may be expected to have a jet velocity of about

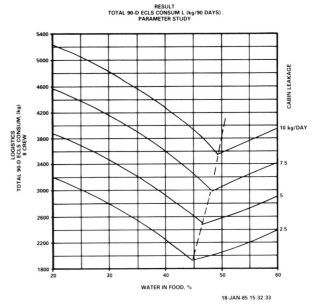

Figure 8.22 EC/LS balance calculation results showing optima in water content of food for minimum resupply. *Courtesy of Boeing.*

1500 m/sec (I_{sp} about 150 seconds). About 6 kg/day are needed for the densest atmosphere. Approximately this amount is available as EC/LS surplus at the minimum-resupply balance point. Thorough completion of such a tradeoff must consider the power to operate the resistojet (on the order of 100 watts), attitude control needs and implementation, the complexity of the fluid supply and feed system, the technical readiness of a suitable resistojet, what backup systems might be needed, how the atmosphere as well as the supply of EC/LS fluids will vary, and so forth.

These examples of design integration trades show that involvement of many technical disciplines and a broad range of design considerations are necessary to obtain valid results. Thorough treatment of design integration trades is one of the most difficult challenges of a preliminary design effort. Examination and review of the resulting interfaces and requirements are important throughout the design and development process.

Chapter 9

Cost and Cost Estimating

"However else the publicly funded space activities of the United States might be described, they certainly would have to be characterized as being very, very costly." - OTA Report on Civilian Space Stations, Congress of the United States, November 1984.

"The Government are very keen on amassing statistics. They collect them, add them, raise them to the nth power, take the cube root and prepare wonderful diagrams. But you must never forget that every one of these figures comes in the first instance from the village watchman, who puts down what he damn pleases." - Sir Josiah Stamp, Inland Revenue Department, England, 1896-1916.

As these quotes indicate, space enterprises are expensive, so expensive as to constitute problems including inhibition of entrepreneurial ventures and considerable resistance in the Congress to the establishment of major new publicly financed space ventures. Often our understanding of why space enterprises cost so much leaves much to be desired.

There are no formulas for cost like those for stress and strain or for orbital mechanics. There are formulas, yes, but they are empirically derived, not based on any sort of physical principles. Cost estimates tend, in many instances, to become self-fulfilling prophesies as explained later in this chapter. Certain popular and widespread beliefs about what causes high cost seem to have little basis in experience.

In this chapter we will examine the contributors to cost, review analytical methods for predicting cost and related economic factors, and conclude with hope for the future, how costs for space systems may be reduced. The intent here is to provide an overview of cost estimating methods, their strong and weak points, and a brief perspective on possible avenues for cost reductions.

The Contributors to Cost

In a sense, cost is very easy to estimate. One need merely take the number of people required to carry out a project, multiply by their average salary, multiply by the appropriate overhead factors, and multiply by the time needed to complete the project. Averages or running sums may be used as necessary to account for variations in numbers of people and salaries.

This is a very accurate method *if* the components of this formula are accurately known. That, of course, is the problem. How many people and how long are the main uncertainties. If these could be accurately estimated, then cost prediction would be an accurate science.

Times required to complete a project are estimated from typical project histories. The intervals between the major reviews such as Preliminary Design Review (PDR), Critical Design Review (CDR), etc., seem consistent from one project to the next. This, as with many other aspects of project estimating, may be in the category of self-fulfilling prophecy. With increasing automation of engineering design and analysis it *should* be possible to shorten some of these times.

To estimate the number of people required, one may call on the experience of seasoned design managers or resort to some sort of statistical procedure. Since seasoned design managers in each important skill are usually not involved in the formative phases of a project when early estimates of total project cost are made, statistical procedures (i.e., cost models) are the usual practice. These take the form of correlative analyses, projecting the cost of the elements of a program using statistical trends of the cost of similar items as a function of physical parameters, often weight (mass). The *major advantage* of cost models is that they enable meaningful cost estimates to be made, and hence cost trades to be run, in the conceptual and preliminary design phases of a program.

Before we can apply any cost estimating methodology, we must define the job to be done. Not so many years ago, this definition was taken to be the specification and the preliminary design. Management concerns over obtaining better understanding and control of costs, and the desire to create a usable statistical data base for cost estimating, have led to a more detailed and structured approach called the Work Breakdown Structure (WBS). A spacecraft doesn't look much like an airplane, but both are constructed of the same basic kinds of engineering subsystems and components, for example, structures and electronics. Statistical inferences indicated that the components could be fitted onto trend curves given suitable adjustment factors. Better statistics were needed. Hence the WBS evolved as a structured system of cost accounts.

A present standard WBS for spacecraft hardware items was given earlier in Table 7.1. The complete cost accounts list includes additional elements of work that do not contribute directly to hardware mass, items such as software development, configuration management, and systems trade studies (to pick three at random). The WBS may also cut across organizational disciplines such as engineering, development shop, manufacturing, and test. Finally it includes a time dimension, the program phases of preliminary design, detailed design, hardware development, flight test, operations, and support. Many of these aspects and their importance differ from one program to another. For a program with a great deal of production, the cost of manufacturing is of paramount importance. For a space station or platform program, the important costs are clearly design and development, and operations support during the lifetime of the system. Design and development will be 60 to 80 percent of the program cost spent to initial operational capability (IOC). With an expected lifetime of 10 to 20 years, the annual operations costs are similarly important.

Analytical Methods

A number of analytical techniques are used in cost estimating. The analytical sophistication of some of these should not be permitted to cloud the underlying issues of what causes cost to begin with and how costs might be reduced.

Parametric Models

It seems intuitively obvious that there ought to exist a cost correlation with mass and size. After all, big cars cost more than small ones, other things being equal. Other things are sometimes not, e.g., a small but exotic sports car may cost much more than a large but common sedan. A large electronics box would be expected to cost more than a small one, but not if the latter resulted from an intensive engineering effort to miniaturize the former. Advances in technology, especially in electronics, can throw carefully developed correlations into complete disarray. For example, a modern programmable pocket calculator weighs and costs about four orders of magnitude less than the original vacuum-tube computer ENIAC but has about the same capability.

These countervailing trends are mathematically modeled using mass/cost trending for similar items and one or more adjustment factors to deal with differences in difficulty of design or manufacture. The principal adjustment factor is a judgmental one called "complexity" (guidelines are provided) that conveys design and manufacturing difficulty. Other factors are sometimes provided for materials of construction, e.g., titanium is harder to machine and runs the

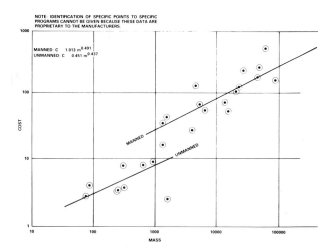

Figure 9.1 Typical cost estimating relationships for structures. *Courtesy of Boeing.*

cost up, and for special requirements such as radiation hardening.

These models exist at two main levels of detail. One considers the entire spacecraft as a single estimate item, and the greater level of detail usually operates at about the level of individual computers, gyros, electrical power supplies, major structural elements, etc. The detailed models sometimes also reflect organizational aspects such as design, development shop, systems engineering, liaison, manufacturing, and systems test. The best of the detailed models estimate in man-hours rather than in dollars. This simplifies historical correlations: the issue of inflation is removed, although human productivity variances remain.

Cost estimating relationships (CERs) are derived from statistical correlations of cost (or man-hours) with a physical parameter. Mass is most commonly used, but area might be more appropriate, e.g., for wings of solar arrays. Memory size or processing speed might be used for a computer. Software cost estimates are usually based on the number of lines of code that must be produced, with due consideration of the type of language to be used. Figure 9.1 illustrates CERs for a typical set of structures. A mass estimate for a structure is entered into the abscissa, and a cost estimate is given on the ordinate. The estimated complexity of the structure, i.e., which CER is used, has a great bearing on the result. The illustrated CERs are typical in being straight-line curve fits on a logarithmic graph. Mathematically, these curves are of the form (cost) = (constant) × ((mass) raised to an exponent). The exponents are on the order of 0.4 for design and development and 0.8 for manufacturing.

Users of parametric cost models must be cognizant of the scaling of the model data base, i.e., what level of detail the model is intended to process. This is important because of the nonlinearity of the CERs. Consider, for example, estimating the cost of a unit of 1000 kg mass, comprised of

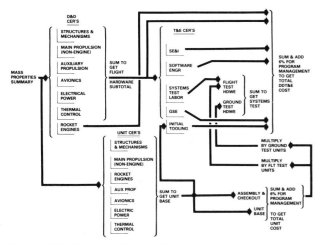

Figure 9.2 Summing diagram for typical parametric cost model. *Courtesy of Boeing.*

ten subunits of 100 kg mass each. Suppose the estimating equation is $C = 650,000M^{0.4}$. For 1000 kg mass, this yields a cost of \$10.3 million. Now, suppose we apply the equation to the subunits at 100 kg. We obtain a value of \$4.1 million each, a total of \$40.1 million for all ten subunits. Clearly it is important that the use of the model be set at the same hardware assembly level as its statistical data base.

Some parametric cost models estimate cost directly; others estimate man-hours for the activities which, taken in total, comprise a program. These activities are then summed up to derive total program costs, as illustrated in Figure 9.2. Most models treat design and development separately from manufacturing. Some hardware must be manufactured to support a design and development program. How this is handled differs from model to model, but the analyst is usually required to estimate how many production units or fractions thereof are needed to support systems test and flight test programs.

The RCA company supplies a cost model under license or lease, called "RCA PRICE." This model has hardware, software, and life cycle cost packages. The hardware package covers design and development and manufacturing.

Parametric cost models require the analyst to make a judgment as to the complexity of design and manufacturing of each element to be estimated. This judgment, as noted, has a large bearing on the results. The judgment must be based on experience and must correlate with the judgment involved in developing the CERs from the historical data in the first place. The analyst must know from experience with the model, and by comparing its results with actual program histories, how complex is complex. The better models provide guides to selection of complexity factors based on technical parameters such as types of material, pointing accuracy, and so forth. Still, the entire business is rather less than highly scientific. Surprisingly, good success is had with these models in the hands of experienced users. One

must, however, keep in mind the point about self-fulfilling prophecy.

A prediction of cost for a developmental item will clearly be too high if estimated as new development when a minor modification of existing hardware is planned. Often, fully developed equipment can be used in new systems. Parametric cost models allow for these economies through off-the-shelf and modification factors. These are usually linear. No modification means no development cost; 100 percent modification is the same as new development. The more sophisticated models reflect the cost effect of a new development in factored costs (systems integration, etc.) even for off-the-shelf items. This is to contend that the effort for these factored items is about the same whether the item is off-the-shelf or a new development.

Some experienced cost analysts argue that the cost of modifying an item equals that of new development at 30 to 40 percent modification rather than 100 percent, and that extensive modification is more costly than new development. I know of no cost model that assumes this.

Most cost models permit a "pass-through" cost for something whose cost is known, e.g., from a vendor quote. Pass-through costs are input by the estimator and not altered by the cost model. They may (and should) be included in factored costs.

It has been observed that the correlations obtained in fitting historical cost data are vastly improved if a factor is included to reflect the developmental environment. Such a factor is called an environment or platform factor. The cost of a given mass item is observed to be systematically different depending on whether the development is for missiles, aircraft, unmanned spacecraft, manned spacecraft, etc. The same effect is true for software; the more emphasis placed on validation and verification (V&V), the higher the cost. An environment factor is included in the RCA PRICE model; results of changing this factor and nothing else are depicted in Figure 9.3. A causality is clearly present, but statistical analyses do not explain causalities, they only infer them. It is tempting to believe, and perhaps true, that these differences in cost arise through differences in program management practices that have recently come to be called "culture." This will be discussed in more detail later.

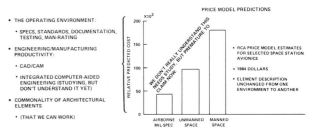

Figure 9.3 Illustration of program environment factor effect in parametric cost modeling. *Courtesy of Boeing.*

Mass growth prediction was discussed in Chapter 7. Since historical cost–mass correlations are based on hardware actual mass rather than someone's design estimate, it may be appropriate to apply an increment to parametric cost predictions to reflect the probable outcome of mass growth. The increment should be applied to both developmental and manufacturing costs. I am not aware of any statistical correlations in this area, but if typical slopes of CERs are assumed to apply, developmental costs should be adjusted by

$$C/C_o = (m/m_o)^{0.4} \qquad (9.1)$$

and manufacturing costs by

$$C/C_o = (m/m_o)^{0.8} \qquad (9.2)$$

Mass growth is not usually factored into cost estimates. If it is to be considered, it should be used in place of, or as a part of, cost growth or contingency allowances and not added in as an additional cost growth. Software has no appreciable mass and its cost cannot be correlated with physical parameters as can hardware costs. The art of estimating software cost is far more immature than that for estimating hardware. Until recent years, the cost of software was not a major program cost item and software costs were usually estimated as a modest percentage of hardware costs. Today, software costs are much too great to be handled offhandedly; there is little agreement in the estimating community as to a best way to predict software costs.

One often used rule of thumb for software cost is that fully validated software can be produced at the rate of about three lines of code per person-day of effort. This figure may seem astounding to the typical programmer of small systems; it seems easy enough to write and check out a program of a few hundred lines of BASIC code in an afternoon. The seeming very low productivity of three lines per day has several roots.

1. The figure includes at least some low-level algorithm development.

2. Full documentation of the code is included—what it does, how it works, explanations of all variables, how to input and operate it, etc. (Try that in an afternoon for even a few dozen lines of BASIC code.)

3. Large systems are assumed, and complete testing is included. Small systems usually have only a few possible states and are straightforward to test; they are usually incompletely tested. Large systems that serve critical functions are tested in every possible state to ensure that there are no hidden software flaws that could precipitate a disaster.

4. All labor charged to the development is included, including clerical, document preparation, and probably computer operator time.

The three-lines rule does not recognize increasing difficulty with size, does not recognize differences in languages and programming environments, and could discourage mod-

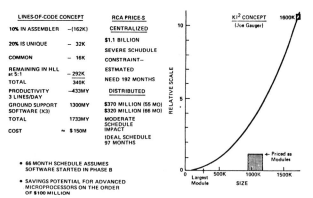

Figure 9.4 Typical results of applying software cost estimating methods. *Courtesy of Boeing.*

ern structured and modular programming techniques that may use more lines of code but are more labor-efficient because they produce code that is easier to read, debug, modify, maintain, and test.

The RCA PRICE model includes a software estimating method. It takes into account some of the items mentioned, such as language and difficulty, and includes a schedule algorithm with severe cost penalties for too little schedule time for software development.

A study conducted by Boeing proposed an algorithm that correlated the cost of software with the square of the number of independent input and output data items to be manipulated; surprisingly good correlations were obtained. This algorithm estimated software cost as a correlation factor multiplied by the square of the number of items to be manipulated.

Figure 9.4 illustrates the use of these software methods to estimate the cost of software for the Space Operations Center (SOC). The estimates of the amount of software needed were very preliminary, but the comparison of results is interesting. Both the RCA PRICE model and the KI^2 model showed great cost advantage for a modular approach. The software in question lent itself easily to modularization as many disparate functions were present, e.g., control of individual subsystems, communications processing, and crew interaction.

Learning Curves

It has been observed that aerospace manufacturing programs improve in labor efficiency with time. For each doubling of the number produced, the labor per unit produced decreases by a certain fraction, expressed by

$$C_N = C_1 r^{\log_2 N}$$

where C_N is cost of the Nth unit, C_1 is cost of the first, and r is the improvement slope fraction.

By manipulation of logarithms this can be expressed as

$$C_N = C_1 N^{(\log r/\log 2)} \qquad (9.3)$$

Table 9.1 Learning curve results for summation approximations.

Unit #	Nth Unit Cost	Exact Sum	Integration Formula	Shields Formula
1	1.000	1.000	1.013	1.000
2	0.85	1.85	1.866	1.853
3	0.7729	2.6229	2.640	2.623
4	0.7225	3.3454	3.363	3.350
5	0.6857	4.0311	4.049	4.036
6	0.6570	4.6881	4.706	4.693
7	0.6337	5.3218	5.340	5.327
8	0.6141	5.9359	5.954	5.941
9	0.5974	6.5333	6.552	6.538
10	0.5828	7.1161	7.135	7.121

where the logs are Napierian, a more useful formula. C_N is the cost of the Nth unit, C_1 is the cost of the first, and r is the improvement curve "slope" expressed as a fraction less than one, the ratio C_{2N}/C_N.

Very often, what is desired is the cumulative or average cost of producing N units, e.g., to find a break-even point if the units are sold at a constant price. Eq. 9.2 can be integrated to give an approximate sum. (Strictly speaking, an integer sum is called for. All of any particular unit costs a certain value. Learning curves are usually not thought of as applying to fractional units.) If one integrates from zero to N, the result is $N^{(r+1)}/(r+1)$. Integrating from 0.5 to $N + 0.5$ is more accurate, yielding

$$C_{CUM} = \frac{(N+0.5)^{(r+1)} - 0.5^{(r+1)}}{r+1} . \qquad (9.4)$$

A still more accurate approximation was found by Ed Shields of Boeing some years ago, and is recommended:

$$C_{CUM} = \frac{(N+0.5)^{(r+1)} - 1.5^{(r+1)}}{r+1} + 1. \qquad (9.5)$$

These expressions are compared for units 1 to 10 and for an improvement curve slope of 85 percent in Table 9.1. Either integral expression is more than accurate enough.

Figure 9.5 presents values for the learning curve expressions for units from 1 to 1000 and for a wide range of improvement slopes. Typical practice is to estimate mechanical manufacturing at about an 85 percent curve and electronics and rocket engines at about 90 percent. There is much reason to believe that learning curves are another self-fulfilling prophecy.

Learning curves are considered applicable to typical aerospace production - that is, production rates of less than 100 units per year, often as low as 1 or 2 units per year, and requiring much manual assembly work. The learning curve represents incremental improvement in production operations, that is, fewer and shorter delays in obtaining and

locating parts, better use of manpower, and on-the-job learning. Many analysts are reluctant to apply learning to cost estimates for very low production rates, arguing that so many things change that improvements in efficiency do not occur. "Learning" production cost improvement is well-demonstrated on commercial aircraft production; less so on government programs. A possibly cynical observation is that the commercial producer must make the learning curve to stay in business while the government contractor has a second option—negotiation of contract changes.

If high production rates are planned, automation of processes is likely to be greater than inherent in typical aerospace parametric cost models. One does not expect learning for a highly automated production process, but one should apply a cost improvement based on the planned production rate and amount of automation. Experience indicates that a 70 percent improvement curve is about right. If the production rate is doubled and the appropriate amount of automation is added for the higher rate, then the unit cost will be reduced by a factor of $1/\sqrt{2}$ or 0.707. Some parametric cost models provide facilities for estimating production rate effects.

One should be cautious in the application of historical trends to automation effects on production costs as the state of the art is advancing rapidly. In historical cases, automation of production necessitated high capital investments in software and equipment. Advancements in the state of the art are making general-purpose equipment, e.g., "flexible manufacturing systems" and increased robot "intelligence," more applicable to small-lot and short production runs.

Compiling Program Costs

Cost estimates, made with cost models or summed up from detailed program manpower and equipment estimates, are usually made at the contract end item level, e.g., pressurized module, power system, or propulsion module. The estimates

LEARNING CURVE FACTORS

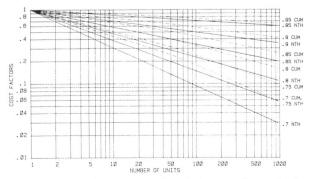

Figure 9.5 Cost improvement (learning) curves for production cost estimating.

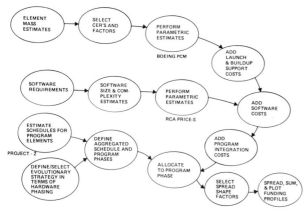

Figure 9.6 Typical method for assembling a total program cost. *Courtesy of Boeing.*

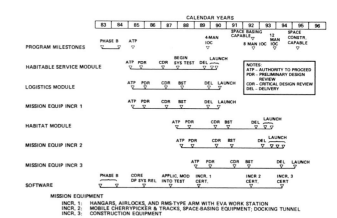

Figure 9.8 Typical high-level program schedule. *Courtesy of Boeing.*

	INITIAL (4 CREW)		OPERATIONAL (12 CREW)		GROWTH (CONSTR. EQUIP. ADDED)	
	DDT&E	PRODUCTION	DDT&E	PRODUCTION	DDT&E	PRODUCTION
MODIFIED SERVICE MODULES	684	564				
LOGISTICS MODULES	106	158				
HABITAT MODULES			550	450		
DOCKING TUNNEL			70	80		
AIRLOCKS	30	50				
HANGARS	70	25		25		
SUPPORT EQUIPMENT	22	76	275	195	25	15
OTV SPACE-BASING EQUIP			200	150		
CONSTRUCTION EQUIP			25	15	250	150
SOFTWARE	150		150		90	
BUILDUP SUPPORT	50	75	100	120		
NO. OF SHUTTLE FLIGHTS		(3)		(6)		(2)
SUBTOTALS	1112	948	1370	1035	365	165
TOTALS	2060		2405 ADDED; TOTAL $$ 4465		530 ADDED; TOTAL 4995	

NOTES:
1) COSTS ARE 1980 DOLLARS IN MILLIONS
2) SHUTTLE LAUNCH COSTS NOT INCLUDED
3) LEVEL I PROGRAM INTEGRATION COSTS NOT INCLUDED

Figure 9.7 Summation of program cost by phase. *Courtesy of Boeing.*

include design, development, test and engineering (DDT&E), and first unit (manufacturing) costs, with appropriate estimating factors for production runs if more than one unit must be built. Even if only one of a large unit is built, it may be appropriate to apply learning factors to those of its components that are used in significant numbers.

First unit costs are sometimes called theoretical first unit (TFU) inasmuch as the actual charges for manufacturing the first unit are inextricably entwined with developmental costs. The value of TFU for a historical program is obtained by extrapolating backward along the actual production cost improvement (learning) curve to unit number 1.

Other costs such as launch charges are often included. A typical summing up of complete program costs is diagrammed in Figure 9.6 and illustrated in Figure 9.7. Finally, it is usually necessary to estimate the annual cost or funding for the entire program.

Annual funding is a primary issue for publicly funded programs because it must be made a part of the annual federal budget and legislated each year by Congress. Annual

funding is also important for privately funded programs as annual budgeting is important for these also. (The difference is that a private institution can obtain credit to cover peak funding. While the government as a whole borrows money, individual agencies cannot.) If detailed manpower estimates against a project schedule are the source of cost estimates, annual funding is an almost automatic fallout. Parametric models, however, estimate in lump sums; these must be spread versus time, using a program schedule such as illustrated in Figure 9.8.

A mathematical device called a beta function is often used to create cost "spreads" (this term is unrelated to the term "spread sheet") for annual funding estimates. The formula for the beta function is:

$$V = \frac{t^r(T-t)^q}{\int_o^T t^r(T-t)^q} .$$

This formula has no particular theoretical significance for cost estimating. It is used because variations in the parameters p and q generate curves that are plausible representations of annual funding. It is easy to program the beta function on a small computer; a few minutes spent exploring its properties will provide more insight than pages of description. Figure 9.9 illustrates the use of the beta function to generate annual funding spreads for the cost data from the previous figures.

Life Cycle Cost and Discounting

Thus far we have concerned ourselves with development and other costs associated with project startup, and production costs as they apply to startup and continuing operations. If we add operations costs, and in certain cases decommissioning costs for project termination, we have all the components of life cycle cost.

The idea of life cycle cost is to estimate and display all costs for a project over its entire life cycle. This is, in a sense, a salutary idea inasmuch as one should be aware of

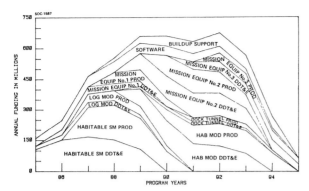

Figure 9.9 Example of a program annual cost estimate. *Courtesy of Boeing.*

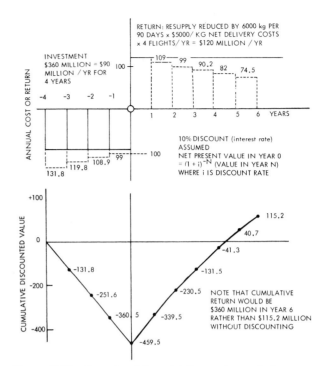

Figure 9.10 Example of financial discounting analysis.

all costs one is committing to when approving a project. It becomes difficult when dealing with projects of indefinite life - the cost is indeterminate—or if the project has infinite life the cost would seem to be infinite. What cost should be estimated for colonizing the Moon? What cost should have been assigned to colonizing the Western Hemisphere? What cost is assigned, for example, to establishing a perpetual chair at a university?

These costs are not infinite. Money has a time value; that is, one is paid interest for an investment or pays interest to borrow. The means of financing a perpetual chair is simple: Contribute a sufficient endowment that the interest on it pays the annual cost of the chair. The amount that must be contributed is called the present value of the perpetual chair for rather obvious reasons.

Present values are calculated by discounting. Discounting depreciates the value of future expenditures to be equal to an initial sum that would accumulate to the future value if invested at a compound interest rate equal to the discount rate. The present value is the amount that need be invested at the designated rate of return (interest rate) in order to accrue to the desired future value at the future date. Mathematically, discounting is related to the integral

$$\int_o^T e^{-rt} dt$$

which clearly is finite even for infinite time T. If interest is continuously compounded, the above integral applies. If interest is compounded at finite intervals, the annual funding to retire an initial amount P is

$$f = P \left[\frac{r}{1 - \dfrac{1}{(1+r)^T}} \right] \qquad (9.6)$$

where r is the discount (interest) rate and T is the number of periods over which the amount P is to be retired. This formula is applicable to calculating the monthly payment on an auto or home loan. The value r is the rate per payment

period (not necessarily the annual rate) and T is the number of payments.

Discounting methodology is sometimes applied to publicly funded projects to evaluate alternatives that involve investing funds early in a project to save later. For example, should we invest in a regenerable life support system in order to reduce resupply costs? Figure 9.10 illustrates this situation to exemplify the technique. Discounting is used in privately funded projects to estimate the internal rate of return to investors. This is exactly equivalent to interest rates. A project with internal rate of return greater than the interest rate available in capital markets is a good investment, all risks being equal (they usually are not).

Discounting is viewed as the appropriate tool for financially evaluating expenditure options in private industry (e.g., should we invest in a new production process to save production cost?). Analysts have argued that it is also appropriate for government projects since government, like industry, pays interest to borrow money. Individual agencies, however, cannot borrow. Consequently, they are often forced to evaluate expenditures based on obtainability of annual funding through the budget process. Whereas an economist might argue that government projects should use a longer-term financial horizon than industry, the reverse is usually true; government decisions (e.g. should we invest in maintainability design features to speed up Shuttle turnaround time), are often made with very short payback horizons. Commonly, optional expenditures whose benefit is reduced production or operating cost are just rejected.

Uncertainty Analysis

Cost estimates for a project are subject to considerable uncertainty, first because the technical parameters used to forecast cost are uncertain, and second because costs are uncertain even if technical parameters are precisely known.

In Chapter 7 we reviewed a statistical method of predicting mass growth based on histories of similar projects. This method applied statistical analysis to the historical data base. It could and has been also used to predict cost growth. The statistical average cost growth for space projects similar to space stations and platforms is on the order of 30 percent. This 30 percent is often applied by government project estimators as a reserve to cover project cost growth. The statistical scatter about this average is large. Projects that more than double in cost are not uncommon; there are also those that underrun. The latter are of course less newsworthy.

Cost uncertainty (standard deviation) may be calculated by

$$\sigma_c^2 = \left(\frac{\delta c}{\delta p_1}\right)^2 \sigma_{p_1}^2 + \left(\frac{\delta c}{\delta p_2}\right)^2 \sigma_{p_2}^2$$

where σ represents a standard deviation, $\dfrac{\delta c}{\delta p_1}$ is the partial derivative of cost with respect to parameter no. 1 (p_1), etc.

An uncertainty analysis technique has been developed based on judgmental estimates on the part of experienced engineers as to the uncertainty in project performance and cost paramaters. This technique is also applicable to mass growth. It is instructive in two ways - first in the use of random variable analytical techniques, and second in what it reveals about the technical psychology of preliminary design and how this contributes to mass and cost growth.

This uncertainty analysis approach produced the unexpected result of predicting mass growth similar to that predicted by the historical correlations described in Chapter 7. It has always been believed that mass growth was the result of unpredictable variables, e.g., changes in program requirements. However, the uncertainty analysis results indicated that growth is a predictable consequence of the natural tendency for engineers to set point design parameters on the optimistic side of the uncertainty range.

This approach requires a parametric systems model (a simple one may suffice, depending on the complexity of the system) to compute the effect of variances in component or subsystem characteristics on the mass and cost of the system as a whole, including any important interrelationships. A typical example is the effect of solar cell efficiency on power system mass and cost. Variance in efficiency causes changes in solar array area to maintain constant power. The effects of area changes on structure mass, control system sizing, propulsion systems (through drag), and so forth must be reflected to obtain a valid result.

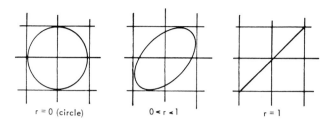

IN THE NORMALIZED ELLIPSE EQUATION, THE ELLIPSE IS A CIRCLE IF r = 0. IF r>0 THE MAJOR AXIS OF THE ELLIPSE IS TILTED AT 45°.

FOR THE NON-NORMALIZED ELLIPSE THE TILT ANGLE IS

$$\alpha = 1/2 \tan^{-1}/2 \left[\frac{2 r \sigma_x \sigma_y}{\sigma_x^2 - \sigma_y^2} \right]$$

Figure 9.11 Probability ellipses and the correlation coefficient.

We assume that all variables are randomly distributed according to the normal (Gaussian) distribution,

$$P(x) = \frac{1}{\sqrt{2\pi}\sigma} e - (v_x^2/2\sigma^2) \qquad (9.7)$$

where σ is the standard deviation of x and v_x is the variance of x from its mean. We also apply the bivariate normal distribution,

$$p(x,y) = \frac{1}{2\pi\sigma_x\sigma_y\sqrt{1-r^2}} e^{-G/2} \qquad (9.8)$$

where $G = C^2 = \dfrac{1}{1-r^2} \left[\dfrac{v_x^2}{\sigma_x^2} - \dfrac{2r\, v_x v_y}{\sigma_x\sigma_y} + \dfrac{v_y^2}{\sigma_y^2} \right]$.

The locus of v_x and v_y for a given value of c is an equal probability ellipse. This ellipse changes shape depending on the correlation coefficient r, as sketched in Figure 9.11. This coefficient measures the functional dependency of y on x. If $r=0$ there is no dependency (that is, no correlation between y and x). If $r=1$, y and x are completely correlated and the problem can be reduced to one with only a single random variable.

The equation for the probability ellipse may be written as

$$x^2 - 2rxy + y^2 = (1-r^2)c^2 \qquad (9.9)$$

where $x = v_x/\sigma_x$ and $y = v_y/\sigma_y$. If a new variable $v_t = Kv_x$ is introduced, we have $x = v_x/\sigma_x = v_t/K\sigma_x$ and eq. 9.9 becomes

$$\frac{v_t^2}{K^2\sigma_x^2} - \frac{2rv_tv_y}{K\sigma_x\sigma_y} + \frac{v_y^2}{\sigma_y^2} = (1-r^2)\, c^2. \qquad (9.10)$$

Note that the correlation coefficient is independent of scaling on x and y.

We may also ask what is the maximum value of x and where does it occur? If eq. 9.9 is solved for x, one gets

$$x = ry \pm \sqrt{(c^2 - y^2)(1-r^2)}. \qquad (9.11)$$

The derivative with respect to y is

$$\frac{dx}{dy} = r \pm \frac{1}{2} [(c^2 - y^2)(1 - r^2)]^{-1/2} [-2y(1 - r^2)] . \quad (9.12)$$

Setting the derivative to zero to find the location of the maximum of x,

$$r = \mp \frac{y(1 - r^2)}{\sqrt{(c^2 - y^2)(1 - r^2)}} \quad (9.13)$$

which solves to:

$$y = \pm rc. \quad (9.14)$$

This can be substituted into eq. 9.11 to find the maximum value of x; namely,

$$x_{max} = \mp r^2 c \pm \sqrt{(c^2 - r^2 c^2)(1 - r^2)} \quad (9.15)$$

which simplifies to $x_{max} = \pm c$, which is independent of r.

In the normalized ellipse equation (which is expressed in terms of x and y rather than v_x and v_y) the ellipse is a circle if $r = 0$. If $r > 0$ the axis of the ellipse is tilted at 45°. For the non-normalized ellipse, it can be shown that the tilt angle is

$$\alpha = \frac{1}{2} \tan^{-1}\left(\frac{2r\sigma_x\sigma_y}{\sigma_x^2 - \sigma_y^2}\right) . \quad (9.16)$$

It can also be shown that the major and minor axes of the ellipse are given by

$$a = \frac{1}{2}\{\sqrt{\sigma_x^2 + \sigma_y^2 + 2\sigma_x\sigma_y\sqrt{1 - r^2}}$$
$$+ \sqrt{\sigma_x^2 + \sigma_y^2 - 2\sigma_x\sigma_y\sqrt{1 - r^2}}$$

$$b = \frac{1}{2}\{\sqrt{\sigma_x^2 + \sigma_y^2 + 2\sigma_x\sigma_y\sqrt{1 - r^2}}$$
$$- \sqrt{\sigma_x^2 + \sigma_y^2 - 2\sigma_x\sigma_y\sqrt{1 - r^2}} \quad (9.17)$$

For the normalized ellipse these simplify to

$$a = \sqrt{1 + r} \text{ and } b = \sqrt{1 - r}. \quad (9.18)$$

These relations can be used to sketch the equi-probability ellipse. As an example, we wish to draw the one-sigma ellipse ($c = 1$) for the case where $\sigma_x = 1$, $\sigma_y = 2$, and $r = 0.5$. The maxima occur at v_x/σ_x and $v_y/\sigma_y = rc$. When either variable is zero, the values of the other are

$$\frac{v_x}{\sigma_x} = \frac{v_y}{\sigma_y} = \sqrt{(1 - r^2)c^2}. \quad (9.19)$$

The major and minor axes for the assumed values are 2.07 and 0.834 respectively. These values allow the ellipse to be sketched with adequate accuracy as shown in Figure 9.12. Similarly, if estimates are available for the variances, these may be used to estimate r. For example, suppose that the information in the lower part of Figure 9.12 is available,

representing 3-σ limits. σ_x is 0.333. A trend line for v_y dependence on v_x is shown, as are estimated 3-σ limits on v_y when v_x is zero. Since these are 3-σ limits, we know that $c = 3$. Also, if the trend line intercepts (at the v_x limits) are the ellipse tangency points, then

$$v_y/\sigma_y = rc = 3r .$$

The limits on v_y when $v_x = 0$ allow setting $v_y/\sigma_y = 3\sqrt{1 - r^2}$.

These are solved to find $r = 0.581$ and $\sigma_y = 0.287$ ($3\sigma_y = 0.862$). The 3-σ ellipse is also sketched in Figure 9.12. Note that the trend line is not the semimajor axis of the ellipse.

A further problem that arises is when the item of ultimate interest, say cost, is a function of other correlated random variables such as mass and efficiency. We need an equation for the uncertainty, e.g., of cost, in such a situation.

Consider a variable U that is a definite function of x and y, the latter being correlated random variables with a known uncertainty ellipse. The problem is sketched in Figure 9.13. In this example, suppose that $dU/dx = 1.3$ and $dU/dy = 1.8$. The angle between the lines of constant U and the x-axis is given by $\tan(\alpha) = -\frac{\partial U/\partial x}{\partial U/\partial y}$. In this example, α is about $-36°$.

We now determine σ_u by a coordinate rotation through the angle α. Consider coordinates (t, u) with the same grid spacing as x and y. Then:

$$v_x = v_t \cos\alpha - v_u \sin\alpha \quad (9.20)$$
$$v_y = v_t \sin\alpha + v_u \cos\alpha.$$

Substituting the above expressions into the equation for G yields

$$G = \frac{1}{1 - r^2}\left[v_t^2\left(\frac{\cos^2\alpha}{\sigma_x^2} + \frac{\sin^2\alpha}{\sigma_y^2} - \frac{2r\sin\alpha\cos\alpha}{\sigma_x\sigma_y}\right)\right.$$

$$+ v_u^2\left(\frac{\sin^2\alpha}{\sigma_x^2} + \frac{\cos^2\alpha}{\sigma_y^2} + \frac{2r\sin\alpha\cos\alpha}{\sigma_x\sigma_y}\right) \quad (9.21)$$

$$\left. - v_t v_u\left(\frac{2\sin\alpha\cos\alpha}{\sigma_x^2} - \frac{2\sin\alpha\cos\alpha}{\sigma_y^2} + \frac{\cos^2\alpha - \sin^2\alpha}{\sigma_x\sigma_y}\right)\right].$$

By comparing terms, we conclude that

$$\frac{1}{1 - r^2}\frac{v_t^2}{\sigma_t^2} =$$

$$\frac{1}{1 - r^2}v_t^2\left(\frac{\cos^2\alpha}{\sigma_x^2} + \frac{\sin^2\alpha}{\sigma_y^2} - \frac{2r\sin\alpha\cos\alpha}{\sigma_x\sigma_y}\right) \quad (9.22)$$

and so forth. Using the identity $\sigma_u^2 + \sigma_t^2 = \sigma_x^2 + \sigma_y^2$ and performing some algebraic manipulation, we obtain

$$\sigma_u^2 = \sin^2\alpha \, \sigma_x^2 + \cos^2\alpha \, \sigma_y^2 - 2r\sigma_x\sigma_y \sin\alpha\cos\alpha.$$

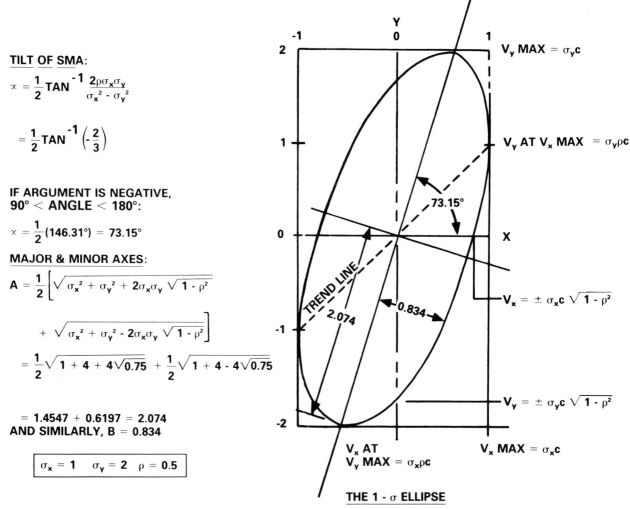

Figure 9.12 Sketching the equi-probability ellipse.

To get σ_U, we need to scale by $\sigma_U^2 = \sigma_u^2\left(\dfrac{\delta U}{\delta u}\right)^2$.

By the Pythagorean theorem, ${\partial U}/{\partial u} = \sqrt{({\partial U}/{\partial x})^2 + ({\partial U}/{\partial y})^2}$

and therefore,

$$\sigma_U^2 = (\sin^2 \alpha\, \sigma_x^2 + \cos^2 \alpha\, \sigma_y^2$$
$$- 2r\, \sigma_x\sigma_y \sin \alpha \cos \alpha)\left[\left(\frac{\partial U}{\partial x}\right)^2 + \left(\frac{\partial U}{\partial y}\right)^2\right]. \quad (9.23)$$

Applying trigonometric identities and performing further algebraic manipulation yield the desired result

$$\sigma_U^2 = \sigma_x^2\left(\frac{\partial U}{\partial x}\right)^2 + \sigma_y^2\left(\frac{\partial U}{\partial y}\right)^2 + 2r\, \sigma_x\sigma_y \frac{\partial U}{\partial x}\frac{\partial U}{\partial y}. \quad (9.24)$$

In the example sketched in Figure 9.13, assume $\sigma_x = 0.55$, $\sigma_y = 0.35$, and $r = 0.5$. Then, from eq. 9.24 we have $\sigma_U^2 = (0.55)(1.3) + (0.35)(1.8) + (2)(0.5)(1.3)(1.8)(0.55) \times (0.35)$, $= 1.359$, and $\sigma_U = 1.166$.

Appendix D presents a worked example of cost uncertainty estimates using the methodology presented here.

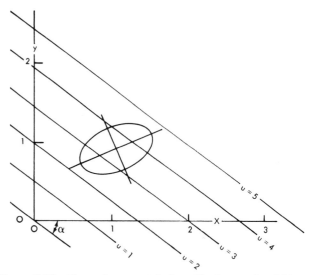

Figure 9.13 Computing uncertainties with change of variable.

Outlook for the Future

Our space activities are today held hostage to the high cost of doing business. Costs are a barrier to commercial enterprise and clearly thwart great ambitions such as permanent settlements on the Moon and expeditions to Mars. Moreover, cost is the primary constraint to space stations and platforms. If we could create a more ambitious space station and platform system for no more investment, this would certainly be accepted. The aerospace community is coming to realize that we can and must do better on cost reduction and control. The conventional wisdom on program management is challenged from within and without.

The "school of hard knocks" long ago taught us that a successful aerospace program must include eight essential ingredients.

1. Excellence of design, including attention to detail, integration, and those things necessary for operation such as maintainability and failure tolerance.
2. Quality parts with the characteristics and capabilities needed for the service intended.
3. Proven processes known to result in quality of finished products.
4. Defect-free manufacture and assembly.
5. Verified capability as established by qualification tests.
6. Verified operability as established by acceptance tests.
7. Verified configuration so that each as-built system is indeed as designed and as tested.
8. Proper operations and maintenance procedures that preserve the integrity of the system.

Fallacies and Myths

In the beginnings of rocket and missile engineering a common view was that a missile was a "one shot deal," and could be cheap and shoddy. A number of design teams learned the fallacy of this the hard way, and in the process early U.S. space rockets earned the reputation of usually blowing up. Today we know that performance, dependability, and safety demand quality in every aspect of design, development, and manufacturing of space systems.

In selecting ideas and approaches for reducing costs of space utilization, we must carefully distinguish between those that would maintain integrity at lower cost by improving human productivity and those that would achieve lower cost by sacrificing integrity. This is not to suggest that we must have ever more integrity at ever more cost, but to point out that compromises of integrity should be clearly understood at the outset.

The Apollo missions to the Moon and the flights of the Space Shuttle have paid a historically unheard-of low price in loss of human life for pushing back the frontiers of ex-

ploration and technology. In the golden age of explorations, the expectancy of returning alive from voyages such as those of Columbus or Magellan was less than 50 percent. Flight testing of high-performance experimental aircraft is also notoriously hazardous. It is sometimes argued that we could avail ourselves of much lower space program costs by being less adamant vis-à-vis reliability and crew safety. While it is certainly true that NASA's high consciousness of safety issues is partly due to the media spotlights under which NASA operates, it does not necessarily follow that relaxation of safety and reliability will generate net cost savings. Every study of which I am aware, and there have been many, shows no cost advantage to compromising present standards in this area. In fact, these studies have tended to strengthen standards for reliability, e.g., by adding more redundancy. Losses due to failures add up faster than savings due to relaxed standards. There is no payoff in "cheap and shoddy." We shall have to search elsewhere.

Another popular belief has it that space programs - criticism is usually directed specifically at NASA - cost too much because NASA undertakes too much technology advancement. This belief reflects lack of understanding of how design and development is actually carried out. The level of technology used in the design process has rather little effect on cost, unless serious development difficulties arise. All of the analyses must be conducted, all the software written, all the drawings produced, all of the tests run, and all of the hardware manufactured regardless of the level of technology. Savings result, of course, when fully developed components or subsystems can be used in a new design. Selection of suitable "off-the-shelf" hardware for use is normal practice in an aerospace program.

When a serious difficulty does arise, solving it is usually not the main contributor to cost overruns, rather it is the cost of supporting all the rest of the program (we can't simply send everyone on unpaid vacation) while the problem is fixed.

Consider the Shuttle. Major program delays were caused by problems in engine and heat shield developments. Both were new technologies. The Shuttle engine has twice the thrust and more than five times the combustion pressure of its largest predecessor. Thrust was dictated by the vehicle size. The increase in combustion pressure was necessary in order to fit enough thrust into the available space in the tail of the Orbiter. There was no reusable heat shield technology before Shuttle. These new technology development problems encountered on the Shuttle program were necessitated by the nature of the vehicle.

Technology advance makes new things possible and old things less expensive. No one, for example, would seriously advocate a return to vacuum-tube computers. The new technology of distributed processing offers major cost reductions as well as user-friendliness for space computer systems, compared to the central processing architecture used on Shuttle and Spacelab. A retreat to proven technology would have but few near-term payoffs and would in the longer term cripple space development.

Some observers argue that NASA should adopt a private-enterprise attitude toward technology advancement, selecting only those that can be shown to generate a positive payoff within the scope of the project under consideration. In fact, NASA's practice is much like this, but the charter of NASA calls for advancing the state of the art, and with good reason. It is the proper role of government to underwrite high technical risks with high potential payoff for all of society. NASA's technology advancements are in the public domain for exploitation by all of industry. The scope of their payoff goes far beyond the projects for which they are made.

Self-fulfilling Prophecies

The cost improvement (learning) curve for aerospace manufacturing is almost an eternal verity. It is almost universally used and believed. It arose from the need to reflect gains in efficiency of manufacturing operations in annual budgeting and program planning. Long-range program plans for production runs and prices for commercial jetliners are based on it. Making the cost improvement curve come true can be a matter of company survival. Little surprise that it becomes a self-fulfilling prophecy.

How this happens is a matter of management psychology. Following the cost improvement curve means gradually improving production efficiency, building more hardware per man-hour. Early in a production run, the production workers improve their performance by learning the fine points of the production tasks, becoming more efficient. Workers learn quickly, and soon better ways of carrying out the tasks must be found - elimination of delays in parts and materials flow, more efficient tooling, for instance. The motivation for managers to do this is strong; their performance evaluations and career growth depend on it. On the other hand, "beating" the curve sets a new benchmark for next year's curve: it still slopes inexorably downward, but from a lower starting point, and is harder to meet. What to do is obvious - follow the curve. This produces the self-fulfilling prophecy mentioned earlier.

The parametric cost models used to predict the cost of new programs are more sophisticated than the production cost improvement curve. Also these models are usually computerized which tends to enhance their credibility. Program plans and budgets are set up based on the predictions of parametric cost models. Programs are organized and started according to the budget plan. We can be sure of spending the planned budget; personnel costs predominate and we staffed to spend it. If technical difficulties cause delays in project completion, we may be equally sure of an overrun. The overrun becomes a part of the historical data base upon which the cost models are based, and their forecasts inch upward in a self-reinforcing cycle of cost escalation. This is not only a self-fulfilling prophecy, but one with built-in deterioration. (Despite this potential for escalation, the overall dollars-per-pound trend of NASA space hardware, when corrected for inflation, is slightly downward. Some productivity improvement is occurring.)

Psychology and Culture

Cultures in aerospace industry exist in the way programs are thought about and carried out by their people. The difference in manned and unmanned spacecraft cost, portrayed by cost models as shown earlier in Figure 9.3, is at least in part a culture effect. The presence of people in a space system should make it cheaper, not costlier (for the same mass; the presence of people may necessitate increased mass). People may be relied upon to accomplish functions such as redundancy management that would otherwise require expensive automation.

There were culture differences, however, particularly during the early years. Early unmanned spacecraft programs were somewhat less meticulous about reliability; many failures occurred. In contrast, the early manned programs had extensive all-up testing. Mercury spacecraft flew unmanned and with nonhuman (primate) passengers before astronauts flew in them. An entire production run of Apollo spacecraft was used for tests of launch escape systems, parachutes, water landings, and so on. These are of course a part of the cost histories on which estimating models are based. And as noted above, history tends to be self-perpetuating.

"Public-sector managers like those of NASA, however, have Congress looking over their shoulders. They have nothing personal to gain if they take a risk and succeed, but Congress may cancel their program if they take a risk and fail. This incentive structure leads NASA, like other bureaucracies, to a risk-avoidance mindset." - Robert Poole, in a paper for the conference on "Space, Our Next Frontier," sponsored by the Center for Policy Analysis, Dallas, Texas, June 1984.

Poole then connects this cogent insight with the reliability fallacy and implies that we should take higher risks by accepting lower reliability. As noted above, thorough quantitative analyses of cost-optimal reliability have never substantiated this notion. These critics want to have it both ways. NASA takes too much risk, they say, in technology advancement, and not enough in accepting lower reliability. Both notions are based on fallacies.

There is truth in the low-risk culture notion. Founded in the need for reliability and safety, it is also manifested in management approach. NASA programs are most vulnerable when they first request significant funding—the Shuttle barely squeaked by in 1973—and later if major delays and overruns occur. It is not surprising that risk avoidance focuses on avoidance of overruns. It is now an accepted fact that early investment in advanced development and technology demonstration can greatly reduce risks of delays due to technical problems, and this is becoming a normal, healthy part of new programs. Avoidance of overrun risk also dictates adequate staffing—enough people to do the job on schedule. And how is one to know how many is enough? The parametric cost model estimate, of course!

There are powerful opposing forces operating here. Risk avoidance says estimate high, but pricing to win says estimate low. Arbitrarily low will not do, as cost credibility tests are applied by the government in proposal evaluation, and cost estimates seen as unrealistic can be cause for a proposal being scored as not technically acceptable. Parametric cost model results serve as a guide both for pricing and for evaluation, as well as for planning and staffing programs.

There are still other barriers to our quest for low cost. Some of these are rooted in management science. Only in the last few decades has there been wide recognition that there is such a thing as management science, and as often true for new ideas, there is an aspect of faddishness. It manifests itself in the idea that if one is well schooled in management science, one need not know anything about the activity being managed. We find managers of challenging technical developments giving their attention to schedule, cost, profitability, customer and public relations, contractual matters, and personnel matters. Indeed, it would seem that these are enough burdens to place on a manager, but not so, especially in the formative phases of a program. The important events in the first two or so years of a development program occur on paper - release of reports, preliminary design drawings, customer briefings, and so forth. These almost always occur on time, and if they don't, technical problems are usually not the reason. During this period, the budget is easily controlled by maintaining the workforce at the planned level. Assessing real technical progress and the quality and integrity of the design requires astute technical insight and a lot of managerial attention.

Problems, if they exist, will eventually manifest themselves as scheduling problems - late final design drawing releases, test failures, late vendor deliveries. By the time these signs appear, the program may be in dire technical straits. It does happen. One hears of instances where the first indication to high-level company management of a serious problem was an angry phone call from a high-level customer official.

Management science is a good thing. It has put some

orderliness into things that once were done entirely by seat-of-the-pants judgment. It is not, however, a substitute for knowing one's business.

The inexactness of cost prediction and management science and the notions and practices of aerospace cultures are strong fetters. Powerful means are needed to break free of them. That means now appears to be at hand - automation in the engineering and development process. The potentials for productivity improvement loom great enough to force a culture change.

Computer-aided Engineering

Computers began to make their way into engineering about 30 years ago. Initially, they carried out calculations impossible or hopelessly tedious for hand calculation. Early applications included the calculation of trajectories and nuclear phenomena. By the 1960s, computers served almost every aspect of engineering, mainly in numerical analysis of complex structures, aerodynamics, propulsion, and the simulation of vehicle flights. They allowed us to do the "impossible": namely, to land men on the Moon and to predict the flight characteristics of the Shuttle so accurately that its first flight into orbit could be safely manned.

New uses emerged in the 1970s. Dramatic cost reductions now put computers at every engineer's fingertips. Computer-aided design, using the fast-developing techniques of computer graphics and data base management, is evolving into a broader concept called computer-aided engineering. Key factors are the proliferation of small but powerful machines, the emergence of user-friendly software, networking of machines together to share and exchange common data bases, and alteration of traditional analytical software to take advantage of the common data bases.

Productivity improvements arise from avoidance of tedious hand manipulation of data (and correction of the mistakes it introduces)and through timely and rapid availability of current data, reducing time spent checking whether results were obtained from the same data base, and speeding up the pace of design iteration.

We cannot today estimate the cost savings potentials. They may be modest, or they may turn out to be staggering. They will surely cause us to challenge present cost prediction practices.

Space is a new, exciting frontier. While space stations and platforms will be our permanent outposts on the edge of this frontier, cost reduction may well be our greatest engineering challenge.

Appendix A

Vector Methods

Consider a spacecraft in orbit about the Earth, with its orbit specified by the six orbital parameters. Common problems include determining the ground track of the orbit and the timing of the periods when the spacecraft is in the Earth's shadow, a situation requiring power from a storage system rather than from solar arrays. These problems are best addressed by vector methods, including coordinate transformations. The latter simply permit expression of position in coordinate systems most convenient for analysis. When the position of the Sun and the spacecraft are both described in Earth coordinates, for example, the condition of solar occultation (eclipse) is easily determined.

A vector is simply a quantity that has both a magnitude and a direction. Accordingly, a vector has components in a coordinate system. A typical quantity not having direction is temperature; a typical quantity with direction is velocity.

It is not the purpose of this book to present a rigorous treatment of vector analysis. Our presentation is confined to practical uses of vector methods for flight mechanics analysis.

Vector methods lend themselves to a sort of "cookbook" technique. A few useful procedures such as dot and cross products and matrix multiplications serve to accomplish most necessary calculations. These may be embodied in computer subroutines; sequences of subroutine calls accomplish desired results.

The dot product is a scalar quantity that is useful for determining the angle γ between two vectors. It is given by $\mathbf{A} \cdot \mathbf{B} = AB \cos \gamma$, written in component form as

$$p = a_1 b_1 + a_2 b_2 + a_3 b_3. \qquad (A.1)$$

If $\mathbf{A}$ and $\mathbf{B}$ are of unit length the angle is $\gamma = \cos^{-1} p$.

The cross product generates a vector perpendicular to the plane defined by the two product vectors (but is zero with undefined direction if the product vectors are parallel). The cross product is given by

$$\mathbf{C} = \mathbf{A} \times \mathbf{B} \quad \begin{aligned} c_1 &= a_2 b_3 - a_3 b_2 \\ c_2 &= a_3 b_1 - a_1 b_3 \\ c_3 &= a_1 b_2 - a_2 b_1. \end{aligned} \qquad (A.2)$$

The cross product is not commutative, i.e., $\mathbf{A} \times \mathbf{B} = -\mathbf{B} \times \mathbf{A}$.

Dot and cross products are diagrammed in Figure A.1.

Matrix multiplication is defined as follows:

$$C = AB$$

where A, B, and C are each matrices. In flight mechanics coordinate transformations, 3×3 matrices are usually used.

Let

$$A = \begin{vmatrix} a_{11} & a_{12} & a_{13} \\ a_{21} & a_{22} & a_{23} \\ a_{31} & a_{32} & a_{33} \end{vmatrix}$$

and

$$B = \begin{vmatrix} b_{11} & b_{12} & b_{13} \\ b_{21} & b_{22} & b_{23} \\ b_{31} & b_{32} & b_{33} \end{vmatrix}$$

Then

$$C = \begin{vmatrix} c_{11} & c_{12} & c_{13} \\ c_{21} & c_{22} & c_{23} \\ c_{31} & c_{32} & c_{33} \end{vmatrix}$$

where

$$\begin{aligned} c_{11} &= a_{11} b_{11} + a_{12} b_{21} + a_{13} b_{31} \\ c_{12} &= a_{11} b_{12} + a_{12} b_{22} + a_{13} b_{32} \\ c_{13} &= a_{11} b_{13} + a_{12} b_{23} + a_{13} b_{33} \\ c_{21} &= a_{21} b_{11} + a_{22} b_{21} + a_{23} b_{31} \\ c_{22} &= a_{21} b_{12} + a_{22} b_{22} + a_{23} b_{32} \\ c_{23} &= a_{21} b_{13} + a_{22} b_{23} + a_{23} b_{33} \\ c_{31} &= a_{31} b_{11} + a_{32} b_{21} + a_{33} b_{31} \\ c_{32} &= a_{31} b_{12} + a_{32} b_{22} + a_{33} b_{32} \\ c_{33} &= a_{31} b_{13} + a_{32} b_{23} + a_{33} b_{33} \end{aligned}$$

Matrix multiplication is not commutative; that is, $AB \neq BA$. However, $(AB)C = A(BC)$.

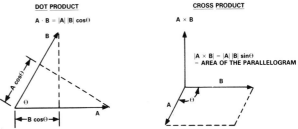

Figure A.1 Vector dot and cross products.

Appendix B
Orbital Calculations: An Example

The orbit coordinate system customarily has its x- and y-axes in the orbital plane. The x-axis extends from the gravity focus of the orbit toward periapsis. The y-axis is 90° in the direction of the orbit path, drawn such that the path direction is counterclockwise. The z-axis forms a right-handed coordinate system; i.e., when the fingers of the right hand are curled in the direction of the orbit path as from the x-axis to the y-axis, the thumb points in the positive z direction.

An example of the use of the dot and cross products is the determination of a specific orbit. Suppose that a particular space station orbit passes over Los Angeles and New York on a single pass. We wish to find the orbital parameters. Los Angeles is located at approximately 118.3° west longitude, or −118.3°, and 34° north latitude. New York is at −74° longitude and 40.4° latitude. The Earth coordinates are given by:

$$x = \cos (\text{lat}) \cos (\text{long})$$
$$y = \cos (\text{lat}) \sin (\text{long})$$
$$z = \sin (\text{lat})$$

Results for these two cities are

	Los Angeles	New York
x	−0.3930	0.2099
y	−0.7299	−0.7320
z	0.5592	0.6481

The great circle distance between the cities can be determined by the dot product, giving the angle between the vectors:

$$\cos \delta = (0.2099)(-0.3930) +$$
$$(-0.7320)(-0.7290) +$$
$$(0.6841)(0.5592) = 0.8142;$$
$$\delta = 35.49° = 0.6194 \text{ radian} =$$
$$0.09858 \text{ orbit.}$$

Multiplying the value in radians by the Earth's mean radius of 6371 km gives a distance of 3946 km.

The Earth, of course, rotates under the orbit. The Earth's inertial rotation rate is 7.292115×10^{-5} radians/sec, about 23.93 hours (not 24!) per revolution. At a typical orbital velocity, a space station will travel from Los Angeles to New York in about 9.5 minutes. During that time, New York will have moved about 2° eastward relative to inertial space. Accordingly, our solution for the orbit will be more accurate if we use a pseudo-longitude for New York of −72° with coordinates:

$$x = 0.2353, \ y = -0.7243, \text{ and } z = 0.6481.$$

The property of the cross product is now useful. The cross product of two vectors in the orbit plane, taken in the sequence of the orbit path direction, i.e, from Los Angeles toward New York, generates a vector colinear with the orbit vector. (The correct sign is obtained when the first term in the product is the first orbital location, i.e., Los Angeles.)

The angle between the orbit vector and the planetary pole vector is the orbit inclination. Further, the cross product of the pole vector and the orbit vector generates the ascending node vector, which lies in the equatorial plane as well as in the orbit plane. The orbit vector in the example is (taking the cross product of the vectors for Los Angeles and New York):

$$x = -0.7299 \times 0.6841 - (-0.7243 \times 0.5592) = -0.0943$$
$$y = 0.5592 \times 0.2353 - (-0.3930 \times 0.6481) = 0.3862$$
$$z = -0.3930 \times -0.7243 - (0.2353 \times -0.7299) = 0.4564$$

The result must be normalized, i.e., the vector must be adjusted so that its length is 1.0, by dividing by $(x^2 + y^2 + z^2)$. We obtain $x = -0.1558$, $y = 0.6381$, and $z = 0.7541$. The orbit inclination is just $i = \cos^{-1}(z) = 41.05°$.

The cross-product of the pole vector and orbit vector is

$$\begin{pmatrix} 0 \\ 0 \\ 1 \end{pmatrix} \times \begin{pmatrix} -0.1558 \\ -0.6381 \\ -0.7541 \end{pmatrix}$$

resulting in $x = -0.6381$ and $y = -0.1558$. Again normalizing, $x = -0.9715$ and $y = -0.2372$.

Taking arctangent (y/x), the longitude of the ascending node is 193.7°. The geometry is shown in Figure B.1. This brief example illustrates the efficacy of vector methods in determining orbit parameters. Spherical trigonometry is also often used in the calculation of orbital characteristics and parameters, but is much less straightforward in its application.

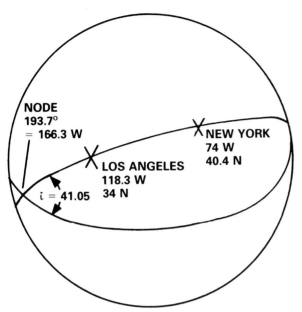

Figure B.1 Overflight geometry.

Coordinate transformations determine the coordinates of points in alternative coordinate systems. Their main use in orbital mechanics is to render the coordinates of points of interest in coordinate systems that facilitate analysis. It is easiest, for example, to find the position of a spacecraft in coordinates referenced to its orbit. The ground track of the spacecraft, however, is most easily found in rotating Earth coordinates.

Orbital mechanics analyses can involve numerous coordinate systems. Examples include heliocentric, fixed Earth, rotating Earth, orbit, and spacecraft body axis systems. A thorough presentation is not practical in this book; the reader is referred to texts on celestial mechanics. We will, however, work through a ground track example to illustrate the principles of coordinate transformations.

The position of a spacecraft in its orbit coordinates is given by

$$(a^3/\mu)^{1/2}(E - e \sin E) = T \qquad (B.1)$$

where T is the time since periapsis passage. In general, this transcendental equation must be solved iteratively (except for the trivial case of a circular orbit, for which $e = 0$), a straightforward procedure on a computer; convergence is rapid. E is the eccentric anomaly, and is related to the true anomaly usually designated as θ by

$$\cos \theta = \frac{\cos E - e}{1 - e \cos E}. \qquad (B.2)$$

With true anomaly determined, the orbit radius is calculated from eq. 3.4 in Chapter 3 and the orbit coordinates are found from $x = r\cos \theta$ and $y = r\sin \theta$. z is always zero in orbit coordinates, i.e., the spacecraft is always in the orbit plane.

The relationship of the orbit coordinate system to the Earth's equator and the first point of Aries (these define the Earth coordinate system with its x-axis toward the first point of Aries and its north polar z-axis) was shown in Figure 3.8. The three angles Ω, i, and ω represent coordinate rotations and are called the Eulerian angles. Geometrically, the coordinate transformation occurs as follows:

1. Rotate the Earth coordinate system about its z-axis until the x-axis coincides with the line of nodes.
2. Rotate about this new x-axis until the x-y plane coincides with the orbit plane. This angle of rotation is the orbit inclination.
3. The z-axis now coincides with the orbit vector. Rotate about this new z-axis until the x-axis coincides with the orbit x-axis, pointing to periapsis.

Such rotations are mathematically specified by multiplying a position vector by a rotation matrix. Presume a position vector $\mathbf{V}$ representing a particular orbital location in orbit coordinates. The first rotation through angle Ω is given by $\mathbf{V}' = D\mathbf{V}$, where

$$D = \begin{pmatrix} \cos \Omega & \sin \Omega & 0 \\ -\sin \Omega & \cos \Omega & 0 \\ 0 & 0 & 1 \end{pmatrix}. \qquad (B.3)$$

The second rotation through angle i is given by $\mathbf{V}'' = C\mathbf{V}'$, for which

$$C = \begin{pmatrix} 1 & 0 & 0 \\ 0 & \cos i & \sin i \\ 0 & -\sin i & \cos i \end{pmatrix}. \qquad (B.4)$$

The third rotation through angle ω is given by $\mathbf{V}''' = B\mathbf{V}''$, where

$$B = \begin{pmatrix} \cos \omega & \sin \omega & 0 \\ -\sin \omega & \cos \omega & 0 \\ 0 & 0 & 1 \end{pmatrix}. \qquad (B.5)$$

The matrix multiplications may be grouped, as $\mathbf{V}''' = A\mathbf{V}$ = where $A = BCD$. If one is using computer routines to perform these analyses, it is convenient to employ a coordinate transform subroutine to carry out the necessary matrix multiplications. Such routines can be easily written to accomplish any sequence of rotations. Note that the Euler sequence does not involve rotations about the y-axis. The latter are sometimes useful. If one is not using computer routines, it is convenient to have the result of the BCD product:

$$A = \begin{vmatrix} a_{11} & a_{12} & a_{13} \\ a_{21} & a_{22} & a_{23} \\ a_{31} & a_{32} & a_{33} \end{vmatrix} \qquad (B.6)$$

where

$$a_{11} = \cos \Omega \cos \omega - \cos i \sin \Omega \sin \omega$$
$$a_{12} = \cos \Omega \sin \omega + \cos i \cos \omega \sin \Omega$$
$$a_{13} = \sin \Omega \cos i$$
$$a_{21} = -\sin \Omega \cos \omega - \cos i \sin \omega \cos \Omega$$
$$a_{22} = -\sin \Omega \sin \omega + \cos i \cos \omega \cos \Omega$$
$$a_{23} = \cos \Omega \sin i$$
$$a_{31} = \sin i \cos \omega$$
$$a_{32} = -\sin i \cos \omega$$
$$a_{33} = \cos i$$

This coordinate transformation will transform a position originally represented in Earth coordinates into orbit coordinates. While this is occasionally done, the reverse is often more useful. An inverse transform accomplishes the reverse and is readily obtained by transposition of the transform matrix:

$$A^{-1} = \tilde{A} = \begin{vmatrix} a_{11} & a_{21} & a_{31} \\ a_{12} & a_{22} & a_{32} \\ a_{13} & a_{23} & a_{33} \end{vmatrix}$$

where the terms are the same as for equation B.6.

As a quantitative example, suppose that a particular space platform is in an orbit having inclination $i = 29°$ with nodal longitude $\Omega = 60°$, argument of periapsis is $\omega = 45°$, semi-major axis $a = 6800$ km, and eccentricity $e = 0.025$.

Even this slight orbital eccentricity gives periapsis and apoapsis altitudes of 252 and 592 km, respectively. These are about the practical limits for a low Earth orbit (LEO) platform. Missions clearly need orbits more near circular than this; the eccentricity was arbitrarily chosen for completeness of the example.

The example ground track solution proceeded as follows. The orbit period factor $\sqrt{a^3/\mu}$ was evaluated and found to be 888.17 seconds. Equation B.1 was rearranged to set $E - e\sin(E) = T/888.17$, where T is time from periapsis. A simple computer routine was used to find E as a function of T for 300-second intervals for 6000 seconds, slightly more than one orbit. The true anomaly, θ, was then calculated from E by eq. B.2.

Values of θ were converted to x and y coordinates in the orbit coordinate system. Orbital parameters or angles of $\Omega = 60°$, $i = 29°$, and $\omega = 45°$ were used in an inverse transform from the orbit system to the Earth system. Rotating Earth longitude was assumed zero at time zero; subsequent

Table B.1 Ground track results.

Time (min.)	E deg	Theta deg	Latitude deg	Longitude deg	Corrected Longitude
0	0	0	20.05	101.17	101.17
5	19.84	20.33	26.14	122.29	121.04
10	39.62	40.54	28.90	144.90	142.39
15	59.29	60.53	27.85	167.63	163.87
20	78.82	80.23	23.33	171.08W	176.09W
25	98.18	99.60	16.31	151.87W	158.14W
30	117.39	118.66	7.84	134.38W	141.90W
35	136.46	137.44	−1.18	117.87W	126.64W
40	155.42	156.01	−10.01	101.43W	111.46W
45	174.32	174.46	−17.95	84.25W	95.53W
50	193.20	192.88	−24.24	65.67W	78.20W
55	212.12	211.37	−28.11	45.50W	59.29W
60	231.12	230.01	−28.88	24.28W	39.32W
65	250.24	248.90	−26.31	3.13W	19.42W
70	269.51	268.08	−20.74	16.91	0.64W
75	288.94	287.58	−12.90	35.59	16.79
80	308.53	307.40	−3.68	53.34	33.29
85	328.25	327.49	6.02	70.96	49.65
90	348.06	347.76	15.21	89.37	66.81
95	367.90	368.10	22.81	109.36	85.54
100	387.73	388.40	27.68	131.18	106.11

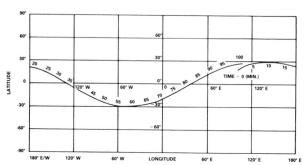

Figure B.2 Representative orbital ground track, corrected for Earth rotation.

longitudes were corrected for the Earth's rotation relative to the orbit. Results are presented in Table B.1 and Figure B.2. Note that the orbit ground track is not a closed path because of the Earth's rotation. This calculation ignored nodal regression, discussed in Chapter 3. Nodal regression would increase the longitude correction by about 0.4° per orbit.

Appendix C
Environmental Control and Life Support Balance Algorithms

Metabolic Rate and Food Consumption

(Note: Calculations are per crewperson.)

Nominal IVA metabolic rate taken as 136 watts = 117 Kcal/hr = 2807 Kcal/day

Average metabolic rate:

$$= \frac{\text{IVA rate} \times (168 - \text{EVA hrs/wk}) + \text{EVA rate} \times \text{EVA hrs/wk}}{168}$$

Example: EVA rate = 400 watts; EVA hrs/wk = 16 per crewperson

Average metabolic rate
$$= \frac{136(168 - 16) + 400 \times 16}{168} = 161.14 \text{ watts}$$

Food Content

Diet:
45% Carbohydrates—equivalent formula $CH_{1.8}O$

40% Fats	50% saturated	$- C_2H_2O_2(15CH_2)$ $= C_{17}H_{32}O_2 = CH_{1.88}O_{0.12}$	
	50% unsaturated	$- C_2H_2O_2 \ (C_{21}H_{31})$ $= C_{23}H_{33}O_2 = CH_{1.43}O_{0.09}$	
	15% protein	$-\overset{\text{H}}{\underset{}{\text{N}}}-\overset{\text{H}}{\underset{}{\text{C}}}-\overset{\text{O}}{\underset{}{\text{C}}}- = CH_{1.6}O_{0.2}N_{0.2}$ C_3H_6	

Composite formula: $CH_{1.71} O_{0.54} N_{0.03}J$

Where J is a pseudo-atom for undigested food and accounts for dry fecal waste.

For nominal input of 0.62 kg/day dry food and 0.11 kg dry fecal waste, pseudo-mol.wt. for J is 4.82.

Generalized formula for input is $A(CH_aO_bN_cJ)$

Food Combustion: Assume the following reaction:

$$CH_aO_bN_cJ + O_2 \rightarrow CO_2 + \frac{a-b}{2}H_2O + \underset{\text{no heat}}{OH} + \underset{\text{no heat}}{N} + \underset{\text{no heat}}{J}$$
$$\underset{\text{Kcal/gmole}}{94.385} \quad \underset{\text{Kcal/gmole}}{57.8}$$

Note that heats are per gram-mole.

The fact that food is partially oxidized by its oxygen content is represented by passing food oxygen through as an OH radical with no heat release.

$$\text{Dry food consumption} = \frac{\text{Metabolic rate, Kcal/day}}{\text{Food Heat Content, Kcal/kg-mole}}$$

Food Pseudo-mol.wt. $= 12 + 1.008a + 16b + 14c + J$

Example: $a = 1.71,$ $b = 0.54,$ $c = 0.03$

$$\text{Heat} = 94.385 + 57.8(1.71\text{-}0.54)/2$$
$$= 128.2 \text{ Kcal/gmol}$$
$$= 128,200 \text{ Kcal/kg-mole}$$

$$\text{Pseudo-mol.wt.} = 12 + (1.008)(1.71) + (16)(0.54) + (14)$$
$$(0.03) + 4.82 = 27.60$$

Heat = 128,200/27.60 = 4645 kcal/kg

$$\text{Consumption (161.14 watts)}$$
$$= 3325.97/128,200$$
$$= 0.02594 \text{ kg-mole/day}$$
$$= 0.02594)(27.60) = 0.716 \text{ kg/day}$$

Water No. 1 - Food

Water from food combustion: (kg-moles food) × (H subscript)/2
Example: $0.02594 \times 1.71/2 = (0.02218 \text{ kg-moles}) \times$
    $(18.016) = 0.3996 \text{ kg}$

Water in food—given as $x\%$ of total food delivery.
    Water mass $= f/(1 - f) \times$ (dry food mass) where $f = x/100$
Example:
    Water in food 40%
    Water mass $= 0.4/(1 - 0.4)(0.71615) = 0.4774 \text{ kg}$
Total water from food = water in food + combustion water
Example: 0.3996 + 0.4774 = 0.877 kg.

Total food intake (without prep water)
= dry + water
= 0.71615 + 0.4774
= 1.1936 kg/day
Water added in food preparation is given as $x\%$ of total prepared food (total = dry + water in + prep water)

Food prep water intake is $f/(1 - f) \times$ (total food)

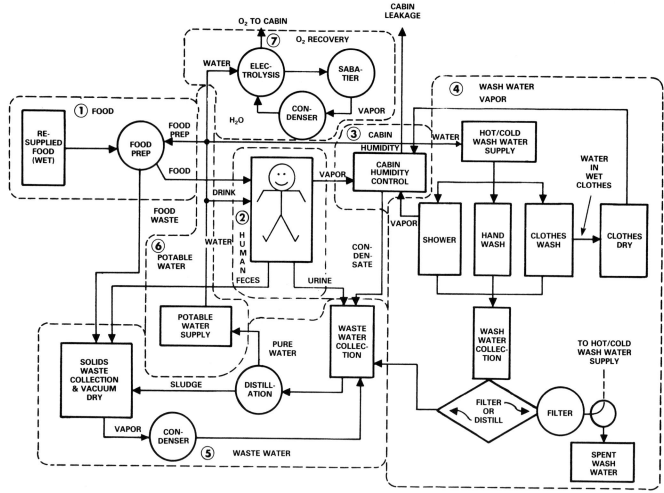

Figure C.1 Water balance diagram with balance algorithm groups.

Example: food prep water 10%
Food prep water intake = $0.1/0.9 \times 1.1936$
                                                            = 0.1326 kg/day

Some food is wasted, e.g., not eaten after prep.
Food waste = $f/(1-f) \times$ (total food intake)
Example: waste = 10%; $0.1/0.9 \times 1.1936 = 0.1326$ kg/day

Similarly, food prep water in food waste = $f/(1-f) \times$ (food prep water intake).
Example: $0.1/0.9 \times 0.13262 = 0.01474$

Total food prep water used = intake + waste
Example: $0.1326 + 0.0147 = 0.1473$.

Food delivered = intake + waste
Example: intake $1.1936 +$ waste $0.1326 = 1.3262$ kg/day

Water No. 2 - Human

Sources: Drink, food, food prep water
Sinks: Urine, fecal waste, water vapor

Calculation Assumptions:
(a) Urine is fixed (assigned or assumptional)
(b) Dry fecal waste is % of dry food intake, per food model
(c) Water in fecal waste is assigned % value
(d) Food and food prep water per above food model
(e) Human thermal output is 75 watts sensible heat and balance as latent heat in the form of water vapor in breath and evaporated from skin.
(f) Drinking water to balance input & output.

Dry fecal waste (DFW) $= AJ$ where A is kg-moles of food and J is the pseudo molecular weight from food model.
Example: $A = 0.02594$, $J = 4.82$; DFW $= 0.125$ kg/day

Assume water = 50% - water in fecal waste = 0.125 kg/day

Vapor = (Metabolic rate - 75 watts) $\times 0.0359$
Factor $0.359 = (24$ hr/day)/(575 kcal/kg water vapor latent heat @ 35°C)(3600 sec/hr)/(4186 joules/kcal)

Example: Metabolic rate = 161.14 watts
        Vapor = $(161.14 - 75) \times 0.0359 = 3.0924$ kg/day

Summary:

	IN		OUT	
Water from food	0.8767 kg	Urine (assumed)	1.5 kg	
Food prep water	0.1326 kg	Water in fecal waste	0.125 kg	
Drink to bal.	3.7081 kg	Vapor	3.0924 kg	
	4.7174 kg		4.7174 kg	

Water No. 3 - Cabin Humidity

Sources: Human water vapor, shower water vapor, clothes wash water vapor.
Sinks: Cabin leakage and airlock loss, balance as humidity control condensate.

Shower is computed from number of showers/day, water/shower, shower water temperature, and cabin temperature.

Water used is showers/day × water/shower.
Example: $1 \times 5 = 5$ kg

Heat absorbed by vapor $= Q_v dX$; lost by water
$= C_p X dT$, and $dX/X = C_p/Q_v dT$

Exact Formula:

$$\Delta x/x = 1 - \exp\left[-(C_p/Q_v)(T_1 - T_2)\right] \text{ or}$$

$$\frac{\Delta x}{x} = 1 - \exp\left[-C_p(T_1 - T_2)/Q_v\right]$$

Since $T_1 - T_2$ is only roughly known, we use the approximate formula

$$\Delta x/x = (T_1 - T_2)/[Q_v + C_{p_1}(T_1 - T_2)].$$

Example: $X = 5$kg, $T_1 = 40$ °C, $T_2 = 20$ °C, $C_p = 1$, $Q_v = 575$ kcal/kg

Exact: $\Delta X/X = 0.03418$, Approximate: $\Delta X/X = 0.03364$ $\Delta X = 5 \times 0.0336 = 0.168$ kg

Clothes Wash:

Clothes wash water = (kg of clothes to wash) × (kg water/kg clothes)

Clothes dry water vapor = (kg of clothes to wash)
$$\times \left(\frac{\text{net clothes mass}}{\text{Dry clothes mass}} - 1\right)$$

Leakage and Airlock Loss:

This section covers all leakage algorithms including oxygen, nitrogen, and water.

Nominal cabin atmosphere used as reference is 28.8 mol. wt., T = 20 °C, pressure = 1 atm = 101,300 pascals, humidity = 0%.

Actual cabin atmosphere calculated from % oxygen in air, % humidity, and cabin pressure.

Water vapor density and pressure at 100% humidity are obtained from Table 5.4 and multiplied by % humidity/100 to get actuals.

Air mol. wt. $= 28 \times (1 - O_2\%/100) + O_2\% \times 32/100$
Air partial pressure = cabin pressure - water partial pressure
Air partial density = $p\mathfrak{M}/RT$; R = 8314 and T degrees Kelvin
Cabin density = air partial density + water partial density
Cabin loss factor = cabin density/nominal density
Cabin leakage = (leakage at nominal conditions) × (loss factor)
Airlock Loss = (lock ops per EVA hr) × (EVA hrs per week per crewmember) × (number of crew) × (lock loss per operation at nominal conditions) × (cabin loss factor)/(7 days per week)
Total loss = cabin leakage + airlock loss
Cabin O_2 partial density = 32(air partial density)/(cabin air mol. wt.) × ($O_2\%/100$)
Cabin N_2 partial density = 28(air partial density)/(cabin air mol. wt.) × ($1 - O_2\%/100$)
Cabin O_2 loss = (O_2 partial density)/(cabin density) × (total loss) - and similarly for N_2. loss and H_2O loss.

These figures are for the total cabin and must be divided by the number of crew members to get a per person basis to be compatible with the other algorithms.

Example:

Assigned values - cabin temp = 20°C; cabin pressure = 1 atm = 101,300 pascals; cabin humidity = 50%; $O_2\%$ = 20; water partial pressure and density from table − 2340 pascals and 0.0173 kg/m³; nominal leakage = 5 kg/day; EVA − 16 hr/wk; 8 crew; lock ops per EVA hr − 1/4; loss per lock operation 0.2 kg

Air mol. wt. $= 32 \times 20/100 + 28 \times (1 - 20/100) = 28.8$
Air partial pressure $= 101,300 - 50/100 \times 2340 = 100,130$
Air partial density $= 100,130 \times 28.8/(8314 \times 293) = 1.1838$ kg/m³
Cabin density $= 1.1838 + 50/100 \times 0.0173 = 1.19245$ kg/m³
Air nominal density $= 101,300 \times 28.8/(8314 \times 293)$ $= 1.1976$ kg/m³
Loss factor $= 1.19245/1.1976 = 0.99567$
Leakage $= 0.99567 \times 5 = 4.9784$ kg/day
Airlock Loss $= (0.25$ ops/hr$) \times (16$ hrs/wk$) \times (8$ crew$) \times (0.2$ kg/op$) \times 0.99567/7 = 0.9103$ kg/day
Total loss $= 4.9784 + 0.9103 = 5.8887$ kg/day
O_2 partial density $= 32/28.8 \times 1.1838 \times 20/100 = 0.26307$ kg/m³
N_2 partial density $= 28/28.8 \times 1.1838 \times 80/100 = 0.92073$ kg/m³
H_2O partial density $= 50/100 \times 0.0173 = 0.00865$
O_2 loss $= 0.26307/1.19245 \times 5.8887 = 1.300$ kg/day
N_2 loss $= 0.92073/1.19245 \times 5.8887 = 4.5469$ kg/day

H_2O loss $= 0.00865/1.19245 \times 5.8887 = 0.0427$ kg/day
O_2 loss/crew $= 1.3/8 = 0.1625$ kg/day
H_2O loss/crew $= 0.0053$ kg/day

Water No. 4 - Wash Water

Wash water consumption includes shower, hand wash, and clothes wash. Shower and clothes wash algorithms were given above. Hand wash is similar - hand washes/day × water use/wash.

In our example, we have 5 kg/day shower, 2.5 kg/day clothes wash, and 10 hand washes × 0.1 kg each = 1 kg/day hand wash for a total of 8.5 kg/day wash water use. We use an assumption of wet/dry clothes mass ratio of 2 with 1 kg/day clothes to wash, giving 1 kg/day of wash water lost to vapor by clothes washing and 0.168 kg/day lost by showering per above cabin humidity model.

If wash water is combined with waste water, wash water to waste water is $8.5 - 1 - 0.168 = 7.332$ kg/day to waste water. If wash water is filtered and separately recycled, wash water consumption is vapor loss + (daily wash water use)/ (number of times recycled). A typical number of recyclings might be five; consumption would be $1 + 0.168 + 8.5/5 = 2.868$ kg/day.

Wash water filtration would be used in a partially closed system where potable water is not reused. An option is to return cabin humidity control condensate to the wash water circuit. This would reduce wash water consumption to about 1 kg per person per day or less, depending on filter effectiveness.

Water No. 5 - Waste Water

Net cabin humidity condensate to waste water is (Human water vapor) + (Shower water vapor) + (Clothes dry water vapor) − (Leakage)
Example: $3.0925 + 0.168 + 1.0 - 0.0053 = 4.2552$ kg.

Total input to waste water is
(Net cabin humidity condensate) + (Urine) + (Wash Water) + (Vapor recovered from solid waste)
Vapor recovered from solid waste is given below - this makes this an iterative algorithm:
→(Total input to waste water) → (recovery from waste water) → (Water input to solid waste) → (Vapor recovered from solid waste)⌐

Example: Total input to waste water $= 4.2552 + 1.5 + 7.332 + 0.425 = 13.512$ kg/day

Recovery from waste water is a given percentage of total input to waste water and balance is waste water sludge; the latter is assumed to be 50% solid.

Example : 95% recovery of 13.512 kg = 12.836 kg
Waste water sludge = 0.676 kg

Total water input to solid waste:
(Water in fecal waste) + (Food waste × % water in food) + (Food prep water in waste) + (50% of waste water sludge)
Example: Total water input to solid waste
$= 0.125 + 0.1326 \times 40/100 + 0.014376 + 0.33779 = 0.530$ kg/day

Vapor recovery from solid waste = given percentage of total water input - Example 80% of 0.530 = 0.425 kg/day

Water No. 6 - Potable Water

Potable water is a simple balance giving any excess available for electrolysis.

Available for electrolysis = (recovery from waste water) - (wash water input) - (food prep) - (drink) + (water return from Sabatier) - see below for latter.

Example: Available for electrolysis $= 12.836 - 8.5 - 0.147 - 3.708 + 0.481 = 0.982$ kg/day

Water No. 7 - Electrolysis and Sabatier

Operation of the electrolysis and Sabatier units is calculated by a simple molar balance. Water available for electrolysis in kg divided by 18.016 is in kg-moles - $0.962/18.016 = 0.0534$ moles/day.

Kg moles of H_2 to Sabatier = kg-moles H_2O; kg-moles O_2 to cabin = (kg-moles H_2O)/2.

$H_2 = 0.0534$ and $O_2 = 0.267$ kg-moles/day $= 32 \times 0.267 = 0.854$ kg/day

The Sabatier reactor reduces CO_2 by reaction with H_2. The reaction is catalyzed so that CO_2 is fully reduced to CH_4. If there is insufficient hydrogen, some of the CO_2 is unreacted. The oxygen from the CO_2 oxidizes hydrogen to H_2O. Thus 4 kg-moles of H_2 are required to reduce one kg-mole of CO_2. Since carbon enters the cycle hydrogenated to something like $CH_{1.7}$ and leaves as CH_4 there will be a hydrogen shortage unless much extra water is supplied in the food. This is not of concern unless there is a negative oxygen balance (see below). In that case it may be beneficial to supply more hydrogen in the form of water.

In the Sabatier reactor with insufficient hydrogen, half of the hydrogen becomes water and the other half becomes methane. Thus kg-moles water = 0.5 kg-moles H_2 and kg-moles $CH_4 = 0.25$ kg-moles H_2. If there is excess hydrogen, all carbon goes to CH_4 and all its oxygen goes to H_2O and the surplus H_2 is vented. In the usual case with insufficient H_2, the water returned from the Sabatier is half the net input to the Sabatier; that is, equal to the input without the return.

Example: CO_2 to reduce = CO_2 produced by food combustion, 0.02594 kg-moles/day. Water available for electrolysis including return from Sabatier = 0.0534 kg-moles. H_2 to Sabatier = 0.0534 kg-moles. CO_2 reduced = 0.0133 (1/4 H_2), and CO_2 left = 0.0126. Water return = 0.0267; oxygen generated = 0.0267 kg-moles = 0.854 kg/day.

Oxygen

Oxygen balance is oxygen generated less that used for food combustion less oxygen loss by leakage and airlock operation.

Example: $0.854 - 0.961 - 0.162 = -0.269$ kg/day. Oxygen to burn food is (kg-moles food) $\times$ (1 + H_2 subscript/4 - O_2 subscript/2).

Example: O_2 to burn food = $0.02594 \times (1 + 1.71/4 - 0.54/2) = 0.03003$ moles (0.961 kg). A negative oxygen balance requires resupply.

Total resupply is food including waste, oxygen, nitrogen loss from cabin, potable water if value available for electrolysis is negative, and wash water as appropriate.

Appendix D
Uncertainty Analysis Example

The following example uses a very simple model of a power system. To simplify the example, practical considerations such as energy storage and power regulation and control have been omitted. Cost and mass figures are for illustration and are not intended to be representative of real hardware. Figure D.1 presents a block diagram of the power system with principal data.

It is assumed that all uncertainties are uncorrelated except array efficiency and cost. In this latter case, it is assumed that $20,000/m^2$ buys a 12% efficient array while $30,000/m^2$ buys a 15% efficient array, and that cost and efficiency are 80% correlated. All ranges above are assumed to be $+/-$ 2 sigma. Finally, it is assumed that the system delivers 75 kW net power from the processor to the load.

The end-to-end efficiency is given by

$$\eta = \pi\,(\eta_y)$$
$$\text{or, } \log \eta = \Sigma\,(\log \eta_y)$$

The latter is the best to use for probability calculations since all $\delta \log \eta / \delta \log \eta_i = 1$.

Similarly, the mass and cost at each stage can be expressed as

$$m = m_s p_i$$

where m_s is specific mass and p_i is power input, and

$$c = c_s m = c_s m_s p_i,$$

where c_s is specific cost.

Then, $\log m = \log m_s + \log p_i$

The solar array gets special treatment since its specific cost and mass are per unit area.

The uncertainties are given by

$$\sigma(\log \eta) = \sqrt{\Sigma[\sigma(\log \eta_i)]^2}, \text{ etc.}$$

(natural) logarithms of the inputs are shown in Table D.1.

The power levels at each state of the efficiency chain are obtained by computing the efficiency and its uncertainties at each stage.

$$\text{Log mean} = (\log \eta_{i\text{HIGH}} + \log \eta_{i\text{LOW}})/2$$

Block Diagram

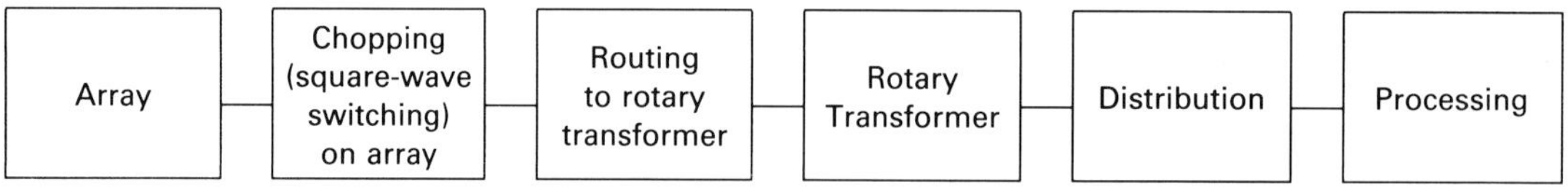

	Array	Chopping (square-wave switching) on array	Routing to rotary transformer	Rotary Transformer	Distribution	Processing
Efficiency						
(min)	0.12	0.95	0.96	0.88	0.90	0.93
(max)	0.15	0.98	0.99	0.92	0.95	0.96
Specific Mass						
(min)	1 kg/m²	0.1 kg/kW	0.05 kg/kW	2 kg/kW	0.1 kg/kW	4 kg/kW
(max)	1.5 kg/m²	0.12 kg/kW	0.05 kg/kW	2.5 kg/kW	0.15 kg/kW	5 kg/kW
Specific Cost						
(min)	$20,000/m²	$500/kg	$500/kg	$1000/kg	$100/kg	$2000/kg
(max)	$30,000/m²	$700/kg	$700/kg	$1200/kg	$200/kg	$2500/kg

Figure D.1 Block diagram and efficiency chain.

Table D.1 Parameter range data.

	log$_e$ (efficiency)			log$_e$ (specific mass)			log$_e$ (specific cost)		
	low	high	sigma	low	high	sigma	low	high	sigma
chopping	−.051	−.020	.0078	−2.30	−2.12	.0456	6.215	6.551	.0841
routing	−.041	−.041	.0000	−3.00	−3.00	.0000	6.215	6.551	.0841
rot. transfmr.	−.128	−.083	.0111	0.69	0.92	.0558	6.908	7.090	.0456
distrib	−.105	−.051	.0135	−2.30	−1.90	.1014	4.605	5.298	.1733
process	−.073	−.041	.0079	1.39	1.61	.0558	7.601	7.824	.0558

Table D.2 Power ranges at each level.

	Log Mean	SumRSS	Eff.	Min Eff	Max Eff	Min Pwr (kW)	Max Pwr (kW)
chopping	−0.317	0.021	0.728	0.684	0.775	96.79	109.60
routing	−0.281	0.019	0.755	0.712	0.799	93.81	105.28
rot. transfmr.	−0.241	0.019	0.786	0.742	0.833	90.06	101.07
distrib	−0.135	0.016	0.874	0.834	0.916	81.90	89.98
process	−0.057	0.008	0.945	0.923	0.968	77.51	81.29

Table D.3 Uncertainty calculation results.

***** No. 1 ***** (Chopping)
Average pwr, logmass, logcost   103.0   −2.211   6.383
Mass: log, value, min, max   2.423   11.28   9.709   13.111
Cost: log, value, min, max   8.806   6674.9   4976.2   8953.4

***** No. 2 ***** (Routing)
Average pwr, logmass, logcost   99.40   −2.996   6.383
Mass: log, value, min, max   1.603   4.97   4.691   5.264
Cost: log, value, min, max   7.986   2939.67   2269.24   3808.18

***** No. 3 ***** (Rotary transformer)
Average pwr, logmass, logcost   95.40   0.805   6.999
Mass: log, value, min, max   5.363   213.33   178.722   254.638
Cost: log, value, min, max   12.362   233691.   186854.   292268.

***** No. 4 ***** (Distribution)
Average pwr, logmass, logcost   85.84   −2.10   4.952
Mass: log, value, min, max   2.352   10.51   7.729   14.302
Cost: log, value, min, max   7.304   1486.83   812.648   2720.33

***** No. 5 ***** (Processing)
Average pwr, logmass, logcost   79.375   1.498   7.712
Mass: log, value, min, max   5.872   354.976   299.768   420.353
Cost: log, value, min, max   13.585   793751.   625716.   1006910.

(Note that logmass and logcost on the top lines are mean log (specific mass) and mean log (specific cost).

Values are obtained from logarithms by

$$\eta_i = \exp(\log \eta_i)$$

Power ranges at each level are tabulated in Table D.2.

Note: the extremes here are 3 sigma rather than the 2 sigma values assumed for the inputs.

Calculations for average power, average specific mass and cost, and values for mass and cost, are tabulated in Table D.3. Note that mean or nominal values are log means, not arithmetic means. The arithmetic mean cost for item 1, for example, is 6965 rather than 6675.

Array:

Solar array area is given by $A = P/(\eta_a S)$ where P, the power output of the array, is equal to the power input to the chopper

(102.996 kW, average); η_a is the array efficiency, and S is solar power per unit area, usually given as 1.353 kW/m². The nominal array area is 567 m² based on a log mean average efficiency of 0.1342. Array mass and cost are mA and cA, where m is assumed to range from 1 to 1.5 kg/m² ($+/-$ 2 sigma) and c, as given earlier, is \$20,000/m² to \$30,000/m², with a correlation coefficient of 0.8 for 12% to 15% efficiency respectively.

Note that the higher efficiency, higher cost array is not a good buy unless other factors are important; its power is very likely to be more expensive per kilowatt.

For mass, $M = (mP)/(\eta_a S)$

Taking logarithms of both sides yields

$$\log M = \log m + \log P - \log \eta_a - \log S.$$

The values of σ are

$\sigma_m = 0.10135$, $\sigma_p = 0.021$, $\sigma_n = 0.055$; $RSS = 0.1172$.

Therefore, $\log M = 0.2027 + 4.6347 - (-2.0087) - 0.3023$ $= 6.5438$

The nominal and 3-sigma extreme masses are

$$M_{Lo} = \exp[6.5438 - 3(0.1172)] = 489 \text{ kg}$$
$$M\ \ = \exp[6.5438] = 695 \text{ kg}$$
$$M_{Hi} = \exp[6.5438 + 3(0.1172)] = 988 \text{ kg}$$

For cost, $C = (cP)/(\eta_a S)$; $\log C = \log c + \log P - \log \eta_a - \log S$

The value of σ_c is 0.10135 (it is coincidentally the same as σ_m)

In this case, because c and η_a are correlated,

$$RSS = \sqrt{\sigma_c^2 + \sigma_p^2 + \sigma_\eta^2 - 2\sigma_c \sigma_n \rho} = 0.06084$$

where P is correlation coefficient = 0.8

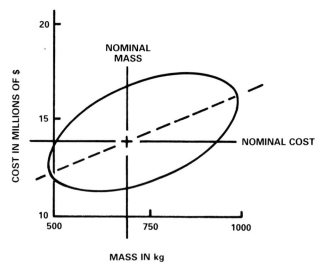

Figure D.2 Array mass and cost 3-sigma uncertainty ellipse.

Log C is 16.4471 (nominal) and the costs are:

$C_{Lo} = \exp[16.4471 - 3(0.06084)] = \$11.28$ million
$C\ \ = \exp[16.4471] = \$13.9$ million
$C_{Hi} = \exp[16.4471 + 3(0.06084)] = \$17.12$ million

Without the cost-efficiency correlation, the cost range would be greater; namely, \$9.77 million to \$19.76 million.

Costs and uncertainties for the elements of the system may now be summed in the usual arithmetic manner. Since the component uncertainties were derived logarithmically, the upside and downside ranges are unequal. They may be averaged, or upsides and downsides RSS'ed separately. Neither method is mathematically rigorous, but the greater complexity of rigor is unwarranted given the approximate nature of cost and cost uncertainty estimates. The cost/mass uncertainty ellipse is sketched in Figure D.2.

Illustrations

Illustrations Continued

Illustrations   Continued

Illustrations   *Continued*

Illustrations   *Continued*

Tables

Glossary

NASA and the civilian space program are notorious for the use of abbreviations and acronymns. I have tried to minimize their use in this book, but there are still enough to merit a glossary.

ALSEP   Apollo Lunar Surface Experiment Package; a radioisotope powered experiment package placed on the lunar surface by the Apollo astronauts. Several were emplaced.

ASL   Along Sun Line; refers to an attitude control strategy where one axis of a spacecraft is lined up along the sun line (pointing toward the sun).

CDG   Concept Development Group; the NASA study group that developed space station concepts during the summer of 1983.

CDR   Critical Design Review; the design review conducted at the completion of detailed design; results in approval to release drawings for fabrication.

CER   Cost Estimating Relationship; a function that correlates cost with a physical parameter, typically mass.

CG   Center of Gravity, the same as center of mass.

CM   Command Module; part of the Apollo spacecraft system.

CMG   Control Moment Gyro; a device for storing angular momentum.

DDT&E   Design, Development, Test, and Engineering; the entire developmental phase of a program after go-ahead. Completion of DDT&E is usually inferred to mean that a system is ready for production or operation.

DOD   (or DoD); the Department of Defense.

EC/LS   Environmental Control and Life Support (system); also abbreviated as ECLS or ECLSS.

EMI   Electromagnetic Interference; in the vernacular, static.

EMU   Extravehicular Mobility Unit; i.e., a space suit.

ESA   The European Space Agency.

EURECA   European Reusable Carrier; an unmanned space platform developed by ESA.

EVA   Extravehicular Activity; what one does in a space suit.

FRR   Flight Readiness Review; a review in which all responsible parties are supposed to concur that a system is ready to launch. It is held to approve a launch.

GEO   Geosynchronous Earth Orbit; 35,786 km above Earth's equator.

GN&C   Guidance, Navigation, and Control (subsystem); all the hardware and software needed to effect these functions except (usually) reaction control thrusters. The latter are usually considered a separate subsystem.

GPS   Global Positioning System; a Department of Defense satellite system that broadcasts precise location and navigation signals.

HGA   High Gain Antenna; usually, but not always, a dish antenna.

HZE   High Z (electrical charge) and Energy cosmic ray particles.

ICD   Interface Control Document; a formal document that describes how, physically and functionally, one system connects to another.

IMU   Inertial Measurement Unit; a system of accelerometers and gyros for measurement of translational and angular accelerations. By integration, velocities and positions may also be obtained.

IOC   Initial Operational Capability; the date upon which a system is formally declared capable of initial operations. This acronymn is also used as an adjective to denote the configuration at the IOC time.

IOP   In (the) Orbit Plane; an attitude control strategy in which one or more spacecraft axes are held in the orbit plane.

IR   Infrared (electromagnetic radiation).

IRAS   (The) Infrared Astronomy Satellite; a cryogenically cooled infrared telescope satellite launched in 1984.

ISO   (The) International Standards Organization.

ITU   (The) International Telecommunications Union; the international deliberating body that allocates the RF spectrum for space and other uses.

IUS   Inertial Upper Stage; a solid-rocket-propelled upper stage used on the Titan and Shuttle launch vehicles, to deliver payloads to high altitude mission orbits such as GEO. Formerly called Interim Upper Stage (same acronymn).

JSC   (Lyndon B.) Johnson Space Center; the NASA Center located near Houston, Texas.

KSC   (John F.) Kennedy Space Center; the NASA center located at Cape Canaveral, Florida.

LET   Linear Energy Transfer; a measure of the energy deposited by ionizing radiation passing through matter.

LM   Lunar Module; the Apollo lunar module that landed astronauts on the Moon.

LV   Local Vertical; occasionally Launch Vehicle.

MMD   Momentum Management Device; any device for angular mementum storage such as a CMG. The common alternate form of MMD is an inertia wheel.

MMH   MonoMethyl Hydrazine; a rocket fuel commonly used with nitrogen tetroxide as an oxidizer. The combination is hypergolic (ignites upon contact).

MMU   Man Maneuvering Unit; a maneuvering spacecraft used by EVA astronauts. It is like an oversized "chair" that a suited astronaut sits (and is strapped) in. It has attitude control and maneuvering propulsion.

MSFC   (George C.) Marshall Space Flight Center; the NASA center located near Huntsville, Alabama.

MSP   Manned Space Program; infrequently used; archaic.

NASA   National Aeronautics and Space Agency.

NASDA   The Japanese equivalent of NASA.

NASTRAN NASA Structural Analysis; a finite-element structural analysis computer program.

NORAD   North American Air Defense (Command).

OMS   The Shuttle Orbit Maneuvering (propulsion) System.

OMV   Orbital Maneuvering Vehicle; a maneuverable propulsive spacecraft. Typical uses include retrieving satellites for servicing at a space station.

ORU   Orbital Replaceable Unit; a unit or part of a spacecraft, platform, or station replaceable on orbit as a routine maintenance action. Usually infers a unit which is the smallest that would be routinely replaced on orbit; further teardown for repair would normally occur after the unit has been returned to Earth. Maintenance engineers like to think of a space vehicle as being made up entirely of ORUs (that is, everything can be replaced).

OSI   Open Systems Interconnect (Standard); a proposed standard for interconnection of computer systems. Also, Operator-System Interface, a fancy name for a controls and displays panel.

OTA   The (Congressional) Office of Technology Assessment.

OTV   Orbital Transfer Vehicle; a propulsive upper stage for delivery of payloads to high-energy mission orbits. It is similar in function to IUS but usually conceived as using cryogenic liquid propellants and capable of delivering much larger payloads than IUS.

PDR   Preliminary Design Review; held at the completion of preliminary design; results in approval to begin detailed design.

PLSS   Portable Life Support System; the "backpack" worn by astronauts on EVA duty. It provides breathing air and body cooling.

POCC   Payload Operations Control Center; a control center dedicated to the control (from the ground) of one or more payloads.

POP   Perpendicular to the Orbit Plane; an attitude control strategy in which one spacecraft axis is perpendicular to the orbit plane. This acronymn also sometimes stands for Program Operating Plan.

PRR   Program Requirements Review; a review sometimes held very early in a program to formally approve and accept the top-level program requirements.

PSL   Perpendicular to the Sun Line; another attitude control strategy.

RBE   Relative Biological Effectiveness; of ionizing radiation, compared to gamma rays. An RBE of 1 indicates that deposition of a given amount of energy by a type of ionizing radiation has the same biological effect as deposition of the same amount of energy by gamma rays.

RF   Radio Frequency; when used as a noun, usually implies radio frequency signals.

RMS   Remote Manipulator System; the Canadian manipulator arm used on the Space Shuttle.

SAA   South Atlantic Anomaly; a part of the Earth's Van Allen radiation belt that is unusually low in the altitude over the South Atlantic. The radiation belt is controlled by the Earth's magnetic field; it rotates with the Earth, hence the fixed location.

SDV   Shuttle-Derived Vehicle; a concept for a heavy-lift launch vehicle derived from the Shuttle propulsion system.

SI   System Internationale; the international system of units.

SNR   Signal-to-Noise Ratio; for communications signals or systems.

SOC   Space Operations Center; a space station concept originated by JSC in 1979 and studied through 1982.

SPAS   A European space platform developed by MBB-ERNO, a German company.

SRR   System Requirements Review; a review to assess and accept system requirements and approve initiation of preliminary design.

STS   Space Transportation System; usually the Shuttle system. The Shuttle system is sometimes designated as NSTS for National STS.

TDRSS   Tracking and Data Relay Satellite System; a system of two or more satellites in GEO for tracking of space missions and relay of spacecraft RF signals. It replaces much of the former worldwide U.S. tracking network.

TFU   Theoretical First Unit (Cost); the projected cost of the first manufactured unit of a system.

TIMES   Thermoelectric Integrated Membrane Evaporative System; a device for distillation of water for purification.

TOPEX   (Ocean) Topographic Experiment; a planned spacecraft for precise measurement of ocean surface height.

TPM   Technical Performance Measurement; a bookkeeping system for tracking the technical performance of a development program. Typically, it would keep track of and score the technical performance of the design as it evolves.

UV   Ultraviolet (electromagnetic radiation).

VCD   Vapor Compression Distillation; another device for distillation of water for purification.

WARC   World Administrative Radio Conference; a conference held every few years by the ITU to allocate the RF spectrum among various users.

WBS   Work Breakdown Structure; a formal accounting system for the collection of accrued costs of a project. Each category of the WBS is defined by a "dictionary" so that all costs, as they are accrued, can be clearly identified as belonging to a particular WBS category and properly accounted.

Index

SOC, 7, 8, 88, 167, 169

Software. *See* Automation

Software cost, 185, 186

Software languages, 114, 115

Solar cells and arrays, 81, 167, 171

Solar flares, 63, 64

Solar generators, 81

Solar intensity, 61, 81, 94

Solar Max (spacecraft), 27

Spacecraft charging, 62

Spacelab, 11–14

Spaceport (in orbit), 35, 36

Space science missions, 15–20

Space sickness, 127

Space structures, large, 20, 24, 37, 40, 167

Space suit (EMU), 134–40

Space Telescope, 10, 15, 24, 38, 106, 140

Spares, 41

SPAS, 24

Specifications, 178

Speech recognition, 115, 117, 132

"Split payload," 32

Spread spectrum, 122

Sputnik, 2

Storage, electrical, 81, 85–87

Storm shelter, 68

Stress, 73, 74

Structural dynamics, 74, 104–6

Structures, 73–78

Subsystems mass estimating, 144

Sunspot cycle, 64

Sun-synchronous orbits, 49

Systems engineering, 178–81

Tankers, 36, 37, 41, 42

TDRSS, 118

Technical interrelationships, 180

Technical performance measurement, 179

Technology development missions, 20, 22, 23

"Tee" concept, 170–72

Teleoperation, 29, 116, 117

Tethers, 38, 57, 58

Thermal control, 88, 89, 93–101, 180

Thermal cycles, 82–86

Thermal management, 26

Thermal radiation, 96

Thermal sources, 94, 96

Thermal storage, 98

Thermal transport, 98

Thrust level, 106

Timelines, 38, 39, 40

Token ring data bus, 111

Tools for EVA, 139, 140

Torques, gravity gradient, 54–57

Trade studies, 178

Truss structures, 73, 75–77

Tsiolkovskii, 1

Ultraviolet effects, 61

Uncertainty analysis, 190–92, 206–8

Unit costs, 186, 187

Van Allen radiation belts, 62

Vector products, 197, 198

Ventilation, cabin, 87–90

Verification, 179

Verne, Jules, 1

Vertical reference, 133, 167

Voice recognition, 115, 117, 132

Volume for crew, 125

Von Braun, Wernher, 1

Wash water, 92, 204

Water, 87

Water balance, 201–5

Wells, H. G., 13

Work breakdown structure (WBS), 141, 183, 184

Zero g, 1

  deconditioning, 125–27

  design considerations, 133

  posture, 133

  restraints, 39, 133